SCIENCE AND TECHNOLOGY EDUCATION AI

Volume 4

Land, Water and Mineral Resources in Science Education

Science and Technology Education and Future Human Needs

General Editor: JOHN LEWIS
Malvern College, United Kingdom

Related Pergamon Journal

INTERNATIONAL JOURNAL OF EDUCATIONAL
DEVELOPMENT*

Editor: PHILIP TAYLOR

Throughout the world educational developments are taking place: developments in literacy, programmes in vocational education, in curriculum and teaching, in the economics of education and in educational administration.

It is the purpose of the *International Journal of Educational Development* to bring these developments to the attention of professionals in the field of education, with particular focus upon issues and problems of concern to those in the Third World. Concrete information, of interest to planners, practitioners and researchers, is presented in the form of articles, case studies and research reports.

*Free specimen copies available on request.

Land, Water and Mineral Resources in Science Education

Edited by

NORMAN J. GRAVES
University of London, United Kingdom

Published for the

ICSU PRESS

by

PERGAMON PRESS

OXFORD · NEW YORK · BEIJING · FRANKFURT
SÃO PAULO · SYDNEY · TOKYO · TORONTO

U.K.	Pergamon Press, Headington Hill Hall, Oxford OX3 0BW, England
U.S.A.	Pergamon Press, Maxwell House, Fairview Park, Elmsford, New York 10523, U.S.A.
PEOPLE'S REPUBLIC OF CHINA	Pergamon Press, Room 4037, Qianmen Hotel, Beijing, People's Republic of China
FEDERAL REPUBLIC OF GERMANY	Pergamon Press, Hammerweg 6, D-6242 Kronberg, Federal Republic of Germany
BRAZIL	Pergamon Editora, Rua Eça de Queiros, 346, CEP 04011, Paraiso, São Paulo, Brazil
AUSTRALIA	Pergamon Press Australia, P.O. Box 544, Potts Point, N.S.W. 2011, Australia
JAPAN	Pergamon Press, 8th Floor, Matsuoka Central Building, 1-7-1 Nishishinjuku, Shinjuku-ku, Tokyo 160, Japan
CANADA	Pergamon Press Canada, Suite No. 271, 253 College Street, Toronto, Ontario, Canada M5T 1R5

First edition 1987

Library of Congress Cataloging in Publication Data

Land, water, and mineral resources in science education.
(Science and technology education and future human needs; vol. 4)
1. Natural resources—Study and teaching. 2. Land use—Study and teaching. 3. Natural resources—Study and teaching—Developing countries. 4. Land use—Study and teaching—Developing countries.
I. Graves, N. J. (Norman J.)   II. Series.
HC59. L3335 1987   333.7'07'101724   86-30527

British Library Cataloguing in Publication Data

Land, water and mineral resources in science
education. — (Science and technology
education and future human needs; v. 4)
1. Natural resources—Study and teaching
I. Graves, Norman J.   II. Series
333.7'07'1   HC28

ISBN 0-08-033915-8 Hardcover
ISBN 0-08-033945-X Flexicover

Printed in Great Britain by A. Wheaton & Co. Ltd. Exeter

Foreword

The Bangalore Conference on "Science and Technology Education and Future Human Needs" was the result of extensive work over several years by the Committee on the Teaching of Science of the International Council of Scientific Unions. The Committee received considerable support from UNESCO and the United Nations University, as well as a number of generous funding agencies.

Educational conferences have often concentrated on particular disciplines. The starting point at this Conference was those topics already identified as the most significant for development, namely Health; Food and Agriculture; Energy; Land, Water and Mineral Resources; Industry and Technology; the Environment; Information Transfer. Teams worked on each of these, examining the implications for education at all levels (primary, secondary, tertiary, adult and community education). The emphasis was on identifying techniques and resource material to give practical help to teachers in all countries in order to raise standards of education in those topics essential for development. As well as the topics listed above, there is also one concerned with the educational aspects of Ethics and Social Responsibility. The outcome of the Conference is this series of books, which can be used for follow-up meetings in each of the regions of the world and which can provide the basis for further development.

John L. Lewis
Secretary, ICSU–CTS

Preface

This publication is the result of a workshop held in Bangalore, India, in August, 1985. The workshop was one of eight within a large conference whose theme was "Science and Technology Education and Future Human Needs". The particular workshop from which this book emanates was one dealing with the teaching of land use problems, water resource development and mineral resource exploitation.

The participants were asked to produce a number of pre-conference papers (listed in Appendix I) and these were used as the basis for the workshop. The members of the workshop were divided into three groups, one for land use, one for water resources and one for mineral resources. Each group was given a chairperson, whose function it was to lead the groups into the production of a teachers' handbook. Prior discussion had established that each section of the handbook would be divided into three parts. The first dealing with the nature of the problems to be tackled; the second with the educational perspectives on these problems; the third would consist of teaching suggestions including exemplar teaching units.

The drafts were produced in Bangalore and subsequently edited by each team leader and by the general editor. The resultant product shows that it was the fruit of an international team's labours, each contributor having his own view of the curriculum process and his own style of unit production. I felt it better to let the text reflect the differences among us, than to attempt to impose some sort of artificial uniformity. The teacher will need to adapt the suggestions made to his or her own circumstances.

May I express my gratitude to Joseph Stoltman, Hans van Aalst and Eileen Barrett, who led their respective teams through many agonizing discussions to produce their manuscripts? I should also like to thank all members of the workshop who in some way or other have contributed to the final product. Alice Henfield deserves my thanks for typing the manuscript that was not always a model of clarity.

Norman J. Graves

Contents

X   CONTENTS

Part III. Water Resources

Part IV. Mineral Resources

PART I

Introduction

1

Education for the Use of Land, Water and Mineral Resources

NORMAN J. GRAVES
University of London Institute of Education, U.K.

Introduction

This chapter is meant to highlight the issues likely to be faced by those attempting education for future human needs in the context of a developing economy. It focuses on the area of land, water and mineral resources which is one of the eight topics which the Bangalore Conference addressed. The rationale for linking land, water and mineral resources is that land provides the space on which other activities take place, and that fresh water and mineral resources are contained within an area of land. The emphasis on the use of land, water and mineral resources implies that what teachers may need to concentrate on is the wise use of these resources and the interaction which inevitably occurs between the use of each resource. The issues which will be addressed are first, the value of teaching about land, water and mineral resources; secondly, the content areas which might be included; and thirdly, the teaching strategies that may be appropriate given the context in which the education is going on.

The value of teaching about the use of land, water and mineral resources in relation to social, economic and cultural development in the future

Not wishing to delve too deeply into the concepts of development and development education, I am assuming that the ultimate aim is to enable a community to undertake modest economic growth, to further the development of the society in such a way that the citizens lead a better life with improved social relations and a richer culture shared by a greater number of people. The question seems to be, therefore, in what ways will

1

learning about the use of land, water and mineral resources aid the development process?

There are no certainties in education. One can only state what it is hoped will be achieved by such learning. First it would seem logical to help people to learn in what way economic growth is dependent on the areas and nature of land available, on the quantity and availability of water resources and on the quantity and kind of mineral resources available. However, it is also important that they should understand that such resources are of no avail unless associated with labour and capital in the process of producing goods and services. Further, that there is no single or simple way in which land, water and mineral resources may be used for development purposes. Much depends on the relative quantities of each available, on their accessibility, on the technology available in relation to manpower and so on. Similarly, it is important to make people realize that there are alternative uses for these resources, that decisions need to be taken as to what kind of development is required and whether the market mechanism is to be used exclusively in allocating resources, or whether central planning is to be used or indeed a mixture of planning and market economy.

It is also important that people should realize that there are costs to any development. Not only opportunity costs (loss of alternative use) but diseconomies which sometimes fall on the community. These diseconomies are usually classed as various forms of pollution whether this be air, water, noise or even aesthetic pollution. The use of land, water and general resources is not independent of the social and political framework within which people operate. It is of value to understand that when all land is privately owned and perhaps concentrated in few hands, then its supply for any purpose may be restricted to raise its price or because of the idiosyncracies of the owner. On the other hand, when the land is owned by the state, its supply for any given purpose may artificially be constrained by bureaucratic processes.

Perhaps one of the important values to make clear is that land and mineral resources are finite and that there is an important need to conserve such resources on "Spaceship Earth". Water is in a slightly different category since it is a re-usable resource, though its scarcity varies enormously from place to place.

Whilst the value of understanding the economic aspect of the use of land, water and mineral resources seems clear, its value in relation to social and cultural development is perhaps not so evident. It would seem that co-operation, discussion of issues, analysis of community needs would all be needed in using those resources and would therefore contribute to social development. There is also the need to discuss how the benefits of any economic growth may be shared and to clarify what view of social justice informs such discussion. By cultural development is understood a greater sharing of scientific knowledge, of art, literature, music and so on and not necessarily only in the "high culture" sense. Clearly any economic development makes such cultural development more possible, though it does not necessarily engender it. In so far as the developing use of land, water and mineral resources creates new landscapes, and those have been created with aesthetic as well as economic criteria in mind, then some cultural development will have taken place. In so far as people have more leisure and are stimulated to use it creatively, then cultural development is taking place.

It is not being suggested that a course be set up in order to develop specifically such understandings about the ways in which development relates to the use of land, water and mineral resources. What is proposed is that when particular aspects of development education are being undertaken, for example in teaching about the development of water supply in practical ways, the fact that where water is in limited supply, a choice has to be made between alternative uses, is something that requires emphasizing.

In a sense what are practical concerns for community development inevitably involve questions of an economic nature.

Content areas which may be emphasized

In this area, namely the use of land, water and mineral resources, the overlap with the other themes of the Conference are avoided as far as possible. It is perhaps important to realize that water and mineral resources may lend themselves to straightforward scientific and technological treatment, but that the use of land is much more related to economic social and political issues. I will therefore deal with each in reverse order: the use of mineral, water and land resources.

The use of mineral resources

Minerals which may be common on the earth surfaces may not be perceived as a resource if there is no knowledge of their use for specialized technical purposes or for building. In terms of community development, the kind of minerals which are likely to be useful are clay, sand and harder rocks for building or road surfacing; iron ore for making into iron for village forges; limestone for cement and agricultural liming and so on. Most of these may be familiar to villagers, but in some cases people may need to be trained to recognize such rocks and minerals in the field. Rarer minerals like copper ores and bauxite are likely to be recognized only after specialized training. An attempt is made in Chapter 8 to show how people with limited schooling may be trained to recognize relevant minerals in the field. A case study of large-scale mining is provided in Chapter 13.

We cannot ignore "high technology" if this is available. This is not so much for direct use by small communities, but rather that these may use information gathered by experts through the use of "high technology". For example, information about possible mineral resources may be obtained by analysing data from remote sensing. The scale of operation of mineral extraction is another aspect which needs examination. Whilst some minerals may only be extracted through large-scale operations, others may be undertaken on a small scale. These labour-intensive operations are very appropriate to a developing community especially where agricultural development has resulted in a proportionate decline of the agricultural labour force. The role of multinational companies and small-scale subsistence operations is examined in Chapter 13.

However, locating minerals and extracting minerals is one thing, and using them is another. Educational institutions could launch minor projects in using building materials, refining minerals and fashioning agricultural tools from the metals so produced.

The extraction of minerals is not without its costs. This may be illustrated by reference to the large-scale extraction of bauxite in Amazonia in Brazil. In a forested area in the tropics, the disturbance of the ecosystem in the area is massive and the natural vegetation and fauna may never regenerate, neither may the soil be restored. Whilst similar exploitations are unlikely to cause as much damage, to educate for awareness of ecosystem destruction is a worthwhile activity. The pressure for development may lead to the abandonment of conservation practices which have been in operation for many generations, having been developed through gradual adaptations to local conditions.

Perhaps another aspect of the use of minerals is that mineral extraction is a form of "robber economy". For practical purposes there is a finite source of minerals whether these be non-ferrous ores, iron ore, fossil fuels or even minerals for use as building materials. Further, if one thinks of many communities as being essentially dependent on the local resources, then the finite nature of such resources is even more evident. Consequently, another educational objective must be to emphasize conservation and recycling. Indeed, many intermediate or small-scale technology projects do precisely this by, for example, using waste organic products for the production of methane gas. In the sphere of mineral resources the stress needs to be on the recycling of scrap and the conservation of the area from which minerals have been extracted. Thus the need to restore land used for mineral extraction for agriculture and not leave an untidy eyesore on the landscape is an aspect of conservation to which educationalists must give attention.

Perhaps one aspect of the use of mineral resources of which communities ought to be aware is that owing to changing technology, certain metals may fall out of favour, for example copper, whilst for others the world demand may be extending, for example aluminium. In some cases the use of plastics may undermine the demand for certain metals. Although these developments affect the world market more than the local use of metals, nevertheless where a cash economy operates, such developments may have a significant impact. Thus knowledge in trends in demand for a particular mineral may be useful to prevent wasted investment.

The use of water resources

Presumably one of the most important ideas which needs to be understood by all those who are likely to be concerned with the extraction and use of water is that of the hydrological cycle. Though some simple idea of the water cycle is probably appreciated, the complex web of relationships between surface run-off, ground water, storage in aquifers and evapotranspiration is not always understood. Thus this will form a suitable subject for a teaching unit for the secondary school level, which might also be used in extension or community work.

The nature of the present demand for water in village communities and the difficulties which they face in procuring water is illustrated from field evidence in the case study by the Vagai project in Tamilnadu. The relationship between water quality and sanitation is touched upon in Chapter 7. Further, understanding how the water supply situation may be improved is dealt with by using some of the material produced by the PLON Project, for example, Water for Tanzania, which is specifically concerned with the improvement of drinking water supplies.

The storage of water is another aspect which merits consideration both on a small scale and a large scale. There is a need to develop an understanding of the physical conditions which make possible the storage of water in an open environment, the conditions which maximize the catchment of water, the cost and benefit of sterilizing a certain quantity of production land and the conditions which allow storage without too heavy a loss through seepage or evaporation.

Lastly, the conservation of water through recycling may be possible. This depends on there being available means of filtering and purifying water at an intermediate technology level.

The use of land

It is important for people to understand that land in terms of a surface on which all kinds of human activities can take place, is finite and can only be added to marginally as for example in the case of The Netherlands and Singapore. As such, there is competition for land as between all kinds of alternative uses. It is also important to realize that land use is as much a product of tradition, of physical constraints and of economic structural forces as of simple competition. The problems of land use in the context of

East Africa illustrate these factors in Chapter 3, though much of what is stated in this chapter has relevance to Asia and Latin America.

Teaching units based on land use problems in various parts of the world are provided in Chapter 5. These examine the complex interrelations between land use, relief, climate, disease, economic development, ethnic and cultural factors. They show that decisions about land use are usually constrained by influences that limit at any one time the available options.

However, there is one aspect of land use which relates to all possible land uses, it is that of aesthetics. Whilst this has some affinity with the concept of environment quality, it is part of the totality. It is a slippery area, but one which of necessity must be addressed. What makes for a pleasant harmonious rural landscape? What makes us react to an urbanscape to decide that it is ugly or tolerable or beautiful? If the environment is to be improved, then land use decisions need to be taken with aesthetic as well as economic considerations in mind.

Teaching strategies

To some extent the nature of the educational activities undertaken must be a function of

(a) the level at which the activity is undertaken (elementary, secondary, tertiary, adult);
(b) the resources afforded by the local environment in which the activity is to take place.

For schools the educational activities suggested would consist essentially of (i) exercises based on data provided in texts or curriculum packs, (ii) field work exercises, (iii) games and simulations. Some of the materials of the British Schools Council Geography 16–19 Project may be useful in this context, as indeed may be a number of Science in Society materials. However, the emphasis in developing countries should be on teachers developing their own resources for teaching, since the possibility of purchasing curriculum packs is probably remote and inappropriate. In tertiary and adult education it would seem important that educational activities should be of use to the community. For example, land use mapping; making an inventory of water and mineral resources; planning the improvement of water supply and conservation; undertaking small-scale exploitation of whatever mineral may be available; suggesting a rearrangement of transport networks, and so on.

The examples provided in the chapters which follow do no more than outline various possibilities. The teacher will need to find those that he can use in his context and develop for the purposes of his community.

2

Land, Water and Mineral Resources: An Overview of Problems

R. P. MISRA
University of Allahabad, India

The problem

We are passing through a stage of impending ecological crisis in the world. The crisis is the consequence of a number of forces. Important among them are:

(a) Our understanding of nature and our attitude towards it.
(b) Pressure of human population on natural resources.
(c) Maldevelopment of the international economy leading to over-industrialization in some regions and no or under-industrialization elsewhere.
(d) Technological and scientific advances giving immense power in the hands of man to destroy things of lasting value.

Incalculable harm has already been done to our natural wealth. Agricultural land of lasting value has been brought under other uses; water has been polluted, mineral wealth has been lost for ever, plant and animal species have been destroyed. We are jeopardizing our health and the survival of generations yet to come. We rarely realize that land is a finite resource and hence must be used judiciously. Our water resources are declining in certain areas and the technology to desalinate sea-water at a reasonable cost is not in sight. The rate at which the mineral resources are being used by the industrialized countries will leave the rest of the world with few in not too distant a future.

Our concept of nature has changed for the worst. We use the term "exploitation" for the use of natural resources. We want mastery over nature as if we were outside the nature system. The ecosystem of which we are a part, is too delicate to be tampered with. It is not the fear of exhaustion

7

that bothers us for we know that our technological ingenuities will help us develop alternatives and increase productivity in the farms and factory. What bothers us is the serious implications of the current approach to the use of our natural wealth for the quality of human life. Our task is now to prepare ourself for a new approach to interaction with nature so that we can use our natural wealth without creating a situation in which it will stand exhausted because of over use or misuse.

Medicine does not make man healthy; technology does not make him happy. Outside nature man is "dead". Nothing should be done to destroy any element of the nature system without giving full thought to the short as well as long term implications for human welfare.

The world population has been increasing at a very rapid rate during this century. It stands at over 5 billions today and would reach 6.5 billions by the turn of the century. It so happens that much of the increase in population is in that part of the world which is economically poor and technologically backward (Table 2.1). Because of this, the demand for natural resources in the Third World countries has not increased at a proportionate rate. But this has been more than compensated by the increased demand for natural resources in the industrially advanced countries of the world. The result is that the output of natural wealth has gone up in the developing countries and its use has increased in the developed countries.

According to Paul Erlich, a biologist, if the present population continues to increase at this rate, by AD 3000 every square metre of the earth's surface (land sea and ice included) will be occupied by 2000 people.[1]* We know that such a situation will not come, but we also know that rising living standards, high aspirations and expectations, improved technology, and rapid industrialization have increased the per capita demand for natural resources beyond the capacity of the ecosystem to adjust. "The amount of most metals and ores used since 1930 is in excess of the combined amount used in all previous centuries".[2]

Landsberg estimates the world will require a three-fold increase in aggregate food and lumber output and five-fold increase in energy and iron alloys by AD 2000.[3] Similarly the ratio between supply and demand for water is likely to drop from 8:3 in 1960 to 3:8 in the year 2000.[4]

The proportion of land area under cultivation is very small in some countries and this may encourage one to suggest further expansion of the cultivated land to meet the requirements for food. The suggestion based on the ample quantity of land waiting for reclamation may be highly misleading. The qualitative aspects of land should be given due importance along with the available quantity of land. In some cases the land use might have attained a stage of maturity and it might not be feasible to make such changes. The African countries, however, have great potential for extension

---

* Superscript numbers refer to References at end of chapter.

TABLE 2.1. *Area and Growth of Population in a Few Selected Countries*

	Area 000 km²	Population (mn)		Annual growth rate* (1972–82) in %
		1982	1972	
World	135,830	4,586.00	3,748.00	2.0
of which				
India	3,287	711.66	563.53	2.4
Australia	7,687	15.17	13.18	1.4
Bangladesh	144	92.62	73.39	2.5
Brazil	8,512	126.81	97.85	2.6
Burma	677	37.07	28.26	2.7
Canada	9,976	24.63	21.82	1.2
China	9,597	1,020.67	854.21	1.8
Egypt	1,001	44.67	34.84	2.5
France	547	54.22	51.70	0.5
Germany (W)	249	61.64	61.67	. . .
Iran	1,648	40.24	30.41	2.8
Israel	21	4.02	3.15	2.5
Italy	301	56.59	54.41	0.4
Japan	372	118.45	107.19	1.0
Kenya	583	17.86	12.07	4.0
Korea, Rep.	98	39.33	33.51	1.6
Pakistan	804	87.13	64.30	3.1
Philippines	300	50.74	38.99	2.7
Singapore	0.58	2.47	2.15	1.4
Sri Lanka	66	15.19	12.86	1.7
Sweden	450	8.33	8.12	0.3
Thailand	514	48.49	38.59	2.3
U.K.	244	55.78	55.78	. . .
U.S.A.	9,363	232.06	208.23	1.1
U.S.S.R.	22,402	269.99	247.50	0.9

* Compound rate.
Source: *A Statistical Outline of India*, Bombay, 1984, p. 200.

of agricultural land in future provided that irrigation water becomes available.

The available land for cultivation is being consumed by other economic sectors at an enormous rate with direct and indirect impact on food supply and environment. "Worldwide more than a hundred square kilometres of arable and virgin land are consumed for housing, industrial buildings and transport routes everyday".[5] We should think seriously about repairing the damage being done to the environment.

Why are we failing? Why have we not been able to make a dent in the ever growing problem of destruction and misuse of our natural wealth? Why do we not realize in operational terms the need to build a social order which will put science and technology to uses which enrich human life and put man in harmony with nature? The intention is not to go back to the non-existent "good old days", but to use the potentials of science and technology to lighten the pressure of man on nature and thus save it from destruction.

The purpose of this chapter is to highlight the problems related to the use of land, water, and mineral resources and to explore the possibilities of improving and reorienting science and technology education so that we, from very early childhood are enabled to understand the symbolic relationship between nature and man and to participate in the reconstruction of a new social and technological order more conducive to the maintenance of the above relationship.

Land resources

Since time immemorial land has played an important role in shaping the life of man. Early civilizations were essentially riverine. Even today, we depend on land for much of our food, fibres and shelter. Land is a nonrenewable resource, it is finite in area. Land including rivers and marshes cover 25.4% of the earth's surface, oceans cover 71% and polar ice and mountain glaciers cover 3.18%. The share of continental lakes is 0.4%. There is some scope for expanding the land area by filling up lakes, sea inlets and low lying coastal regions. Cases of Holland, Hong Kong, Japan and Singapore may be cited as examples. The net gain from the global or continental perspectives is, however, marginal.[6]

The global land use data[7] reveal that the agricultural land, which is responsible for nearly 71.0% of the total edible products, is only 2% of the total area of the globe. Forests cover 8.6% of the area, and contribute 10.4% edible product per annum; grass lands cover 7.2% of land and produce 15.3% of edible products. Other lands including wet land and swamps, tundra, hot deserts and cold deserts, extend over 10.4% of the area and make only a marginal contribution to food. The remaining part of the globe is covered by oceans and lakes.

The optimum production potentialities of known resources are yet to be reached and vast tracts of land in various parts of the world are yet to be explored scientifically. But we do not know whether we can use these lands without inviting global ecological disaster. Nature does not recognize national boundaries and nations unfortunately have failed to recognize nature's unity.

It is this 2% of the land already under agriculture which needs immediate attention for even this is being depleted at an enormously rapid rate; soil erosion alone takes away thousands of hectares of land per annum. Add to this the land being diverted to non-agricultural uses. Desertification and salinization of irrigated land is well known.

The problem of land is more acute in the developing countries where agriculture constitutes the main source of livelihood. Table 2.2 shows the dependence of economically active population on agriculture in selected countries of the world. The dependence of economically active population on agriculture is phenomenally high in case of Bangladesh (84%), India

(67%), China (59%), Pakistan (53%), Burma (51%), and Sri Lanka (53%). In African countries the dependence on land is much higher. In Kenya, Tanzania and Uganda more than 80% of the population is dependent on land while in Burundi and Rwanda, this is over 90%.[8]

While in North America the average annual agricultural output per person is 2.5 tons, it is less than 0.25 tons in Asia and 0.125 tons in Africa. This low productivity of people may be attributed to several factors such as lack of irrigation, poor technology, complex land-tenure system, etc.[9] The data given in Table 2.2, indicates the very limited use of modern technology for crop production in these countries. The use of fertilizers is very limited indeed.

So far, we have examined only the physical availability of land. What is physically available is however not necessarily socially accessible. Land

TABLE 2.2. *Man–Land Relationship in Selected Countries*

	Economically active population engaged in agriculture as % of total	Arable land* (million hectares)	Per capita arable land (hectares)	Fertilizer consumption per hectare of arable land (kg)
India	62	169.1	0.25	33.8
Australia	6	44.4	3.06	27.9
Bangladesh	84	9.1	0.10	43.6
Brazil	37	62.0	0.51	37.5
Burma	51	10.0	0.28	n.a.
Canada	5	44.4	1.85	41.9
China	59	99.2	0.10	150.1
Egypt	50	2.9	0.07	247.5
France	8	18.6	0.35	298.4
Germany (W)	4	7.5	0.12	418.4
Iran	38	16.0	0.42	n.a.
Israel	7	0.4	0.11	199.6
Italy	11	12.5	0.22	163.3
Japan	10	4.9	0.04	387.2
Korea Rep.	37	2.2	0.06	351.3
Mexico	35	23.3	0.33	66.6
Pakistan	53	20.3	0.23	53.1
Philippines	45	9.9	0.20	32.4
Sri Lanka	53	2.1	0.14	n.a.
U.K.	2	7.0	0.12	329.6
U.S.A.	2	190.6	0.84	102.7
U.S.S.R.	16	232.0	0.87	82.6

Note: Data relate to 1980–81
      * Including area under permanent crops
Source: *A Statistical Outline of India*, Bombay, 1984, p. 204.

tenure is a social institution which mediates between man and nature. Who gets what, where, how much and when depends on the land tenure system of a country. Most cultivators consider land as property and hence it has been used as wealth to be owned by the privileged few. It did not necessarily belong to those who tilled it. As a result the land distribution among different sections of population in many countries is very skewed. While a few hold large areas of land, millions of those who actually till the land own only a small or no holding at all. In countries like India, Bangladesh and Pakistan the splitting up of land into small and uneconomic size of holdings is the result of laws of inheritance insensitive to changing man–land relationship.

The recent land reform measures undertaken by various governments to give land to the tiller are noteworthy but their total impact on the overall situation has been marginal. For example, in India rural and urban Land Ceiling Act, 1976 and the U.P. Zamindari Abolition Act, 1950 as also the U.P. Land Consolidation Act 1952 were enacted to reduce the fragmentation and skewed distribution of land. But ownership pattern continues to be heavily skewed (Table 2.3). Nearly 55% of the holdings which spread over just 2% of the total are marginal holdings. The size of such

TABLE 2.3. *Operational Holdings in India*

Size of holding (hectares)	No. of holdings ('000s)	% to total	Area of holdings (mn hectares)	% to total
Marginal				
Below 0.5	30,050	36.8	7.1	4.3
0.5–1.0	14,473	17.7	10.5	6.4
Small				
1–2	14,728	18.1	20.9	12.8
Semi-Medium				
2–3	7,497	9.2	18.1	11.1
3–4	4,169	5.1	14.3	8.8
Medium				
4–5	2,831	3.5	12.6	7.7
5–10	5,381	6.6	37.1	22.7
Large				
10–20	1,943	2.4	26.0	15.9
20–30	323	0.4	7.6	5.7
30–40	91	0.1	3.1	1.9
40–50	36	—	1.6	0.9
50–above	47	0.1	4.5	2.8
	81,569	100.0	163.3	100.0

Note: Data relate to 1976–77 Agricultural Census.
Source: *A Statistical Outline of India*, Bombay, 1984, p. 60.

holdings ranges from 0.5 to 1.0 hectares. Large holdings which vary between 10 to 50 hectares are only 3% and cover nearly 27% of the total cultivated land. In countries like Brazil, the multinational corporations and land speculators are buying tracts of land, dispossessing those small holders who cleared the land and cultivated it for years. Even in high density populated countries like India and Bangladesh landlessness is on the increase.

Urban land

The problem of urban land is not less acute. True, it occupies only a small area of the earth's land, it is most valuable and has been expanding at a rapid rate encroaching the nearly agricultural lands. Urban land is most contested as well as congested land . . . and provides examples of intense land use competition.[10] The problem of urban housing in the Third World cities needs no special emphasis. The mushroom growth of squatter settlements is an indication of the failure of our social system to use land for the benefit of the poor. The complicated land tenure system, illegal sub-division and outmoded building codes and norms are the means by which the poor are kept outside the land market. A study of popular settlement in Allahabad city (India) undertaken by the International Institute for Development Research, Allahabad,[11] reveals that the city's complex land tenure system has encouraged the growth of illegal self-built housing units on government and other vacant lands and also on unclaimed land with disputed titles. Many of these settlements are located in marshy, swampy or low lying areas.

Land use planning

This brings us to the question of land use planning. This exercise has to be done in its total context (i.e. relief, soil, vegetation, climate, population, food, housing, clothing, energy, and environment). The mechanization of agriculture in many developing countries has failed to meet the agricultural goal of maximum production. Yakuba observes that "Physically the land had been degraded (in Ghana) by the uneducated use of technology on it. Soil erosion has escalated and the soil continues to be infertile year after year".[12]

Land use planning should aim at:

(a) earmarking each piece of land for specific uses keeping in view the ecology and economic imperatives;

(b) indicating the potentialities of each piece of land given different levels of technological inputs;

(c) preserving and improving the fertility of land by appropriate conservation and management tools;

(d) advising governmental agencies on land reform including consolidation of holdings; and

(e) suggesting appropriate control over urban land use to stop speculation and to make urban land available to poor especially.

Water resources

Water is vital for human life and is present as a major constituent in the cells of all animals and vegetative tissues and in the crystals of many minerals.[13] It is used for a variety of purposes; domestic, agricultural, industrial, transport, recreation, etc. Its social and economic importance cannot be over-emphasized. It has political significance too because on many occasions water disputes between nations or between states within a nation have been the cause of continuing conflicts.

World water resources

Water is found in liquid, gaseous and solid forms. Its purity or impurity depends upon the sources from which it is obtained and what is added to it subsequently. Snow is the purest natural source of water followed by rainwater. Mountainous lakes, streams, springs and wells are also relatively free from organic impurities but contain some inorganic salts. Table 2.4 presents a detailed breakdown of the distribution of world water resources of the earth. The earth's total volume of water is assessed to be about 1386 billion km^3 which will be sufficient to enclose the globe in a layer 2718 m deep.[14] Oceans constitute nearly 96.5% (1338 billion km^3) of the total world water resources. The share of land-water is 3.5% (47,971,710 km^3) only. Yet another estimate[15] suggests that the oceans share 97.2% of the total global water storage and the remaining 2.8% is shared by land which includes ice sheets and glaciers (2.15%), ground water (0.62%), and stream channels, freshwater lakes and other lakes, soil water and atmospheric water combined (0.03%). The water of land consists of:

(i)   Surface water   Water flowing or ponded on the land.
(ii) Subsurface water   Water occupying openings in the soil or rocks.
(iii) Soil water   Water retained by soil as soil moisture.
(iv) Ground water   Water found in the bedrock.

The proportion of fresh water which is of consequence to human beings, is 2.53% of all water (35 million km^3) only or 73.0% of the total land-water. The major proportion of the fresh water is found in frozen form and is underground. The fresh water, in its liquid form on the earth's surface constitutes only a small proportion (0.3%) of the world's resource of fresh water and 0.008% of the global water. The lakes, marshes, river water and biological water[16] which are most frequently used by man represent only

TABLE 2.4. *The World's Water Resources*

Zone of the resources	Catchment area (km^2)	Volume of water (km^3)	Depth of stratum (m)	% of world's water resources related to	
				Total resources	Fresh water resources
World's oceans	361,300,000	1,338,000,000	3,700	96.5	—
Land of which Ground water (gravitation and capillary water)	148,800,000 134,800,000	47,971,710 23,400,000^a	322 174	3.5 1.7	
Of which Fresh water	134,800,000	10,530,000	78	0.76	30.1
Soil moisture Polar ice Glaciers, Snow	82,000,000 16,232,500	16,500 26,064,100	0.2 1,483	0.0001 1.74	0.05 68.7
Of which Antarctic	13,980,000	21,600,000	1,545	1.56	61.7
Greenland	1,802,400	2,340,000	1,298	0.17	6.68
Arctic	226,100	83,500	369	0.006	0.24
Mountains	224,000	40,600	181	0.003	0.12
Ice in Permafrost	21,000,000	300,000	14	0.022	0.86
Fresh water Lakes	1,236,400	91,000	73.6	0.007	0.26
Saltwater lakes	822,300	85,400	103.8	0.006	—
Marsh land	2,682,600	11,470	4.28	0.0008	0.03
Water courses	148,800,000	2,120	0.014	0.0002	0.006
Biological water	510,000,000	1,120	0.002	0.0001	0.003
Water in the atmosphere	510,100,000	12,900	0.025	0.001	0.04

^{a} This does not include ground water resources in the Antarctic which are estimated at 2 million km^3 of fresh water.

Source: Keller, R., The World's Fresh Water: Yesterday, Today, Tomorrow. *Applied Geography and Development*, Institute for Scientific Cooperation, 1984, Vol. 24, p. 8. The above table has been extracted in this publication from *World Water Balance and Water Resources of the Earth*, Leningrad, 1974, p. 47 (Russian).

a very small proportion of the earth's water resource. The quantity of water vapour in the atmosphere which is responsible for all fresh water on land is also very small, i.e. 12,900 km^3 or 0.001% of the world's water resource. This inequitable distribution and the limits imposed by nature have certainly great implications for future planning and development of the world's water resources.

The notion that fresh water supply on the earth is unlimited, is not based on fact. Water supply in areas of habitation is too precariously balanced to be misused. Much of the fresh water is far away from human settlements. Even if technological know-how permits us to use frozen water, we may not utilize it for ecological reasons. We have to be content with land water alone for years to come.

Hydrological cycle and world water balance

Unlike land and minerals, water can be recycled and is renewable. It is true that the usable water available is only a small fraction of total world's water, it gets renewed by the global hydrological cycle. Water on the surface of earth evaporates under the influence of solar heat and this returns back to the earth in the form of fresh water precipitation. "A particular molecule of water might, if we could trace it continuously travel through any one of a number of possible circuits involving alternatively the water vapour state and the liquid or solid state".[17]

This complex hydrological cycle tries to maintain the global water balance which may be explained by the formula

$$P = E + R$$

where P = precipitation, E = evaporation and R = runoff.

Future demands for water

The water balance of world's land areas is expected to change (see Table 2.5) in future due to various ecological changes resulting from indiscriminate use of land by man for agriculture, industry and settlement. Table 2.6 compares the present and future demands upon the world's water resources. It is abundantly clear that irrigation is the major consumer of water. But its unscientific use may prove to be detrimental as it may increase evaporation, salinization of soil, and waterlogging.

Human settlements, especially urban agglomerations and industries are the next important consumers of water. The demand for water by these two sectors is increasing due to rapid urbanization and industrialization. Two sets of problems have already cropped up. While the large scale use of water by industries and consequent discharge of effluents in the lakes and rivers is creating a problem of water pollution, the shortage of protected water supply in human settlements is responsible for diseases like jaundice, diarrhoea, dysentery, cholera, typhoid, worm infestations etc. These diseases are the major killers of children in the Third World countries. A study conducted recently in a community of 492 people in the city of Allahabad (India) reported more than 50% of people suffering from worm infestations. The incidence was more (about 55%) in the case of children

TABLE 2.5. *Estimated Changes in the Water Balance of the World's Land Areas (volumes given in km³) from M. I. Lvovitch)*

Elements of balance	1970	Balance 2000
Precipitation on land (P)	110,300	110,300
Runoff from land (total runoff) excl. ice runoff from polar glaciers	38,800	37,500
Basic runoff (= stable runoff) of which	14,000	22,500
Ground water runoff	12,000	17,000
Controlled discharge from lakes and reservoirs	2,000	5,500
Surface runoff (= direct runoff from land surface, e.g. flood waves)	26,800	20,500
Total moisture stored on the land surface, (R) including superficial soil moisture	83,500	89,800
Total evaporation (E) (Evaporation + Transpiration = Evapotranspiration)	71,500	72,800

Source: Keller, R., *op. cit.*, p. 21.

TABLE 2.6. *Present and Future Demands upon the World's Water Resources (in km³) (from M. I. Lvovitch, 1974)*

Types of use	Water extracted (WE) 1970	Water consumed (WC) 1970	WE in 2000	WC in 2000
Water supply (settlements, industry, thermal power stations, livestock production)	600	130	1500	1050*
Agricultural irrigation	2800	2100	3950	4000**
Rain-fed irrigation (i.e. unirrigated)	500	500	1200	1200
Hydropower and navigation	170	160	500	500
Fishing	65	15	175	85

* Excluding 450 km³ of sewage used for irrigation.
** Including 450 km³ of sewage used for irrigation.
Source: Keller, R., *op. cit.*, p. 19.

below 14 years of age.[20] The situation is no way better in the case of villages. Many villages do not have a potable water supply in the dry season. Most of the rivers and lakes of the world are polluted. Efforts are afoot in many countries to clean these water bodies by treating the industrial effluents at the source. The creation of Ganga Valley Authority by the Government of India is a laudable effort in this direction.

The drying up of the underground supplies because of excessive use, is another problem which has emerged in many parts of the world. The replenishment of underground water takes place at a rate determined by the rock structure, and the amount and periodicity of rain fall in the catchment area. Modern bore wells can draw water at a much faster rate than that of natural replenishment. This leads to the lowering of the water table and in due course to the drying up of the source.

Water resource planning

The problems mentioned above call for a very judicious use of water resources of the world. Land and water are inextricably linked with each other. Land use planning, therefore, implies water resource planning. Land use should be such that it obstructs runoff allowing the water to percolate in the soil to re-charge the underground and sub-surface water. We must give up the age old method of irrigation by flooding. It amounts to not only a callous misuse of water but also the destruction of the soil caused by salinity. We have to be frugal in the use of water to avoid water famine in the years to come. Many African countries are already in the grips of water scarcity. The day may not be far off when the human civilization will be threatened by water famine.

Appropriate steps are necessary to maintain the ecological nexus between land, water, minerals and trees. Soil conservation efforts should be speeded up all over the world. Barrages and storage reservoirs should be built in drought prone areas. Only 5% of the total world's water power potential is being used[21] at present. Wherever the ecological principles do not militate against the construction of dams etc. this potential should be harnessed speedily. This will also minimize soil erosion and transportation of silt to the sea. The two case studies; one by P. E. Spargo[22] on the Orange River Project and the other by E. G. Vedanayagam[23] on Periyar-Vaigal project reported at the Bangalore conference speak well of the benefits accruing from such projects. All these activities should however form part of a grand design to harness the natural resources for the benefit of man.

Mineral resources

Minerals like land and water are invaluable treasures of the earth. Without them, we cannot think of industrialization and hence the development of our economy. In many countries they are the main source of national income. Important among these are Nigeria, Brunei, Ghana, Mauritania, Zambia, Liberia and Venezuela. The most important characteristics of minerals which have bearings on our present and future well-being is that they are practically lost once used. They are nonrenewable resources. The mineral wealth being finite in nature, once depleted it cannot be replaced. The need to conserve these resources and to recycle them if possible cannot be over emphasized.

Among the many causes of the fall of the Roman Empire the depletion of mineral deposits and the erosion of soil is said to be one. During the recent past several mining towns have turned into "ghost towns" in many parts of the developed world. The Canadian township of Elliot Lake which turned out to be "the first nuclear-age ghost town" is the most recent example of this process. Built at an enormous cost in response to the discovery of uranium in the mid-fifties, its population declined from 25,000 in 1958 to 5,000 in 1961 as soon as an alternative source was found by the U.S.A.[24]

Apart from the problem of depletion, mineral extraction has led to serious environmental damages. Mountainous areas which contain much of limestone, coal, iron ore, etc., have been subjected to immense vandalism by man. Deforestation, land slides and floods have increased beyond the capacity of the ecosystem to control. Lack of appropriate conservation devices has made coal-producing areas inhospitable.

Minerals should therefore be extracted only after careful ecologically sound land use planning. Such a plan should look to the continuing prosperity of the area.

Occurrence of minerals

The occurrence of minerals is the result of long-term geological processes. It is associated with the formation of the earth's crust which is composed of minerals. When mineral matter is sufficiently concentrated, it is known as "ore". Unless adequately concentrated it does not warrant commercial exploitation. The mode of occurrence determines the relative cost of extraction.

Minerals may be found in igneous, metamorphic and sedimentary rocks. They may also be found in the oceans. More will be said about this in Chapters 11 and 12.

Minerals production and world reserves

The data pertaining to production, distribution and reserves of mineral wealth are still unreliable. Tables 2.7 and 2.8 show the production, and reserves situation of some minerals in the world between 1973 and 1979. We note from Tables 2.7 and 2.8 that:

(1) The total volume of workable mineral deposits is an insignificant fraction of 1% of the earth's crust and once consumed, there will not be a second "crop".[26]

TABLE 2.7. *World's Mining Production of Some Mineral Raw Materials and Their Distribution (in %) between Industrialized Nations (I), Developing nations (D), and State-economy Nations (S)*

	1973				1979			
	World total (10^6 tonnes)	I	D	S	World total (10^6 tonnes)	I	D	S
Copper	7.5	42	38	20	7.9	36	41	23
Lead	3.6	54	19	27	3.6	51	20	29
Zinc	5.9	58	20	22	6.3	53	20	27
Tin	0.2	9	76	15	0.2	8	76	16
Iron	420.0	41	26	33	510.7	42	25	33
Manganese ore	22.0	23	33	44	24.5	28	26	46
Chromite	6.8	33	27	40	9.6	38	27	35
Nickel	0.7	50	26	24	0.7	38	32	30
Bauxite	73.1	38	48	14	87.9	43	44	13
Fluorite	4.8	40	39	21	4.9	35	31	34
Phosphate	95.0	43	29	28	127.8	43	33	24

Source: Schippers, H. J., Mining and infrastructure in developing countries, *Natural Resources and Development*, Institute for Scientific Cooperation, Tubingen, 1982, vol. 16, p. 28.

(2) The production of all minerals has increased during 1973–1979, which is in consonance with the increasing demand for raw materials. It has been observed that despite recycling, the primary production of most of the raw materials has increased since the 1950s.[27]

(3) The share of developing countries in the total production dropped during the same period but only slightly. It was about 29% in 1979.

(4) The life of world reserves has increased considerably during 1973–1979 in case of all minerals listed in the Tables 7 and 8 except for manganese and iron ore.

(5) The percentage increase in proven reserves has been greater in developing countries. This implies that developing nations will assume greater importance in mineral output in future. This also implies that mining activities will expand in those areas where infrastructural facilities are presently poor. This is bound to make mining expensive and this situation calls for public policy for adequate investment in the infrastructure of developing nations.[28]

Mining and the ecosystem

The ecosystem can be adversely affected by the mining activity. It has already been discussed how mining has converted several settlements into "ghost towns". The working of minerals inevitably produces permanent scars on the landscapes through dumps of waste, surface subsidence and tailing ponds. It also results in chemical changes of soil and underground water, and water and air also get polluted. No matter what methods and or

TABLE 2.8. *World's Mining Reserves of Some Mineral Raw Materials and Their Distribution (in %) between Industrialized Nations (I), Developing Nations (D) and State-economy Nations (S)*

	1973				1979			
	World total (10^6 tonnes)	I	D	S	World total (10^6 tonnes)	I	D	S
Copper	375.5	41	45	14	550.8	29	58	13
Lead	103.6	70	13	17	156.7	67	15	18
Zinc	185.3	69	15	16	241.0	73	12	15
Tin	4.3	4	79	17	9.7	8	66	26
Iron	87,700.0	35	29	36	93,600.0	35	31	34
Manganese ore	1,920.0	52	19	29	1,835.0	53	9.	38
Chromite	1,690.0	96	3	1	3,541.0	65	29	6
Nickel	68.0	44	41	15	82.0	22	48	30
Bauxite	11,871.9	38	56	6	23,400.0	25	72	3
Fluorite	135.3	52	39	9	303.0	58	32	10
Phosphate	4,649.3	39	43	18	70,920.0	17	70	13

Source: Schippers, H. J., Mining and infrastructure in developing countries, *Natural Resources and Development*, Institute for Scientific Cooperation, Tubingen, 1982, vol. 16, p. 28.

operation are adopted, the loss of useful land and vegetable cover is bound to occur unless appropriate scientific and technological measures are adopted to ward off the ill effects mentioned above.

Science and technology education

Given the above perspectives how can we meet our basic, and developmental needs in the future is a question that occurs to many of us from time to time. Land area is finite and non-agricultural uses of it are likely to increase in future. Water resources are renewable if used judiciously. The mineral resources are fixed and inequitably distributed in the world. The limitations imposed by these resources can be partly overcome by science and technology. Productivity of agricultural land can be increased several fold, water can be recycled on a mass scale and new irrigation methods adopted to minimize its uses, and metals can be substituted by plastics. All the bounties of nature can be used without destroying the ecosystem. Here lies the importance of science and technology education for future human needs. The needs which are so inextricably linked with natural resources of the world.

Science and technology education for future human needs should aim at:

(a) providing learning opportunities to various sections of people to understand the close relationship between nature and man; bringing home the importance of land, water and minerals for the present and future welfare of man;

(b) educating people in the use of the scientific knowledge appropriate technological know-how to get over the problems emerging from the use and misuse of the world's resources.

Such an education has to be provided at various levels starting from the pre-elementary stage. How to interact with nature must be taught from a very early stage in life. We need to redraft and reorient our curricula. Students are not to be taught; they have to learn partly by experience, partly by interaction with the teacher and partly by experimentation.

By the time, a pupil has passed the primary stage, he or she should understand the following aspects of land, water and minerals:

(a) origin,
(b) uses,
(c) current state of utilization,
(d) importance in relation to future human needs,
(e) relation to overall ecological system,
(f) how science and technology can help solve the emergent and emerging problems.

Our target groups, however, include not only children but also adults. In most developing countries of the world, much of the adult population is illiterate and these countries do not have the resources to build an adequate number of schools and colleges to provide learning opportunities for all those who must be schooled. The use of modern technological devices to impart education through TV, radio etc, has thus acquired considerable importance. New opportunities have thus been opened up for imparting science and technology education to the masses. The potentials of science and technology must be used more than hitherto, to enhance the welfare of people without damaging the world's fragile ecosystem.

References

1. Hagget, P., *Geography: A Modern Synthesis*, Harper & Row, New York, 1975, p. 144.
2. Ibid, p. 197.
3. Landsberg, H. H. *et al.*, Resources in America's Future; *Pattern of Requirements and Availabilities 1960–2000*, Johns Hopkins Press, Baltimore, Md., 1964.
4. Keller, R., The World's Freshwater: Yesterday, Today, Tomorrow, *Applied Geography and Development*, Institute of Scientific Cooperation, Tunbingen, Vol. 24, p. 14, 1984.
5. Stein Volker, Mining and Environment, *Natural Resources and Development*, Institute of Scientific Cooperation, Tunbigen, Vol. 29, 1984, p. 8.
6. Graves, N. J., The Use of Land, Water and Mineral Resources, *Science and Technology Education and Future Human Needs*, CTS and ICSU, 1985, p. 9.
7. Hagget, P., *Geography: A Modern Synthesis*, Harper & Row, 1975, p. 136. The data in this book has been extracted from R. U. Ayres, *Science Journal*, Vol. 3, No. 10, 1967, p. 102.
8. O'Connor, Anthony, Studying the Problems of Land Use in East Africa, *Science and Technology Education and Future Human Needs*, CTS & ICSU, 1985, p. 1.
9. Hodder, B. W., *Economic Developments in Tropics*, Methuen, 1979, p. 16.
10. O'Connor, Anthony, *op. cit.*, p. 4.

11. Misra, H. N., *Popular Settlements in Allahabad City*, IIDR, 1985.
12. Yakuba, J. M., A Case Study of Technology in Relation to Land Use in Ghana, *Science and Technology Education and Future Human Needs*, CTS & ICSU, 1985, p. 10.
13. *Encyclopaedia Britannica of Social Sciences*, p. 403.
14. Keller, R., *op. cit.*, p. 1.
15. Strahler, A. N., *et al.*, *Geography and Man's Environment*, John Wiley & Sons, New York, 1977, p. 94.
16. Biological water is the water absorbed by the flora and fauna. This accounts for more than 50% of the flowing water (Keller, R., *op. cit.*, 1984).
17. Strahler, A. N., *op. cit.*, p. 93.
18. Ibid, p. 93.
19. Ibid, p. 93.
20. Misra, H. N., *Health and Habitat in Popular Settlements: A Case Study of Chheetpur, Allahabad City*, IIDR, Allahabad, 1984.
21. Rao, K. L., *India's Water Wealth*, Orient Longman, 1975, p. 135.
22. Spargo, P. E., The Orange River Project – A Case Study, *Science and Technology Education and Future Needs*, CTS & ICSU, 1985.
23. Vedanayagam, E. G., Case Study of Periyar-Vaigal Project, *Science and Technology Education and Future Human Needs*, CTS & ICSU, 1975.
24. Knowels, R. and Wareing, J., *Economic and Social Geography*, W. H. Allen, London, 1976, p. 166.
25. Ibid, p. 162.
26. Lovering, T. S., Mineral Resources from the Land, in *Resources and Man*, W. H. Freeman, London, 1969, p. 110.
27. Schippers, H. J., Mining and Infrastructure in Developing Countries, *Natural Resources and Development* Institute for Scientific Cooperation, Tubingen, Vol. 16, 1982, p. 27.
28. Ibid, p. 30.

PART II

Land Use

Team Leader: J. P. STOLTMAN

3

Viewpoints and Problems of Land Use

Introduction

JOSEPH P. STOLTMAN

University of Western Michigan, U.S.A.

Teaching on land use, in most areas of most scales (local, national, global), at most levels, involves consideration of at least eight issues.

Land as a finite resource

This is quite evident globally with all acknowledging the ultimate "limits to growth" though no consensus exists on where these limits lie. It may be less evident from the perspective of individual families or even local communities where pressure on land resources is not yet severe. Of course, land (resources) may not be finite in vertical terms, either literally up and down (multi-storey buildings, under-ground railways) or in respect of increasing intensity of land use (see Misra, Chapter 2).

Land as a dynamic system

Units of land must be seen to relate to each other, e.g. valley sides and valley floor, or a "hill top" is not just the land surface, but also includes the soil beneath and the flora and fauna above. A complex physical system and an even more complex ecosystem is always involved (again at every scale).

Land related to water and minerals

The links have been indicated in Graves' introduction. "Land" is sometimes taken to embrace surface and ground water, and all minerals, but in this volume land, water and minerals are reviewed side by side. In some respects they differ greatly (e.g. minerals are commodities that can be moved to where they are needed) and are a major element in international trade. This is not the case with land. Mineral use often involves directly only a few decision-makers, but land use often involves directly innumerable decision-makers. In each case water perhaps lies somewhere between the other two. Such differences have sufficient educational implications to justify separate treatment in this book.

Optimum or appropriate use of land

If land is to contribute its share to meeting human needs, optimum use must be the goal. This is easily said, but who is to determine what constitutes the optimum (or even what is appropriate)? Value judgements are involved here, and the optimum will rarely be the same from all perspectives. From a nation-state viewpoint military land use may have a place, whereas from both an individual and a global perspective, it has no place in the optimum. Furthermore, from every viewpoint what is most appropriate may differ as between the short term and the long term, and a sequence of different uses may ideally be involved. Perhaps the nearest to the optimum use of land may be where the possibility or recycling its use is maximum.

Competition between alternative land uses

Competition will always be involved, again at every scale and in all situations – both rural and urban. Wildlife sanctuaries, reservoirs (water!) and factories are all land uses that are likely to be the outcome of competition, and to be against the interests of someone. This implies decision-making (individual, local, national, global), so we are educating people both to make decisions themselves and to understand the dilemmas of those making decisions elsewhere or at a higher (or lower) level?

Impact of science and technology

Land use will always be affected by science and technology, and will vary from place to place according to the technology available. An agreed appropriate or optimum use may depend on adoption of new technology. However, there is not just one universal evolving form of science and technology. Each society has its own scientific notions (ethnoscience) and its own technologies in particular fields, and often teachers must recognize a duality arising from the co-existence of indigenous and introduced knowledge, each of which has a vital contribution to make to land use decisions. This theme is taken up briefly on p. 40.

Demographic, cultural, economic and political influences

These considerations will all be relevant in almost every situation. The rate of population growth, male/female roles and land ownership structures provide obvious examples. Any use of land is a response to an economic demand for some product or service, whether on a commercial or a subsistence basis. The extent of the power of the state varies immensely from country to country and may often be a critical factor. The key educational problem here seems to be just what proportion of the time available, can be given to such considerations when the teaching is essentially in a "science" context. (It is unlikely to be the same as when teaching is in a social studies context.)

Personal and aesthetic dimensions

The last point made above applies with at least equal force to aesthetic considerations, or indeed to other non-material dimensions. Different societies differ greatly in the priority they give to aesthetic and spiritual, as against material, "needs". In most of the more affluent societies where the basic material needs of almost everyone are fully satisfied, the unmet needs may be mainly non-material. Even within any one society individuals will differ greatly in the priority they give to aesthetic, emotional and spiritual needs, and teaching on many topics, including land use, must encourage students to recognize this.

In order to exemplify the range of land use problems in developing countries, the following case study is provided.

Studying problems of land use in East Africa

ANTHONY O'CONNOR, *University College, London*

This section is provided by a geographer whose teaching experience has been almost entirely in universities, both in Africa and in Britain. It indicates and illustrates themes which seem to need attention at that level. Some may be equally relevant for teaching at secondary level. That is for the teacher to decide. A focus on land use combines the two traditional, and still central, themes of geography, firstly man–environment relationships and secondly spatial differentiation and organization. The same focus could appropriately be more evident than it now is within various interdisciplinary studies, providing the opportunity to explore how the most basic of all natural resources is managed in efforts to meet some of the most basic of human requirements.

Land use issues are examined here with particular reference to East Africa, though many points made are applicable elsewhere in Africa and perhaps beyond. There is no part of the world where land is of more intense concern – to individuals, to communities, and to the state. In Kenya,

Tanzania and Uganda over 80% of the population still directly depend upon it for their livelihood, while in neighbouring Burundi and Rwanda the figure is over 90%. The ethnic groups with which most people still strongly identify are closely associated with specific tracts of land, and even most urban dwellers have a powerful attachment to the land of their original rural home area. In Kenya especially, issues of land ownership and occupance, land alienation and land resettlement, land-grabbing and landlessness, have long been at the heart of political life as well as economic affairs.

In most parts of this region basic human needs, however defined, are by no means fully satisfied, even if the situation is not as desperate as in neighbouring Ethiopia. It is a region of immense cultural richness, but also of indisputable material poverty. On all indicators of development Burundi and Rwanda are among the lowest ranking countries in the world. Tanzania's achievements in political and social development over the post-independence period have not been matched on the economic front. At least parts of Uganda were relatively prosperous in the 1960s, but a mixture of tyranny and anarchy under Amin shattered its economy. Kenya has much the best economic record in aggregate terms, but there inequality is greater than in the other countries, and while material gains have been more widely distributed than some critics suggest, at least half the population has had little share in these.

Inevitably, therefore, *future* human needs are far from assured, especially in view of a population increase as rapid as any in the world, and probably now exceeding 4% a year in Kenya. Both in that country and in Burundi and Rwanda scarcity of usable land must present increasingly severe problems, whereas in Uganda fears for the future rest more on the establishment of socio-economic structures that will make effective use of the land. Throughout the region perceived needs may well increase even faster than population numbers, for aspirations are rising, fuelled by the rapid expansion of education – the one facet of development in respect of which even the most ambitious targets have been largely attained.

The aim of this paper is to raise a wide range of issues involved in studying land use in East Africa rather than to examine any specific land use situations in depth. Some of the issues are essentially conceptual, some relate to basic description, some concern attempts at explanation of existing patterns, and some concern alternative policies for the future. The structure of the discussion will be based on these distinctions.

Conceptual issues

Different people will undoubtedly mean different things by the phrase "land use". There is necessarily a contrast between a macro view of how the total land resources of a country or region are exploited and what determines this, and a micro view of what the individual does or should do with any patch of land under his or her control. The view offered here is the macro view of someone who has been privileged to work and travel in East Africa but who is still an outsider. Perhaps almost any insider would have a different perspective. Equally, however, the ideas of most academics in Dar es Salaam or Nairobi would differ from those of "the man in the street" or indeed "the woman in the field". We might also speculate that the phrase "land use" however translated, would have quite different connotations for most Kikuyu cultivators from those it would have for most Turkana pastoralists.

Among the academic outsiders there are some who would see the study of land use as largely synonymous with the study of agriculture, and others whose interpretation would be much broader. A discussion of land use confined entirely to agriculture is surely as unjustified as the all-too-frequent discussion of rural dwellers as "farmers", as if they undertook no other forms of economic activity. Just as most of these people are also part-time builders, cooks, fuel suppliers, nurses, and local politicians, so rural land use involves much beside cultivation and stock rearing. The gathering of fuelwood is a particularly relevant case in the present context. Following the broadest interpretation, matters such as city planning and the growth of unplanned settlement within the cities would also require attention. Urban areas occupy far less than 1% of the land of East Africa, but it is often contested land, as well as congested land, and is used to house an increasing share of the population. Conversely, National Parks and Game Reserves are of minor importance even in East Africa in terms of numbers of people directly affected by them, but they occupy a larger proportion of the total land area here than anywhere else in the world, and again provide examples of intense land use competition.

The matter of competition raises the distinction between the social and political question of land use *by whom*, which will be of most interest to some people, and the economic question of land use *for what*, which will interest others more. Furthermore, any comprehensive discussions of East African land use should involve a dialogue between these social scientists and the technologists, who may take the matters of "who" and "for what" as given, concentrating their attention on "how". Certainly the prospects for the satisfaction of human needs from the land will depend on the answers to all three questions.

The time dimension is relevant in other ways in addition to projecting into the future. It was highly significant on a grand scale when Europeans occupied large tracts of Kenya that appeared then to be unused. Much of this land certainly had previously been used by the local population, and would have been so used again if this settlement by outsiders had not occurred. At a more mundane level the time dimension affects measurement of present day land use in terms of conventional categories such as arable or cultivated land, especially in an area where much land is still managed on the basis of shifting cultivation systems. Even the bush fallowing or land rotation systems now practised by far more people involve the use of much larger areas than are under cultivation at any one point of time. Seasonality is another vital theme in the understanding of East African land use.

The most challenging conceptual issues are perhaps political or ethical issues. One concerns who has the right to determine use in any locality. It might arguably be the individual land-holder, the extended family, the local community, or the nation-state. In some situations ultimate responsibility may even be seen as global, for instance in relation to wild life sanctuaries. A second issue concerns who determines the priority needs. The perceptions of those in authority (e.g. needing electricity and thus a dam) may differ from those of the local community (e.g. needing more cattle and thus more grazing land) and study of the situation involves considering what should be regarded as "needs" rather than merely "wants". Such questions are essentially the same in East Africa as anywhere else, but the answers may depend on local circumstances.

Basic description

Education relating to land use in East Africa is greatly hindered by a lack of accessible and reliable data. Individuals may know exactly what use they make of their own land, and small communities may have almost as comprehensive collective knowledge, but the patterns over whole districts and countries are not known accurately by anyone. The data published by national governments and by organizations such as FAO involve much guess work as well as uncertain definitions. It should be more widely acknowledged that no one knows how much land in East Africa is used in any year for cultivation, for livestock or for fuelwood, nor at what rate such use is increasing. With regard to individual crops, complications arise also from the fact that intercropping is widespread, and that the cultivation of ten crops in one field is not uncommon. Our knowledge of the nature of the land use in such respects as male versus female labour, or use of ploughs or fertilizers is equally imprecise.

With respect to some elements in the description of current land use the advent of remote sensing has vastly increased the potential knowledge. Already a vast store of information does actually exist in the form of satellite imagery, though some technical, and more financial and political, problems stand in the way of its transformation into knowledge accessible to any decision-makers in East Africa as well as to anyone teaching about the region's land use. Furthermore, there is much that could be learned from this material regarding untapped land resources and hence potential land use. Here lies one of the most obvious opportunities for the application of science and technology and hence education in these fields, to the problem of satisfying future human needs. Such information sources can certainly overcome the need for immensely time consuming comprehensive surveys on the ground, but it must be stressed that sample surveys in a variety of areas remain a vital tool of research if the data are to be correctly evaluated, and that these involve both technical and social components.

Some other approaches to the description of land use in a region such as this are a matter much less of technical expertise and much more of personal interpretation. Some relate to basic concepts in social science, and two will be mentioned here even though they are often used for explanation as well as description. As a supplement to distinctions between functional land uses such as cultivation or forestry one might see land use in East Africa as a manifestation of cultural and technological dualism. For most of this century there has been a sharp contrast between tracts of agricultural land managed by the indigenous people operating on a small scale and using mainly traditional techniques, and tracts managed by aliens operating on a far larger scale with imported technology. A similar distinction has existed between traditional grazing areas and ranch land. Even within cities some land has been used according to traditional, though evolving norms, and other land has been used following systems imported from overseas. For many years this distinction was especially clear within Kampala.

This duality can of course be exaggerated. Introduced systems always required some modifications, and even in the Kenya highlands land is not used in quite the same way as in England. Meanwhile, indigenous systems of land use were much modified by the colonial impact, notably in the form of the introduction of new cash crops. If distinctions were somewhat blurred even in the colonial period they are far more so today. In Kenya nearly all farms really were then of either less than 5 or more than 50 hectares: but how many former large farms have been taken over by groups or co-operatives and are operated at an intermediate scale, while some individuals in the small-farm areas have expanded their holdings and operations also to an intermediate scale. Even so, the notion of contrasting systems juxtaposed and co-existing, not necessarily implying one superior to the other, remains of value for understanding present patterns of land use in East Africa.

Equally relevant, and in some ways related, is the notion of dependency. A distinction might be made between land uses that represent the tapping of local land resources to meet local needs, and those that involve much external contact, influence and even control. In the rural areas the latter often take the form of using the land to produce commodities such as coffee or tea that are exported overseas in exchange for imported goods such as oil or various manufacturers. These may help to meet basic local needs, or they may satisfy mainly the highly limited demand for luxuries. Some observers, however, would argue that penetration from outside has been so comprehensive that it is a matter of recognizing such dependency everywhere rather than making a distinction as above. Certainly a full description of land use in East Africa today should note the ways in which much of it is part of a worldwide system of human activity, and is dependent on decisions taken far outside the region: but this issue is perhaps even more significant in relation to attempts to explain the observed patterns of land use.

Attempts at explanation

Explanation may be attempted from a variety of intellectual perspectives, and debate at cross purposes sometimes results, for the approaches may really be complementary rather than contradictory. One group of approaches, which might be labelled as positivist, emphasizes apparently objective facts and tries to correlate variations in these with the diversity of land use. A second group, which we might call either behavioural or humanistic, stresses the decision-making processes involved, and involves asking the individuals involved why they use the land as they do. A third group of approaches, often termed structuralist, is less concerned with observable and measurable facts, or with what individuals say about their own motivations, and more concerned with underlying economic, social and political structures which are considered to determine very largely what happens and where.

Studies of the first type have shown that climate, notably total amount, seasonality and reliability of rainfall, soil conditions, incidence of disease, population density, various cultural attributes and accessibility have all played a part in influencing patterns of rural land use, along with historical accident and government policy. There is a close correlation between population density and intensity of land use, though it is rarely clear which is cause and which is effect. The tsetse fly prevents cattle keeping over large areas, while infestation by those species which spread sleeping sickness in humans has caused certain well-watered and fertile lakeshore areas in Uganda to be used only as forest reserve. The distribution of nomadic pastoralism reflects not so much the prevalence of suitable climatic conditions as the prevalence of conditions that inhibit settled agriculture and the distribution of game reserves is similarly influenced by climate unsuited to agriculture as well as by the density of game animals. Accessibility has been most significant for export crops, especially those of low value for weight such as sisal, and for activities such as commercial dairying.

Explanations in behavioural terms require more attention to the question of who determines land use, and an effort to see the situation from the perspective of this individual, group or agency. Climatic factors still emerge as highly significant, but it is now the climate as perceived, often with a strong emphasis on matters of security and risk. In many tsetse-infested areas there is not only little cattle rearing but also little cultivation: often far more land could be cultivated, but few people choose to live there because most wish to keep some cattle. The highly distinctive pattern of land use in the remaining large-farm areas of the Kenya highlands reflects various objective facts about these areas, but also depends on the choices made by a few thousand European settlers early in the century. Another set of decisions, this time by politicians and government officials, determined which of these (white Highland) areas had their land use transformed through post-independence resettlement schemes.

In the case of some tea and sugar estates the land use decisions have been made far away in the headquarters of multinational corporations, but the influence of such agencies in East Africa is generally much more indirect. Where rural land use is not determined by the rural community themselves it is most often determined by some branch of the state. In Tanzania the pattern of rural land use was modified in almost every part of the country in the 1970s as a result of the villagization programme pushed forward by the government and party. At a local scale government community and personal decisions have all played a part in determining who uses what land in what way around the new villages. In each country forest reserves constitute a form of land use that has resulted largely from government decisions over a much longer period.

The value of behavioural or humanistic approaches to the explanation of land use patterns is perhaps most evident within the cities. Many features which persist today reflect the attitudes of colonial planners and administrators, notably a sharp separation between functional and residential areas, and a massive contrast between low-density high-income (formerly European) and high-density low-income (formerly African) residential areas. Both Dar es Salaam and Nairobi also have distinctive areas occupied almost exclusively by people of Asian origin, and the persistence of these must be explained partly in terms of personal preference and communal cohesion rather than considerations such as income levels.

Those seeking explanations in structural terms, however, would stress that urban squatters for example, make their choices within very severe constraints, and that the fact that Mathare Valley (Nairobi) and Manzese (Dar es Salaam) are occupied by squatter settlements is largely the result of economic inequality and social injustice. Emphasis is placed upon impersonal forces rather than individual decision-makers as determinants of both urban and rural land use patterns. In these terms most changes in rural land use in East Africa during this century have resulted from the spread of capitalism and the incorporation of the peasantry into a system over which they had no control. A contrary view is that capitalism has largely failed to capture the peasantry, and that land use is essentially determined by persisting pre-capitalist structures.

On a more limited scale the patterns of land use in the semi-arid areas of East Africa are sometimes seen largely in terms of conflict between cultivators and pastoralists, with the land use practices of the latter increasingly governed by the pressures exerted by the spread of cultivator groups into their territory.

Alternative policies

Just as all the approaches indicated above have something to contribute to explanation, so also each of them is of some relevance for policy-making. If future human needs are to be satisfied in East Africa a wide range of land use problems will have to be tackled at local, national and supra-national levels. Little can be done to alter the climate but there is scope for much more irrigation than takes place at present, and for the breeding of crop varieties that are less exacting in their rainfall requirements. With more widespread use of improved fertilizers more intensive forms of land use could often be adopted, while there are many ways in which the control of human, animal and plant diseases could assist more productive forms of land use. Many observers of the East African scene would also advocate population policies designed to reduce pressure upon the land, both by a reduction in the general birth rate through the spread of contraceptive practice and by planned redistribution of population towards areas now experiencing least pressure. Numerous other policy measures designed to change specific circumstances, in the field of transport and energy for example, could also influence future land use patterns.

The second approach would place much more emphasis on attitudes, both of the policy-makers and of the population in general. It is possible that the specific measures agreed by government matter less than the sincerity with which they are adopted, and both the enthusiasm and sensitivity with which they are implemented. At the same time the state can achieve very little in East Africa unless the people give their whole-hearted support. Indeed, the most effective measures for improved land use to satisfy basic needs in each area might be those which the people of the area would suggest if they were given the opportunity. Most often both "above" and "below" have something to contribute, and the problem is how to organize an effective dialogue. Tanzania has put far more effort into this than most countries, but with only limited success.

Education within the region clearly has a vital part to play, especially in countries where half the population is under eighteen. It will affect the degree to which "technical" policies ranging from irrigation to family planning can actually be implemented, but it will also affect the extent to which local people are able to formulate their own responses to land use problems and pressures. Only through education can those from cultivating communities become aware of the pastoralists' perspective and vice versa. No educational programmes will prevent an ultimate confrontation between those arguing for game reserves and those who insist that the land must be used to grow food, but some mutual understanding may mitigate the conflict.

The third approach indicates that the only policies that get to the root of problems of poverty, including specific land use problems, are those that tackle basic economic, social and political structures. It is argued that neither well-planned irrigation schemes nor attempts to listen to the suggestions of the land users will provide lasting solutions as long as macro-structures remain as at present. At a national level this viewpoint is now put forward most often and most eloquently with regard to Kenya, especially with reference to how much land is controlled by whom, but also in terms of broader class and power structures. It is in Tanzania that most deliberate action has been taken to alter fundamental structures, and some are sure that it has largely failed, though others are more cautious and merely acknowledge that it has not yet succeeded in ensuring that basic needs are met. Perhaps it is actually in anguished Uganda that there is the greatest need for attention to be concentrated in the basic economic, social and political structures within which life goes on.

Fundamental structure at the international level may be equally significant. The use of much of the most fertile land in East Africa to grow coffee for consumption in Europe and North America may or may not be in the interests of the people of East Africa, depending partly upon the price that is paid for it. That price is totally outside the control of the growers, and indeed such forms of land use put much of the control over East Africa's future into the hands of decision-makers elsewhere in the world. No one in East Africa can alter global power structures, but there is a degree of option regarding the extent of incorporation into or withdrawal from global networks.

It must by now be evident that this writer does not believe that any one approach has a monopoly of the truth, with respect to either understanding the present situation or policy prescription for the future. Visible "facts" and human attitudes underlying structures are all relevant in every situation. There is not even much point in debating their relative importance with respect to such a topic as land use in East Africa, especially since this almost certainly differs from one area to another and one situation to another. What is important is that all should be taken into account in any attempt to understand the present or to prescribe for the future.

4

The Educational Implications of Land Use Problems

JOSEPH P. STOLTMAN
University of Western Michigan, U.S.A.

The contemporary development of most educational systems has two major elements. The first is general education at the primary and secondary levels. During that period of schooling the student is introduced to a wide body of educational experiences designed to develop basic skills, intellectual processes, and as preparation for lifelong learning. The second is tertiary, professional and specialist schooling. While some aspects may indeed begin at the secondary school level, most require technical and professional skills and development available only through higher education. The general education focus upon land and land use should occur across the primary and secondary curriculum incorporating information, attitudinal investigations towards the land, ethical considerations and field studies in a formal curriculum structure. Professional, specialist and technical education may occur in a formal curricular structure or in an informal structure. The universal presence of land use questions necessitates that both formal and informal educational practices be incorporated.

General education

Children begin to explore the land and places on the landscape at a very early age. They learn to make their way through the maze of structures and pathways in the local village, community, or neighbourhood. The child's perception of the land is ever expanding. The personal space of the home gradually extends out to include much larger areas. It is this view of the land which the child brings to formal education, with considerable variation from individual to individual based upon rural or urban background, or a number of other conditions. The fact is, that children bring to school with them a wide range of views towards and information about the land.

Within formal education, the primary years are a time for the development of observational and classification skills regarding the land. Instruction should be true to the local area and expand the child's knowledge of land and the uses of the land. The ways in which the family unit is tied to and makes use of the land should be a focus as it provides an example of the close link between people and land resources.

In the upper primary and early secondary years the students should begin to make a comparative study of the land as a resource. Contrasting land uses in the local area may be identified, data about each of them collected and the information analysed and evaluated. Considerations of slope, soil, land value, site and situation provide larger conceptual structures within which land use may be studied.

The upper secondary school is where the more detailed and perhaps technologically based, study of land and land use should be introduced. A scientific exploration of soil science as it is related to land use may be developed, incorporating both field work and laboratory work.

Small- and large-scale studies of land use may be undertaken using aerial photography and other remotely sensed data. The benefits of using remotely sensed images with students provides both an application of new technologies to land and land use studies as well as permitting a spatial or graphic analysis of information regarding the surface of the earth. However, scientific understanding must be matched with a similar appreciation of the social and economic context. Only when this occurs will such scientific understanding be truly applicable.

The educational implications of teaching about land, land use, science and technology ultimately relates to the people who occupy the land. While the focus is usually on new technology there is a broad category of indigenous technologies which must also be recognized. This technology exists virtually everywhere but is most important in non-Western societies. One aspect of education's mission is to preserve indigenous knowledge as well as introducing new knowledge. Education must assist in the diffusion of indigenous knowledge and technology where they offer a solution to local problems. It must be recognized that indigenous technology or knowledge does not have all the answers. Indigenous knowledge may not be the appropriate technology to use in solving a problem. This is especially true when people have migrated and taken technology to a new environment where it does not fit or may not help solve a land use problem. However, indigenous technology and knowledge observed in a local area will usually contribute to the blend of indigenous and introduced technology and scientific information essential to successfully dealing with land use problems. For example, preventing soil erosion may be done by combining traditional terracing methods with western methods of strengthening terrace walls.

Formal technical education

Good land use requires informed politicians and planners, and a high level of technical expertise on the part of, for example, soil scientists, extension workers, agriculturalists and foresters. The scientists need accurate, up-to-date knowledge of existing and ever changing patterns and relationships in the environment. Technical education at the tertiary level has a vital role in this context. Although this expertise is required across a whole spectrum of science disciplines, it seems that progress should, and is likely to be made in two areas related to land use studies. Soil science in the developing world is hampered in so far as much of the classical understanding of soils has been obtained in the temperate climates of the northern hemisphere. Here soils are largely of recent origin, whereas in much of the developing world soils have developed in tropical and sub-tropical climates with their higher temperatures and intense rainfalls. Whilst the principles remain the same, the land use practices found satisfactory in temperate lands may be quite unsatisfactory given the different limiting factors which apply in developing countries. It is suggested that courses on soil science in the developing countries, at whatever level but particularly at the tertiary, should emphasize the effects and relationships of soil (soil chemistry) the role of plants, animals and micro-fauna and flora (soil biology) and the variations encountered in soils in the field. All these should have special reference to tropical and sub-tropical soils.

From a practical standpoint any attempt to plan, modify or reclaim land requires spatial information that is economically acquired as well as up-to-date and accurate. During the last decade at least, remotely sensed images have been periodically available enabling recognition of major changes in land use at the regional scale. These photographs can be enlarged to 1:250,000 without loss of detail. By and large such information has been limited to specialist uses and tertiary level education. But it is a technology that will have a far ranging impact if used fully. The extent of soil erosion, zones of dense natural vegetation, wetland areas, wasteland, the spread of shifting cultivation practices, crop types, the availability of ground-water and the changing urban landscape can be assessed using satellite images or aerial photographs, with a stereoscope for three-dimensional viewing. The technical skills of photographic interpretation could be developed in secondary schools as well as at the tertiary level. Adoption of such tools in classrooms clearly depends on their availability and the willingness of teachers to handle such equipment.

Informal technical education

This type of land use education is represented by the foresting extension programme which is found in Nepal. The purpose is to raise the productivity and standards of living of people dependent on forest products. Communal forest custody and management succeed only if there is a concerted effort by entire communities. Thus, the training of the community leaders is vital, to develop awareness of the responsibility of the community for the forests and the technical understanding of silviculture. Informal technical education depends upon a number of *different learning resources*. Its approach is distinct by virtue of the vast array of ways it is presented to the recipient (e.g. radio, newspaper, television, posters).

Summary

Learning about land resources and land use begins at an early age in the local community. Through the use of scientific and technological means, the ability to study land use problems and issues develops to include larger areas and regions as well as to delve into soil, water balance and other such topics. The pervasive issue of land as a finite resource, the scientific and technical means to manage that resource, and the fact that the world's people are inextricably tied to the land, all provide a rationale for the educational implications of land use.

5
Teaching Examples

Land: its human uses

JOSEPH P. STOLTMAN
University of Western Michigan, U.S.A.

Strategy

The teaching strategy proposed in "Land, Its Human Uses" is guided learning. The materials may be used in other ways, including using the maps and diagrams for brainstorming. The ethical considerations may provide an opportunity to focus mainly upon attitudes and values in learning. Finally, the questioning of data and future projections may permit an extension of the lessons to inquiry. The teacher will have to judge which strategy is appropriate in the classroom.

Module overview

This teaching module or unit introduces students to the concepts associated with the ways in which the surface of the earth has been used. Among the numerous resources of the earth, land is the most important. Within its structure are found the natural elements which humans have learned to incorporate in the maintenance of life. On the surface of the earth, land more directly meets the demands of the human inhabitants. All the activities of humans, whether they are for the provision of food, clothing, and shelter or some other endeavour, are inextricably tied to the land.

Description of materials

Courses and topics

The concepts presented in the module are appropriate for students studying geography, earth science, and natural resources topics.

Grade level

The materials are designed for 12- to 13-year-old students, but could be incorporated with more advanced classes if supplementary materials were added.

Time required

Usually one class period of 40 to 50 minutes will be required for each activity in the module.

Concepts and skills

Broad concepts presented include land use and human welfare. More specific objectives are listed with each activity in the module. Skills developed in the module include map reading, map making and graph, chart and diagram reading. Field observation skills are developed through the recommended local examples in each lesson.

Instructional objectives

Upon completing the activities in this module the students will be able to:

1. Describe the different uses which humans have for the surface of the earth.
2. Explain the relationships between the land resources of the earth and human welfare.

Sources

Thomas, Wm. (ed.) *Man's Role in Changing the Face of the Earth*. Chicago: University of Chicago Press, 1956.

Iozzi, L. *et. al. People and Environmental Changes*. New Brunswick: Institute for Science, Technology and Social Science Education, 1980.

Iozzi, L. *Technology and Changing Lifestyles: Teacher's Guide*, Longmont, Colorado: Sopris West, Inc., 1982.

Lesson 1. Land use decisions – people using the land

Key Concepts

Land use, conservation, soil degradation

Lesson objectives

The students should be able to:

1. Apply land use principles to their community;
2. Describe the importance of land use decisions;
3. Evaluate the way land is used.

Introducing the activity

1. This lesson develops the social impact of land use, including soils as an essential element in land use decisions.

   Begin the discussion by asking the students how they depend upon soil. How have the uses of the land changed in their community during the past 50 years? For example, the school may not be 50 years old. What was here before the school? Before the school, this area was devoted to a different type of land use. The soil has changed little, but the land use has changed a great deal. Why did the land use change? Possible explanations may include population change, urban sprawl, a new town, or the spread of formal education.

2. Develop discussion which enables the students to list the things they use which come indirectly from the soil. As an example, many foods come directly from the soil. However, many manufactured products indirectly relate back to the soil. Aluminium containers, for example, began as bauxite ore. After processing and manufacturing, the containers are used for many different things. Ask the students to list the things they use on a day-to-day basis and classify them on the basis of their ties to the soil and land.

3. Define the following terms and have the students record them. Land use – The way in which people use the surface of the earth (e.g. agricultural use, urban use, transportation use). Land cover – The natural state or cover on the land (e.g. swamp, rocky, outcrops, grassland). Conservation – The practice of caring for the natural environment, including land, water and wild life, so that it provides for different needs, as well as meets the essential requirements of society and is not degraded or lost. Soil degradation – Practices which result in the reduced quality and productivity of soils.

Developing the activity

4. Present the class with Fig. 5.1, the Development Map. The map may also be presented on the board or overhead projector. Instruct the students to work either individually or in pairs and plan an agricultural community. A map of the local area may also be used. Students will need to take into account the basic necessities (e.g. shelter, transportation, water) but every element of the design should be of their own making. They may consider relief, village location, soil quality. However, rather than listing all the elements they must consider, provide them with adequate hints and begin work. Provide the students sufficient, but limited time to complete their development map either in school or as a homework.

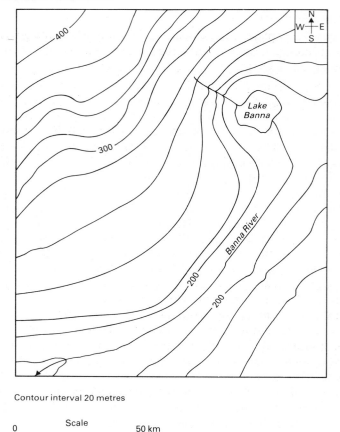

Contour interval 20 metres

```
        Scale
0                        50 km
└──┴──┴──┴──┴──┘
```

FIG. 5.1. Development map.

5. The next step is have the students analyse the completed development maps by looking at the following questions. What did you imagine your map to be like before you added anything to it?

Why did you decide to locate the various elements of the agricultural area where you placed them?

Classify the elements that you took into consideration in developing the area. What types of objects take up space on the land?

Estimate or measure the percentages of the areas of the map which are devoted to various land uses. What types of and how much land is left for future development?

The answers will, of course, vary from student to student. Ask how they came to the decision regarding how much land to devote to various uses. The importance of the land for agriculture uses was a part of this development plan. In a similar fashion land is used to meet the needs which place it in demand, or in a way which the governmental authorities determine. When the government classifies certain areas for specific uses, this is referred to as land use planning.

Concluding the activity

6. Begin the discussion by asking the students why land is considered a natural resource. What can people get from the land? Why does land have value to people? Do all groups of people view the land as being used in the same way? Conclude the discussion by reviewing how people depend upon the land and the soil.

Local examples

7. Make a classification of the different ways in which land is used in the local area. If it is a non-agricultural area, the different land uses may be classified. In an agricultural area the crops may be classified as specific land uses, as may residential and transportation uses.
8. It is important to begin studying how technology and science have helped in determining the uses of land. List the ways in which machines or agricultural science have altered the ways in which land in the local vicinity is used. Has its fertility been enhanced with chemical fertilizers? Are new types of crop grown? Were machines used to change the way the land is arranged so that more or less agriculture could take place?

Concluding the activity (Fig. 5.2)

9. Look at the vegetation map of the world and review the regions where the tropical rainforests are being converted to agricultural land. What problems might this present in the future? Do the people of the world rely upon the rainforests to provide any other of the world's resources? What about the rainforest as a drainage basin? As a place where thousands of species of plants, birds, insects and animals live? Should we continue to reduce the size of the rainforest?

Local examples

10. The clearing of the tropical rainforest is viewed by many environmentalists as a global situation similar to cutting the trees in a public park or community green. The question is one of ethics regarding whether or not one group has the right to alter the environment which another group shares. This is the root question of

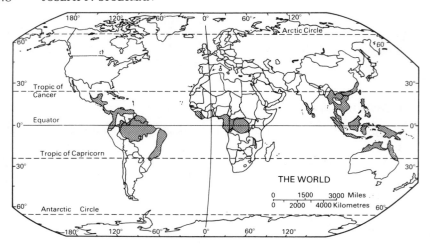

Fɪɢ. 5.2. Tropical rainforests.

land use decisions. Point out and discuss an example of converting a natural environment to a human made environment in your local area. Was it controversial? Why? Do you think that changing global land use patterns should be decided upon by all nations of the globe?

Lesson 2. Land use decision – agricultural to urban

Key concepts

Land value, site, situation.

Lesson objectives

The student should be able to:

1. Evaluate land in urban areas by site and situation for its value to individuals and society;
2. Analyse the importance of local and global connections to land value;
3. Graph and interpret data related to land use and other human activities.

Introducing the activity

1. Begin the lesson by drawing on the board, on an overhead transparency, or on a handout a map showing the location of a nearby city (perhaps the national capital). Select an appropriate hypothetical case in which a new airport, market centre, or highway is being built and apply it to the city. It will be more appropriate to the lesson if the

land upon which the new activity is being located is agricultural land, or open land. Instruct the students to suggest the various activities which might be attracted to the new development. What might they produce or manufacture? What kind of services might they require? List the suggested activities on the board. Which of the activities might involve the largest amount of return to be earned by the people?

2. Point out to the students that the suggestions made regarding various activities require land. Because they require land they will make land use decisions necessary. Define each of the following terms for the students.

Land value – the worth which is placed upon a parcel of land based upon its overall suitability for use. In a socialist society, the value is often related to the overall benefits which society in general receives from the land being used in a particular way. In a capitalist society, the value of the land is often based upon the economic returns it will bring to the landowner.

Site – the physical attributes of the location of the land, including soil, water, slope, and vegetation.

Situation – the relative location of the site to all other sites, either in same vicinity or at greater distances. Transportation and communications are important considerations.

Developing the activity

3. Place a map of your region, state, nation, or the world on the board. If maps of all areas are available, it is useful to have more than one area represented. Discuss with the class the degree to which your local area is connected to other parts of the region, state, nation, and world. Identify this as the situation which may have some bearing upon land use decision. If, in your judgement, the local vicinity is not suitable to develop the concept of situation, then use the capital city of the state or nation. Because it is the capital city, it has a situation which can be identified and described. Lead the students in a discussion which develops the concepts of situation as applied to that place.

4. Begin the next focus of the lesson with a view of the largest cities of the world. Cite London, New York, Delhi, Mexico City, Bangkok, Tokyo, Moscow, São Paulo, etc. Ask the students if the cities of the world are growing. Present them with the data in Fig. 5.3 which shows changing world urbanization.

5. Turn back to the question of land use. With a greater and greater number of people living in the cities, what will the cities require? Land! Where will the new land for urban development be found? What might be one of the present uses for the land which will be changed by urbanization? Urban areas provide one of the best examples of the

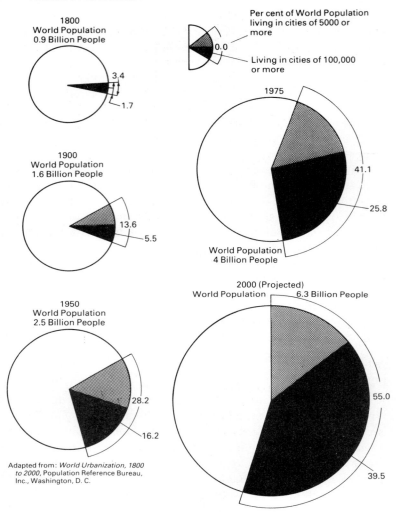

FIG. 5.3. Global urbanization.

change in land use from agriculture to another use, usually related to urban or economic development. Why does that change take place? Use the two examples which follow to help explain land use change from agricultural to urban.

a. Graph A (Fig. 5.4) shows the value of the same unit of land for six different land uses. Unless there is land use zoning which prohibits the development of the land use which brings about the higher return per unit of land, then it will be the preferred use.

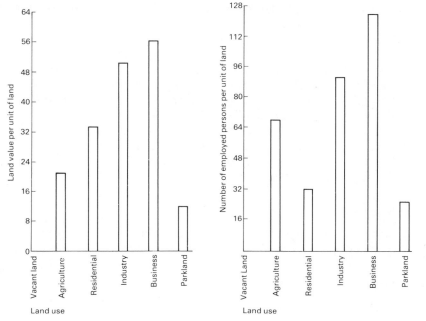

Fig. 5.4

b. Graph B (Fig. 5.4) shows six different land uses contrasted against number of employed persons per unit of land. Since employment in urban areas is an important factor, it might be judged that the greatest social good results if the land is used to employ the largest number of people. What are the ethical issues related to the provision of employment opportunity?

c. Using a blank graph paper have the following data entered by the students. Use the same land use categories:

Number of employed persons (Vertical axis)	Land value per unit in local currency (Horizontal axis)
2	2.5
16	20
48	40
90	60
116	80
126	100

What is the relationship on the graph between the number of employed persons per unit of land and land value? What types of land use might take place at the various points on the graph? Where would industry be located? Where would agriculture be located?

6. The remaining important consideration is the suitability of the site for a particular land use. The site of the city or town must be considered. Is it too hilly? Is there a large enough tract of land? Is the soil suitable for building upon? If it is proposed to build a factory, where will the workers live and how far will they have to travel to the workplace?

7. Instruct the students to suggest the various points which must be considered when a land use decision changing agricultural land to some other use is being made. Be certain to include the human considerations, such as the displacement of people from their homes as well as their farms. Include the land value, situation and site considerations.

Concluding the activity

8. Select an issue related to land use (e.g. traffic, air pollution, land value, human displacement). Restrict the discussion to the human element of the issue. What are the ethical issues which must be considered regarding the land? Is providing jobs to individuals more important than uprooting a community? What are the alternatives to major land use changes in favour of further development?

Local examples

9. Develop a land use map of the local area. The student may begin with the school and gradually extend the map outward, incorporating adjoining areas, the teacher may pose a hypothetical situation, such as what if a new factory were to be located on a nearby parcel of land. What issues would have to be considered? What problems might develop? What benefits might the community experience?

Lesson 3. Land use decisions and the future

Key concepts

Land pollution, cropland reduction, desert-creep.

Lesson objectives

The student should be able to:

1. Describe the relationship between land use and population distribution;
2. Develop a cost benefit analysis of a major project affecting land use;
3. Use a time and space matrix to evaluate the types of local land use changes which have occurred and project them into the future.

Introducing the Activity

1. Begin the lesson by projecting Fig. 5.5 with an overhead projector, placing it on the board, or distributing a copy to each student in class. Ask the student to identify the main categories of elements shown in

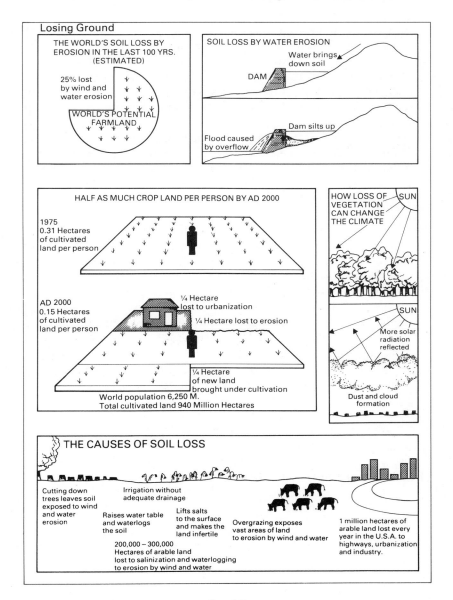

FIG. 5.5

Fig. 5.5. These are: erosion, urbanization, and land use change. Discuss ways in which those concepts have been developed in earlier lessons. Are there examples of additional land use issues which appear in Fig. 5.5? How does the example of the causes of soil loss in Fig. 5.5 demonstrate land use change?

2. Define each of the following items for the student. Land pollution – the process by which the land is rendered unsuitable for human activity. Pollution may result from over use of chemical fertilizers or herbicides, dumping of industrial refuse, and salt buildup from irrigation.

   Cropland reduction – the removal of land from active production of crops as a result of soil loss, salt buildup, urbanization, or chemical contamination.

   Desert-creep – the degree to which the vegetation of an area diminishes due to variations in weather patterns or from human use. Often referred to as desertification.

Developing the activity

Steps:

3. One of the important relationships to introduce is that of population distribution in relation to land use. Figure 5.5 projects those relationships to the year 2000. Get the students to evaluate the diagram as it might apply to the local area, the nation, and the world. How will the long term effects of urbanization and erosion bring about changes in the future? Notice in Fig. 5.5 that new land is being brought under cultivation. Will new land always be available in the future?

   Do not accept the information in Fig. 5.5 as absolutely true. It is a projection. How might such projections be inaccurate? What technical and social changes might alter the projection?

4. Read the article, "Consequences of the Aswan Dam, Egypt", Fig. 5.6, to your students or have them read the article as a homework assignment. Analyse the article for the benefits and costs of the project designed to increase the agricultural land of Egypt. Arrange the points from the article as in the Table 5.1.

TABLE 5.1

Benefits	Costs
1. Flood control	1. Salt buildup in soil
2.	2.
3.	3.

CONSEQUENCES OF THE ASWAN DAM, EGYPT

The annual Nile floods have now been controlled. These flood waters previously had three indispensable functions: (1) they flushed away salts from the soil that would otherwise choke plant life; (2) they swept away the snails carrying Bilharzia larvae, which causes a debilitating or fatal intestinal infection in humans; and (3) they left behind a new layer of fertile soil.

Built without sluices, the dam is trapping all the Nile's silt in its reservoir. The loss of this sediment load has led the clear river water to scour its bed, undermining numerous bridges and dams downstream. To prevent this, the Ministry of the High Dam proposed plans to build ten barrier dams between Aswan and the sea at a cost of $250 million – one-quarter of what the high dam cost.

Due to the decline in sediment discharge and, therefore, delta out-building, the Mediterranean Sea is eroding the delta and advancing inland, threatening many square kilometres of rich agricultural land. Approximately one-third of the delta front is actively eroding, some sections as rapidly as 2 metres per year.

Deprived of the Nile's rich sediment, much of the land already has depleted nutrient levels and needs artificial fertilizer. Two-thirds of the annual fertilizer usage is needed to make up for lost fertility and mineral content since Nile silt stopped coming. A number of minerals will also have to be added to the soil with time.

The marine food chain in the eastern Mediterranean has also been broken. The loss of nutrients formerly carried with Nile sediment has reduced plankton populations. As a result sardines, mackerel, and crustaceans have either died off or been driven away. Approximately 30,000 Egyptian fishermen have lost their livelihood.

The one undisputed benefit of the dam has been the conversion of 2,800 square kilometres from flood to canal irrigation, so that several crops can be produced on the land each year. The drawback has been that the canals are providing habitats for the snails that carry the Bilharzia larvae. A healthy human scarcely need set foot in the water to pick up the disease.

Adapted from: Griggs, G. and Gilchrist, J. *The Earth and Land Use Planning*, Massachusetts: Duxburg, 1977, pp. 290–292.

Fig. 5.6

5. Evaluate each of the items in the cost–benefit analysis and identify which of them relate directly to land use. What other land use activity may be evaluated using a cost–benefit analysis? List the consideration which might be made when deciding the future of a land use decision. How might land use decision affect people in 20 or 30 years?

Concluding the activity

6. The values of the past are important when considering land use decisions presently and for the future. Table 5.2 presents a matrix for classifying information and placing it in both a time and space framework. Direct the students to work in groups of two or three individuals and complete as much of the matrix as possible. Encourage the students to speculate regarding future land uses and how they will affect people. Table 5.2 has been partially completed in order to provide ideas for the teacher.

TABLE 5.2. *Land Use Over Time: The Case of Bangalore, India*

Aspects of Land	Earliest Residents	Scientific and Technological Events	Grandparents Time	Scientific and Technological Events	You (Now)	Scientific and Technological Events	Future (your predictions for the year 2050)
Feelings about the land	Spiritual Affinity	Water storage Food storage	Land as a resource Land as a source of wealth	Better transport	Conservation of land Planning for the future use of land	Chemicals for plants and pests Machines of various kinds	Environmental Ethic Value of land increases Holistic views
Direct activities with land							
Use of land resources	Forests Farming Grazing Village sites	Use of draft animals Irrigation systems	Urban areas Manufacturing Construction materials	Specialized machines for agriculture and mining, Green Revolution	Urban sprawl Suburban sprawl Transportation uses increase	Computer Nuclear Power Regional water supplies	Renewable energy from land Recreational uses High rise buildings
Type of Man-Made Structures on Land							
Owners of the land	Maharaja Tribal	Irrigation tanks, Pottery and brick making	Corporations Government Banks Individuals	Tractors Harvesters Deep wells	Small farmers Government Corporations Development agencies	Grain storage for long term Biogas, market data	

Adapted from: *People and Environmental Change*

Local examples

7. Use the idea of a matrix as demonstrated in Table 5.2 and develop a similar matrix for the local community. The entire community might be the subject of the investigation, or several parcels of land within the community may be selected for analysis. Students should rely upon family and community members as sources of information.
8. Complete a local study to determine the number of people who are employed on units of land where the use is quite different. For example, a farm might be compared with a local market, or business centre. A local manufacturing or processing plant may be available and the number of employed persons obtained. In some instances, data on a land use which is not in the community may be obtained and compared with the local land uses. The results may be plotted on a graph similar to Graph B in Fig. 5.4.

Agricultural land use – a case study of Sri Lanka

MICHAEL MORRISH

Introduction

This is a case study designed for lower secondary pupils. It uses a guided learning strategy with a strong skills element. The teacher seeks to direct the pupils through a set of questions. Alternative approaches might be to start with the land use pattern and to follow with questions as to why the pattern occurs (i.e. what, where, why). The graphs could be partly drawn, requiring only completion by the students.

This case study sets out to investigate the factors affecting agricultural land use patterns in a small Third World country, named Sri Lanka in South Asia. This material is intended to illustrate the effect of interaction between social, economic and physical factors in the development of agriculture in this country.

Sri Lanka has favourable physical factors for agriculture. Conversion by the British during the colonial period of agricultural land producing food crops to plantation crops required an increased labour force. This component was brought in from India, the neighbouring country. This has resulted in ethnic conflict with many attendant political, social and economic problems.

Physical factors: relief and climate

Sri Lanka is an island north of the equator. It has a central highland sloping towards the coast on all sides. It can be divided into a wet zone and a dry zone, which reflect differing annual rainfall totals and distributions. In May and June the southwest monsoon brings rain to the SW quarter of the island when the remainder of Sri Lanka experiences its dry season. Between

July and September the rain slackens and then in the October to December period the whole island experiences an important rainy season as unstable air masses remain stalled over the area by the doldrums. The Northeast monsoon does not occur until after the period of maximum precipitation, but in March and April the doldrums return to bring more rain, when the dry zone experiences its "little monsoon".

This climatic pattern leads to the recognition of two distinct crop seasons: Maha from October to March and Yala, from April to September.

Cultural and historical background

The original settlers of Sri Lanka were the Sinhalese, who entered it from India at an early date and maintained close links with the mainland. In the third century BC they adopted the Buddhist faith and have preserved this religious allegiance ever since. During the first millenium AD an advanced Sinhalese civilization developed in the north-central lowlands. It was based on the cultivation of paddy rice, irrigated from tanks on the valley floors, and on a system of shifting cultivation (Chena), carried out on the wooded hills between the valleys. Agricultural methods in this region changed little before the mid-20th century.

In the 11th and 12th centuries AD a series of invasions by the Tamil people from Southern India forced the Sinhalese to move southwards and a Hindu Tamil Kingdom was established in the north, based on Jaffna. A new Sinhalese Kingdom grew up, with its capital at Polonnaruwa, but anger over the Tamil's intrusion created a deep division between the two groups that is still a cause of political conflict today.

A new element was introduced when the Portuguese founded a trading station at Colombo in 1505. All trading links that had existed before this had been primarily Asian, when the island was used as an entrepôt on routes between the Middle East and Far East. The main export product was wild cinnamon, which was obtained from the bark of trees that flourished in the west coastal lowlands. Since the beliefs of the Sinhalese made them unwilling to work for others, from the 14th century onwards labourers were brought in from Southern India to peel the cinnamon twigs. In the mid 17th century the Portuguese were displaced by the Dutch, who created the first organized plantation system. Gardens of cinnamon were planted, peppers and coffee trees were introduced and the planting of coconut trees was increased. Sugar-cane and tobacco were also encouraged. The transfer of land to the production of commercial crops caused a shortage of subsistence foodstuffs and rice had to be imported from India. Slave labour was also required to provide a workforce for the plantations and more Indians were brought in.

When the Dutch were defeated in the Napoleonic wars at the beginning of the 19th century Britain took control of their colonial possessions in the East

Indies. The British were responsible for the consolidation of the whole of Sri Lanka's plantation structure. They put an end to the Sinhalese Kingdom, which had maintained its independence throughout the period of Dutch influence. Under the British direction a new era in plantation development was initiated, with the lowlands of the southwest being converted to a more specialized commercial economy.

Coffee was slowly replaced by tea, which unlike coffee could be harvested all year round and therefore required a permanent workforce. Consequently villages were established on the tea estates to house the workers, who consisted of poor Tamils brought in from southern India by the British.

After World War II Sri Lanka was one of the first countries to demonstrate the dramatic effects of DDT spraying against the malaria-carrying *Anopheles* mosquito. A sudden fall in the death rate lead to a significant and sustained increase in population.

When Sri Lanka became independent in 1948 (it was then known as Ceylon), it had an economy based on plantation agriculture, the exports of which paid for half its food imports and all its manufactured imports. However, since that time the country has found itself under increasing pressure; the rapid rate of growth of its population and its reliance on the export of primary products as a mainstay of the economy. To add to these problems were the "Indian Tamils" who were brought in as a labour force for over a century and who remained unenfranchized non-citizens.

Sri Lanka-agricultural production

The chief problem facing Sri Lanka in agricultural terms is the difficulty of increasing home food supplies without harming the productivity of its export crops. If it can reduce the amount of foodstuffs imported into the country this will release additional funds for the purchase of manufactured goods from abroad. Therefore, since independendence, Sri Lanka has made concerted efforts to improve productivity and extend the cultivated area of paddy rice, its staple crop.

Since 1950 the area of rice harvested has increased by 110%, or 43,000 hectares. Since most of this has been gained in the dry zone it is not surprising that more of the increase has been in the area harvested in Maha (124% increase) than in Yala (77% increase). Maha rice now accounts for 2/3 of the total crop area. Irrigation plays a large part in this and the percentage of land irrigated in the dry zone is double that in the wet zone.

Rice yields have improved considerably since 1950 (by 187% in Maha, by 168% in Yala) as a result of the introduction of high yield varieties and better cultivation methods associated with the "green revolution". The irrigated rice crops are the ones that have benefited most from these developments, since they are in the best position to take advantage of "green revolution" innovations such as fertilizer use, pesticides, insecticides, and a more efficient water supply.

Although the west zone contains 71% of Sri Lanka's population it only possesses 47% of the country's paddy area. Yields are considerably lower than those in the dry zone. Maha is the more productive season in the wet zone, despite the lower rainfall. In Yala conditions are less favourable, the higher rainfall giving rise to flooding, encouraging pests and diseases, and making harvesting more difficult. Rice growing in the wet zone relies largely on direct rainfall although some irrigation is provided by water led from streams in small channels called "elas". In general cultivation techniques are of mediocre quality and the transplanting of rice is rare. The widespread system of sharing land use over time also prevents long-term improvements in paddy production.

In the dry zone annual rainfall is almost universally below 2,000 mm, and large areas receive less than 1,500 mm. Not only is the rainfall highly seasonal but it also varies markedly from year to year. Therefore irrigation has been a feature of this region since ancient times, and many of the old systems of tanks, storage dams and river barrages are still in evidence today. The whole of the Yala rice crop relies on irrigation, as does over three-quarters of the predominant Maha crop. Modern development schemes, in particular that based on the diversion of water from the Mahaweli Ganga river, are all designed to provide the irrigation necessary to increase the cropped area still further.

Homestead gardens play an important role in subsistence agriculture, especially in the wet zone where paddy rice tends to be more scarce. The range of crops grown is varied and cultivation occurs at several different levels simultaneously. Trees producing coconuts, breadfruit, mangoes, kapok, areca and cashew nuts are interspersed with coffee bushes, pawpaws and plantain, which are themselves under-planted with manioc (cassava) and pineapples. Pepper vines are also grown as climbers. While the normal rainfall provides adequate moisture for homesteads in the wet zone, dry zone gardens need to be close to the irrigated water supply. In recently colonized areas water is often too far away, and the gardens are dry, dusty and unproductive. This removes an important part of the peasant farmers' subsistence food supply.

Shifting cultivation on "chenas" is common in the dry zone and the transitional areas on its borders. It is found on the wooded interfluves. Woodland or secondary forest is cut and burnt from June onwards. Seeds are sown in September and the Maha crops include millets, sorghum, maize, chillies and vegetables. If moisture allows, a second crop of oilseed may be grown in the Yala season. Plots are normally abandoned after 2 or 3 years, when weeds become obstructive, and the jungle is allowed to recolonize the area for 15 to 20 years. However, pressure of population has shortened the cycle of rotation and land is now being cultivated again after a gap of only 5 to 8 years. In some cases absentee entrepreneurs have made the Chena system a commercial operation, and cash inputs allow the use of fertilizers to offset declining natural fertility.

Perennial crops for export occupy twice the land area devoted to paddy rice and are produced mainly in the wet zone. Tea is grown at all altitudes, but 80% of the cropped area is found above 600 metres. Rubber is confined to the wet zone below 400 metres where rainfall is regular all year round; holdings tend to be smaller than the tea estates because the product is easier to process by a small scale operator. Coconuts are distributed widely and occupy an area second only to paddy rice. Their production is less highly organized than tea or rubber but coconut oil, dessicated coconut and goods made from coconut fibre find a ready market inside Sri Lanka.

Question 1

Find a map of Sri Lanka in an atlas.
(a) Between what lines of latitude does it lie?
(b) What are the basic dimensions of the island?
(c) Roughly how large an area does it cover? – compare with the area of your own country.
(d) Describe its position in relation to surrounding countries and major physical features.

Question 2

Refer to the data in Table 5.3.
(a) Construct a graph with birth/death rates on the vertical axis and time on the horizontal axis. Use different colours to plot lines showing the change in birth and death rates from 1881 to 1983.

TABLE 5.3. *Population of Sri Lanka*

Year	Millions	Birth rate per 1000	Death rate per 1000	Natural increase %
1871	7.4			
1881	2.8	27	23	0.5
1891	3.0	29	24	0.5
1901	3.6	34	28	0.7
1911	4.1	38	29	0.9
1921	4.5	38	30	0.7
1931	5.3	40	27	1.3
1946	6.7	37	23	1.4
1953	8.1	38	17	2.1
1963	10.6	37	10	2.7
1971	12.7	33	8	2.5
1983	15.6	28	6	2.2

(b) On a separate graph plot a line to show the increase in Sri Lanka's population over the same period.

(c) In what way are the two graphs related? How is Sri Lanka's population likely to increase over the next 30 years?

Question 3

Compare Figs 5.7, 5.8 and 5.9.

(a) Describe the distribution of population in Sri Lanka, as shown in Fig. 5.7. Use an atlas to identify the urban centres which represent marked concentrations of population.

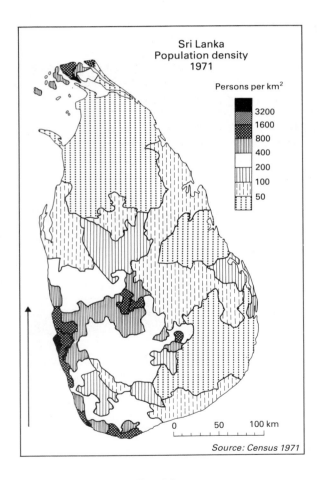

FIG. 5.7

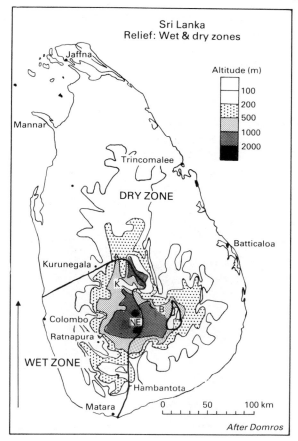

FIG. 5.8

(b) To what extent does the pattern of population distribution appear to have been influenced by (i) relief, (ii) rainfall? Now read the information sheet entitled "Sri Lanka – The cultural and historical background".

(c) What human factors have helped to produce the present population pattern?

Question 4

Refer to the data in Table 5.4 and study Fig. 5.10.

(a) Draw rainfall/temperature graphs for Colombo and Trincomalee. Compare and contrast the patterns shown by the two graphs, giving as much detail as possible.

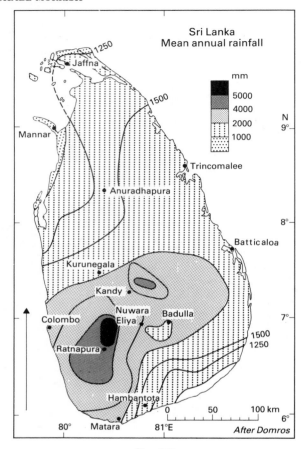

FIG. 5.9

TABLE 5.4. *Climatic Statistics*

	J	F	M	A	M	J	J	A	S	O	N	D
Colombo Average temperature (°C)	26	26	27	28	28	27	27	27	27	27	26	26
Average rainfall (mm) Total: 2,397 mm	88	96	118	260	353	212	140	124	153	354	324	175
Trincomalee Average temperature (°C)	26	26	27	29	30	30	30	29	29	28	26	26
Average rainfall (mm) Total: 1,727 mm	211	95	48	77	68	18	54	103	89	235	355	374

(b) Identify Colombo and Trincomalee on the two maps in Fig. 5.10. How do these maps help to explain the patterns shown by the two climatic graphs? Now read the information sheet headed "Sri Lanka – Climatic factors".

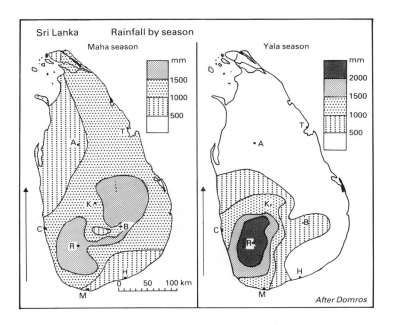

Fɪɢ. 5.10

Question 5

Study very carefully the two land use maps, Figs 5.11 and 5.12.
(a) Write a paragraph describing each one in terms of (i) the range of land use, (ii) the distribution of the different types of land use, (iii) the proportions of each land use type.
(b) Compare the overall layout and features of the two land use maps. Now read the information sheet headed "Sri Lanka – Agricultural production".
(c) Using the information at your disposal, write an account of the factors influencing the development of the two land use patterns.

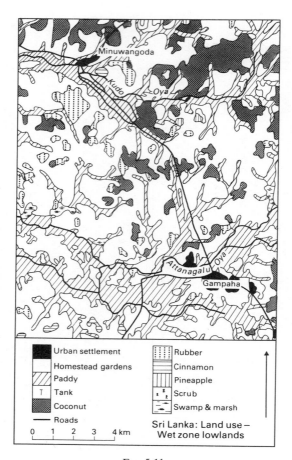

F IG. 5.11

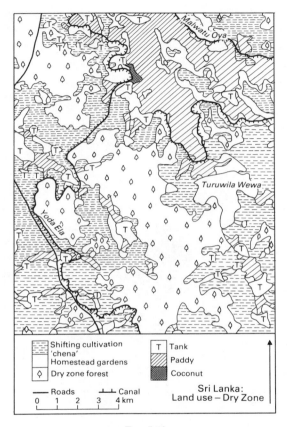

Fɪɢ. 5.12

Question 6

Study Figs 5.13 and 5.14.

Referring to specific administrative districts, describe:

(i) the overall pattern of paddy rice production,
(ii) its distribution between the Maha and Yala crops in different parts of Sri Lanka,
(iii) the areas where irrigation is *most* important and *least* important in paddy.

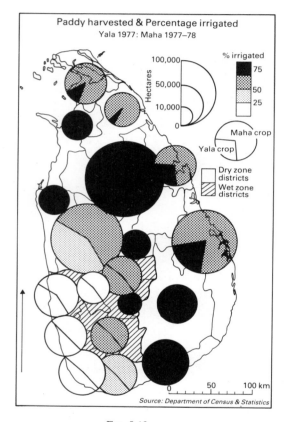

Fig. 5.13

Question 7

Use the data in Table 5.5 to draw two pie-charts showing the pattern of Sri Lanka's import and export trade in 1980. What weakness do they reveal in Sri Lanka's economy?

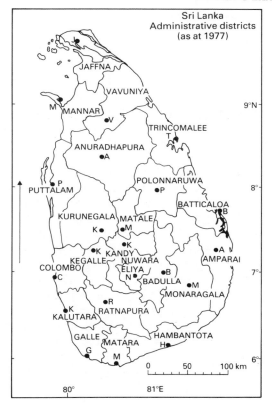

Fig. 5.14

Source of all figures: *South Asia* by B. L. C. Johnson, Heinemann, 1981.

TABLE 5.5. *Trade data, 1980*

	Imports %	Exports %
Food and live animals	20.0	45.5
Beverages and tobacco	0.1	0.1
Crude materials, except fuels	1.5	19.8
Mineral fuels/lubricants	24.2	15.3
Animal and vegetable oils/fats	0.1	0.3
Chemicals	8.3	3.0
Manufactured goods	17.3	4.2
Machinery and transport equipment	24.8	0.4
Miscellaneous manufactured goods	2.7	10.8
Miscellaneous products	1.0	0.6

Photographs and posters in land use studies

JULIAN ELLIS

Visual material can be a powerful educational medium when dealing with topics such as the use of land, water and mineral resources. In a few countries video recordings and slide presentations can be used as a focus for learning about faraway lands or issues of global concern. But many teachers have to rely on a few posters and maps on their classroom wall, photographs in newspapers and magazines, plus perhaps their own black and white snapshots. How can the teacher gain the most educational mileage out of a visual stimulus?

At an early stage simple skills of recognition can be emphasized – objects, species of animals, what people are doing. Towards the secondary level it is suggested that a more rigorous approach be adopted. Photographs need to be scoured for all the information they contain on land use practices. At more advanced levels new techniques of remote sensing, using false-colour imagery, require special visual skills. Vast amounts of land use information become available to the experienced eye. This paper develops an example of using photographs at the secondary level, with reference to a poster published by UNESCO as part of their Man and Biosphere programme.

A teacher could show a child a photograph and ask "what is this a picture of?" Again she may state "this is such and such an environment". A better teaching approach and one which would use the visual stimulus more fully is one where the teacher guides a child to "see". A picture tells us what sort of people, land, animals, vegetation, constructions and technology exist in an area. It also affects our feelings. It provides us with a message. A teacher can

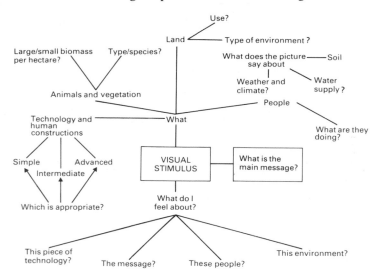

Fig. 5.15. Basic "splay" diagram to develop a visual stimulus.

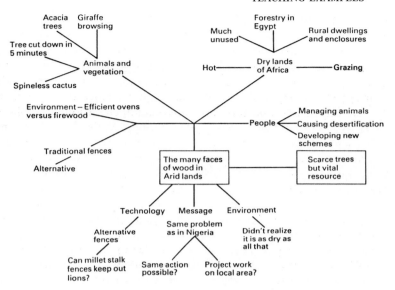

FIG. 5.16. "Splay" diagram developed by a Nigerian teacher.

try to develop a child's thoughts in all three of these areas – perhaps along the lines shown in the "splay diagram", Fig. 5.15. For comparison, Fig. 5.16 shows a splay diagram developed for a Nigerian teacher about to use the poster: "The many faces of wood in arid lands".

Once the teacher has decided on the information context of the picture, she can draw it from the pupils. The key question for the teacher is how may the ideas be developed so that the pupils learn, understand, and most importantly, remember?

One method is fully developed here. Pupils are guided in their learning. Ideas from the splay diagram (Fig. 5.16) are in italics in the expository script, and questions for recall of knowledge or development of understanding are posed. Specific project work in the local environment on the related topic could link in with this unit.

Perhaps the pupils could develop their own poster, putting together a series of pictures or sketches with some writing. Although a picture may be better than words in conveying information, an activity-based exercise related to the local area can be better still.

The many faces of wood in arid lands

Trees are becoming more and more scarce the world over. In much of the tropics trees are cut down without being replaced, both in the rainforest and in the drier areas. But dry areas like the Sahel in Africa have only a few slow growing trees and bushes in the first place. They are often scrubby and thorny, rarely in a forest, and mostly found scattered around the dry landscape. The *photographs on the poster show trees and bushes in the dry lands of Africa, and how they are used by the local people.*

Q.1. Use an Atlas to help you name six countries in the Sahel dry zone of Africa, just south of the Sahara.

Although scarce and becoming *scarcer, the trees* of the Sahel are a vital *natural resource.* Their roots bind the sandy soil together, reducing soil erosion. Leaves hold the moisture of the rains and provide food for the browsing animals. If present in sufficient numbers the trees may alter the local climate to cause an increased amount of rain to fall. Their wood is also greatly used for fuel, construction of homes and fences, and for household crafts. The trees are a vital part of the social and economic systems of Sahel people. They are also a vital element in the ecosystem.

The loss of woody trees results in "desertification". Desertification is the spread of unproductive deserts. This is occurring at an alarming rate. Minimum wood and fuel needs of people to the north and south of the Sahara are estimated at 400 to 500 kilogrammes of dry wood per person per year. To meet one person's basic needs the woody vegetation covering 0.3 to 2 hectares of good savanna land has to be removed each year.

This makes the amount of woody vegetation removed in the northern fringe of Sahara 1 to 2 million hectares a year. At this rate there will be no more wood left in the area at all by the year 2000.

Q.2 Describe in as much detail as possible what effect the removal of wood might have on people, livestock, climate, water and soils in the northern Sahara region. Use the diagram to help you.

Firewood and fuel

Even now *firewood* is becoming scarce in the cities and rangelands around the Sahara. But there are alternative sources of energy such as oil, gas, solar power, heat storage devices, wind-powered generators, methane (biogas) production from human and agricultural waste, and in some areas geothermal heating. If these fuels are available and cheap for the local people they will use them. The farmers in two areas of southern Tunisia are relying less on the use of firewood as a source of energy and are increasing their use of gas and oil.

Sources of energy for households in southern Tunisia

	Zougrata area	*Bir Lahmar area*
Wood only	30%	17%
Oil only	1%	12%

	Zougrata area	*Bir Lahmar area*
Gas only	2%	51%
Mainly wood	30%	—
Mainly oil	22%	—
Mainly gas	15%	—
Wood, oil and gas	0%	20%

Q.3 List the various alternative sources of energy. In each case (a) describe how the energy may be obtained; (b) state the likely problems of their use in any parts of the marginal lands of north Africa.

In some parts of the Sahel alternative fuels are either not available or are too expensive. *Energy efficient ovens*, as shown in one of the photographs, are a simple but effective solution. The average Sudanese family requires 50 kilogrammes of wood for cooking and heating each week. With the use of closed ovens this figure could be reduced by 20 kilogrammes. How many trees would this save? A 20 kilogramme acacia tree has a crown diameter of about 4.75 metres, and a trunk at ground level 10 centimetres in diameter. Some 50 of these could be saved per household per year.

Construction and fences

Rural dwellings and *fences* are constructed out of local acacia trees in countries like the Sudan and Kenya. The pastoralist people of northern Kenya use large amounts of wood to build night *enclosures (bomas)*. These bomas keep their animals together and protect them from jackals, hyenas, leopards and lions. At each temporary camp a boma is constructed. It is occupied for as short a time as a week before the livestock are moved to a new area and a new boma constructed. In more permanent Kenyan settlements ticks and other parasites accumulate in the bomas. To rid the animals of these pests the construction of new bomas has been the major cause of woodland destruction in northern Kenya. This in turn has led to the increased desertification of the region.

Permanently settled Rendille people of the Marsabit area of Kenya use 800 kilogrammes of wood per household per year for all purposes. The size of an average household is four adults, seven children. More nomadic Rendille families use 1,060 kilogrammes of wood a year. This represents some 50 slow growing 20 kilogramme acacia trees – but far more if younger trees are used. In the Marsabit area, amongst the Rendille people, the Integrated Project on Arid Lands (IPAL) is studying woodland and depletion. IPAL scientists propose the provision of alternative fencing materials for the construction of bomas. These could be provided free for local people. The new fencing materials will have to come from outside the Marsabit region.

Alternative fencing and building materials are shown in one of the photographs on the poster. Straw, millet and sorghum stalks have long been used in northern Nigeria's dry areas as cheap and useful construction materials. IPAL workers see the possibility of transferring Nigerian construction ideas to other arid areas – like Marsabit in Kenya.

The vegetation of nearby wetter zones, such as bamboo, could also be used as building material in places like the Sahel. But it would have to be transported some distance over difficult roads and this would add to its cost.

Animal fodder

Woody plants as well as grasses are important in the diets of animals. One of the photographs in the poster shows *giraffes* browsing on the leaves of acacia trees. With trees becoming scarcer, and with the animal population increasing as a result of better vaccines, it is important to find alternative fodder crops. The *spineless cactus* shown on the poster, is one example.

Q.4 How can the planting of the spiny fig cactus in Tunisia halt desertification?

Tree planting

It takes 50 years for an *acacia tree* to reach maturity. It takes 5 minutes to *cut it down*. Widespread cutting creates a landscape that is the beginnings of a desert – "desertification". Planting of trees can help to stop the advancing desert. One of the photographs shows a *forest in Egypt*. It consists of trees not normally found in the dry zones of Africa. The trees have been especially selected from species found outside of Africa, noted for their ability to live in poor soils. They also grow rapidly. The eucalypts, found in dry parts of Australia, and the casuarina, are two examples of species being used in northern Egypt. However, tree planting should mainly be of local trees that are best adapted to maintain the fragile balance between local climate, soils and vegetation.

Widespread planting of woodlots of local trees around villages will reduce the distance people have to travel to obtain wood, and the time spent gathering it. The villagers could plant and look after the woodlots themselves. Around the towns larger areas can be set aside for forests.

Q.5. In 10 years after the drought of 1968 to 1973 the Sahel region of Africa had 7½ billion dollars of aid poured into it. One fifth of this money went to building new roads, one fifth went on irrigation and water supply, much went on direct food aid, some was "lost", and one hundredth was provided for forestry projects.

(a) How might aid become "lost"

(b) How might new roads help to solve the problems of the region?

(c) How might better irrigation and water supply help?

(d) Suppose you are a scientist working on the IPAL project, write a letter to the President of Sahelia, stating the extent to which you think aid should be put into wood projects in dry lands. (Note that Sahelia is a fictitious country.)

Using local resources in the classroom for teaching land use in secondary schools

JULIE N. OKPALA

Introduction

Local resources available to the teacher for teaching land use in the classroom are of two types namely, material and human. For most teachers the former implies asking pupils to bring in products and tools from the locality for demonstration while the latter involves using resource persons, guest speakers and demonstrators. While these resources are invaluable there is need for the teacher to explore other inexpensive and easily available local resources not only for variety but also to make learning more challenging and stimulating to the learners. The two local resources suggested in this paper, one material and the other human, are media information and the learner respectively.

Sources and their importance

Media information

Information on land use contained in newspapers, local journals, government publications, radio and television could be utilized by the resourceful teacher for effective teaching. Media information should be utilized in teaching because they contain decisions, facts and opinions which directly or indirectly affect the student's life in the environment. If the child is being prepared to benefit from and improve his environment, it is essential that he should be provided the opportunity to deliberate on policies and people's opinion on land use. It is only after weighting such deliberations against information collected from texts, personal observation and experiences that he starts questioning propositions and policies made on land use.

The learners (mental map)

The learner is the most readily available teaching resource in the classroom but is unfortunately often under utilized. He comes to class with a wealth of experiences resulting from his interaction with his environment. His environment is physical, social, political and economic. The ideas, experiences, convictions which he has and structures in form of a mental map could be externalized and utilized in teaching. Mental mapping otherwise known as cognitive mapping is a technique concerned with processes for externalizing personal cognitive maps. Personal cognitive maps as constructs assume that people store information on their feelings and perceptions about their environment in their heads. Such cognitive maps influence to a large extent their behaviour and response to their environment. Cognitive maps of the school compound, the vicinity of the school, farm lands, facility centres for the community, could form the focus at the secondary school level for discussing appropriate and optimum use of land.

Application to teaching

The local resources suggested in this paper could be utilized at any level in the secondary school but the material selected, in terms of scope and concept, should be appropriate to the level. For example in discussing land use in Nigeria at the senior secondary level, fundamental elements for the purpose and the machinery for implementing the 1978 Land Use Decree, which declared all lands in the country as belonging to the government, should be taught. Hence extracts from the land policy statement should be utilized as a teaching resource. At the lower secondary school level, some information on the purpose of the policy should be given to the students.

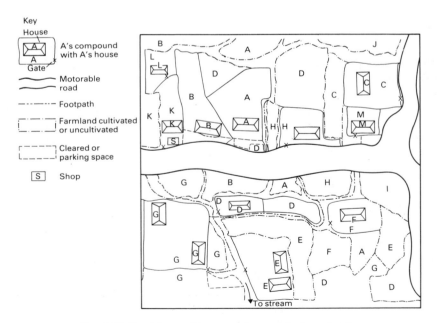

FIG. 5.17. Possible cognitive map of an area in Anambra State.

Mental mapping

Topic	Pattern of Land Use in the Locality (Agulu in Anambra State, Nigeria)
Class	Secondary I
Time	30 minutes
Objective	Using information from mental maps students should be able to identify and explain how the pattern of land use in the locality creates problems for economic activities, communication and infrastructural development.
Entering Behaviour	Students have acquired the concept of appropriate use of place direction, sketching and use of mapping symbols.
Resource Material	Mental maps produced by the students e.g. (Fig. 5.17).

Teaching procedure

Time allocation	Teacher Behaviour	Student Activities
2 Minutes	Instruction to students: Draw a map of your compound and nine other compounds around it indicating areas used for various activities. (i) Residence (with wall, barn, houses) (ii) economic activities e.g. farmlands, shops (iii) communication e.g. footpaths, roads (indicate where the routes lead) (iv) Show a key	Listening
8 minutes		Drawing mental maps individually
10 minutes	Divide pupils into groups of 6 to discuss these issues (i) How is land use in the area? (ii) How are the houses, farmlands and routes located?	Working in groups Record key points

Time allocation	Teacher Behaviour	Student Activities
	(iii) Do you think that people in your area have some problems because of the way things are located? (what problems) Teacher listens to groups and gives guidance.	
8 minutes	Teacher selects different groups to express their ideas on the issues raised.	Class discussion

Characteristics of the environmental setting mapped

Settlement	— Walled compounds
	— dispersed settlement
	— distance between walled compounds 0 to over .5 km
	— areas of compounds 1,500 sq. metres (+ or −)
	— Compound area contains house, barn, a few fruit trees (some – poultry, vegetable garden)
	— Settlement interspersed by pieces of land
Land	— individually owned
	— mostly cultivated
	— various sizes some less than 20 sq. metres
Routes	— A main road
	— Motorable tract lead to most compounds
	— Footpaths link most compounds
	— footpaths lead to the direction of water supply

2 minutes	*Question:* If the government wants to distribute pipe borne water and electricity in your area would the way the land is used pose any problem? Ask different individuals for positive or negative responses.	Response taking instruction

Instruction:
That's a take home assignment. Take a stance and give reasons.

A possible follow-up for this lessson in the next period could be:
(1) Discussion of the take home assignment.
(2) Instruction for students to draw a map of the way they would like land to be used in their area (group work)
(3) Give reasons for the proposed plan produced by different groups. Questioning, argument, illustrations and defence of stance.

Media information

Topic	Land inaccessibility as a problem facing development in Nigeria.
Class	Secondary 4
Time	A double period of 40 minutes each.
Objective	Students should be able to:
	(a) recognize the adverse (linkage) effect which shortage of land has on agriculture and various aspects of people's lives.
	(b) explain why some idealistic land policies and proposals are not implemented.
	(c) suggest some workable means of minimizing the effect of land problems on agricultural activities.
Some ideas to be involved	Population density, land ownership system, fragmentation of land, co-operative farming, foreign exchange, 1978 Land Use Decree.
Entering Behaviour	Students should have been aware of purposes of.
	(a) 1978 Land Use Decree.
	(b) Co-operative farming.
Resource Material	Media information "Land Shortages hamper agro industry" (see INSET 1).

Inset One

LAND SHORTAGES HAMPER AGRO-INDUSTRY

Agro industries in Imo state have had to contend with the twin problems of land shortages and insufficient foreign exchange to finance essential imports.

The land issue is particularly problematic in Imo, the country's second smallest and second most densely populated state. Peasants' reluctance to yield land, over which they have traditional rights, to the state government has sometimes led to open conflict, particularly along the border with Cross River State. And, large-scale agro-industries face serious obstacles to land acquisition from the highly literate and litigious population.

Agriculture and natural resurces commissioner Tobias Enyinnia recently advised farmers to pool their land in order to attract government incentives, and said they must be encouraged with grants and credit facilities. To be eligible, farmers must cultivate at least one hectare and be members of registered co-operative societies.

Enyinnia has also told the Imo State Association of Chambers of Commerce, Industry, Mines and Agriculture that his ministry is ready to go into partnership with agro-based organizations to assist them to boost raw materials production. "The call for a return to farming will be meaningless if all we hope to achieve is subsistence farming", he said. And in mid-August he announced government plans to set up a land bank to help acquire farming land and settle any social problems that arise.

But the most immediate obstacle facing modern agro-industry is insufficient foreign exchange for essential imports. And the poultry industry has been particularly hard hit. The scarcity of concentrates and yellow maize, two essential ingredients in the manufacture of livestock feeds, is biting harder each week. Many poultry farmers are selling off their layers and breeding stock as meat, because the low-quality feeds available lack the protein additives necessary for daily egg production.

While a number of small poultry farmers have already gone out of business, larger operations such as the Anambro-Imo River Basin Development Authority (AIRBDA), funded and administered by the World Bank, have been able to obtain feed. AIRBDA cannot grow maize directly "because of constraints on cultivable land", a representative says. But it sells farmers high yielding maize varieties and has distributed 167,420 bags of subsidized fertilizer so far this season. It buys feed from Maris Brothers Feed Mills, Uturu Okigwe and from Livestock feeds at Aba for its poultry scheme, pending commissioning of its own feed mills.

More than half the country's poultry farms have closed because of the maize shortage, according to Poultry Association of Nigeria president Aliyu Danmarayo. Another 30% are operating at reduced capacity. Due to drought and lack of import licences, only 150,000 tonnes of the 900,000 tonnes of maize required last year were available, of which 90,000 were imported, he added.

Source: (AED Special Report, Nigeria p. 31) October 1984.

Teaching procedure

(1) Teacher divides students into groups, six in each group. Give out "Land shortage hampers agro-industry" together with the questions for discussions.

Instruction:

(30 minutes)   Read the extract and in your group; jot down your main points on the following issues:

(1) What is the major problem facing agriculture as discussed in this report.

(2) How far does land ownership system and foreign exchange situation contribute to the problem facing agriculture?

(3) Couldn't Government measures have solved this problem?

(4) What are the possible effects of this problem facing agriculture on other aspects of people's lives, including the peasant farmers lives?

Suggest

(1) (a) How the peasant farmers can help in solving the problems facing agro-industries as they could not form co-operatives.

   (b) How the government can help the peasant farmers?

(40 minutes)   (2) Class discussion on the issues raised as each group presents its point of view.

(10 minutes)   (3) Summarize the issues involved with the assistance of the students

Main issue

1. Land ownership system creates problems – scarcity, fragmentation and makes co-operative farming difficult.

2. Land Use Decree 1978 could not enforce co-operative farming. (Why?)

3. Foreign exchange availability is not a permanent solution to the problem facing agro-industries.

4. Small farmers could be encouraged to produce maize. (How?)

Conclusion

Local resources discussed here no doubt would enhance active participation of students in lessons on land use. Concepts and ideas would be better understood. Nevertheless it should be realized that if teachers could be induced to utilize such sources, these should form a component part of questions asked in certificate examinations.

Environmental deterioration – an issue based unit for secondary schools

JULIAN ELLIS

Public concern often focuses on certain topics of global, national or local importance. They become issues about which the teacher and students wish to become informed. They are highly relevant to the day to day life of the student, and thus provide a real source of motivation. The teacher can use issue-based topics for developing concepts, provoking discussion, perhaps leading to the students' own projects and even direct involvement. If the issue is deforestation the students may be moved to plant trees. Here the issue is environmental deterioration, more specifically desertification.

This unit presents facts, provides an analysis, and encourages the student to grapple with the problem and its possible solutions. Finally students are encouraged to relate the issue of desertification to their local landscape.

The specific objectives of the unit are to increase students' awareness and understanding of:

(1) the nature of the desertification process,
(2) the main human and other factors giving rise to the problem,
(3) the methods being made to arrest desertification,
(4) the social and environmental implications of the desertification,
(5) desertification as a local and global issue,

For teachers the aims are:

(1) to provide information about desertification,
(2) to emphasize the need to link students local experiences with a world view,
(3) to demonstrate how articles and newspaper reports can provide material.

The unit includes suggestions for procedures in the classroom, ideas for written and out-of class assignments, and a selection of teaching materials. Materials include:

(1) notes for teachers,
(2) a map of world desertification,
(3) an article on desertification in Tanzania,
(4) climatic statistics for Dodoma, Tanzania.

Notes for teachers

It is assumed that the students already have an adequate knowledge of tropical farming practices. Secondly, it should be clear in the teacher's mind that Tanzania is not an extreme case of desertification, but an area where the issue could become a problem in the future.

Warm-up questions, or introductory notes:

(i) Under what conditions do soils become eroded?
(answer: high velocities of agents of erosion-heavy rains creating rapid runoff, high winds, steep slopes, long slopes, lack of soil resistance, sandy soils, lack of vegetation).

(ii) What is desertification?
(deterioration of the vegetation cover so that the effectiveness of rainfall to promote plant growth is reduced).

(iii) What is our mental picture of a desertified area?
(A rocky or sandy wasteland with a dead tree outlined against the horizon: this is an extreme case.) Most deterioration takes the form of:

— overgrazed shrub-infested pastures,
— gully erosion on hills,
— sheet erosion on flat lands,
— accelerated run-off,
— sand or silt choked rivers,
— destructive floods following rains,
— sand dunes encroaching on fields and homes
— reduced yields of dryland crops,
— periodic famines.

If you have photographs or slides, these would be useful.

(iv) What are the effects on humans, livestock and crops?
(Desertification leads to diminished biological productivity and consequent reduction in vegetation cover, in the land's carrying capacity for livestock, in crop yields, and in human well-being.)

(v) What might cause desertification?
(Natural factors such as climatic changes may cause desertification or it may be induced by man. More often it results from the interaction of both man and nature.)

(vi) which ecosystems are most at risk?
(The greater the physical vulnerability of and human pressure on an ecosystem, the higher the risks of desertification. Therefore the ecosystems most liable to be affected by it are the arid and semi arid lands. To some extent, however, sub-humid ecosystems undergoing intensive exploitation are also susceptible to desertification.)

Students may now look at H. E. Dregne's map of the world desertification (Fig. 5.18), and read the accompanying notes. (From Dregne, H. E. "Degradation by Degrees", in *The Geographical Magazine*, August 1977, pp. 708–710.)

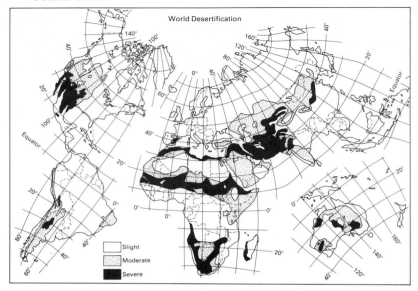

FIG. 5.18

DEGRADATION BY DEGREES

(adapted from an original article by H. E. Dregne)

The degree to which the arid regions of the world have been affected by desertification is shown on the *map*. Three categories of desertification have been used: slight, moderate and severe. Slight desertification represents little or no deterioration in vegetative cover or soil due to man's activities. The Sahara and Atacama, as well as other climatic deserts, automatically fall within the slight category. This is because the plant life in climatic deserts is so sparse in the natural state that even man cannot do very much to make matters worse. Deserts cannot be further desertified.

Moderate desertification consists of a level of environmental deterioration that: (1) degrades the plant cover to the point where the range condition is only fair; or (2) causes accelerated wind or water erosion that shows up as sandy hummocks or as small dunes or small gullies; or (3) increases soil salinity sufficiently to reduce crop yield by about 25%. A moderate degree of desertification is serious because it represents a significant loss of productivity that will become worse unless management practices are improved. At the moderate level, land improvement is economically feasible and relatively simple to accomplish.

Severe desertification indicates that: undesirable broad-leaved herbs and shrubs have replaced desirable grass and shrubs or have spread to such an extent that they dominate the flora; or wind and water erosion have removed much of the top soil and have largely denuded the land of vegetation or reduced crop yields by 50% or more; or salinity controllable by drainage and leaching has made the land unsuitable for sustained crop production. At this stage of desertification, recovery will be slow and costly. Some continents have very severe desertification, though these are not shown on the world map. Though numerous, generally these areas are small (a hundred square metres to several square kilometres). This category includes land covered with large shifting sand dunes, large and numerous gullies, or salt crusts on nearly impermeable soils. One hundred square metres may be reclaimed at moderate cost. Reclamation of several square kilometres will usually be uneconomic except for places where mobile sand dunes are encroaching on settlements, transportation routes, or high-value irrigated fields.

The students should be prepared to answer:

   (i) Why the Sahara is in the "slight" category?
  (ii) At what level does control of desertification become slow and costly?
 (iii) Which continent has the greatest problems with desertification? (This is a very open-ended question. The answers to (i) and (ii) are in Dregne's text).

The teacher may suggest that students graph Table 5.6 as pie-charts or barcharts.

Students should now become involved in a case study of Tanzania (see following article by Darkoh). It could be that there is a similar suitable article or newspaper report from the student's own country – this would increase the impact and relevance of the task. So much the better if the article has photographs.

As an out-of class assignment,

   (i) Locate Tanzania on the map of world desertification.
  (ii) Assess the climatic statistics for the new Tanzanian capital, Dodoma, in the central zone of the country. Students to summarize the data, perhaps graphing the information. They should state, probably with help from Darkoh's article, the elements of climate that the climatic statistics do not show. (Variations in rainfall from year to year are not shown; neither is evapo-transpiration.)

Students must read the article "Desertification in Tanzania" and answer the following questions, quoting specific examples.

TABLE 5.6. *Desertification of arid lands, by continents*

Continent	Degree of desertification	Per cent of arid lands	Per cent of continent
Africa	slight	28	12
	moderate	36	22
	severe	36	22
		100	56
Asia	slight	7	3
	moderate	66	26
	severe	27	10
		100	39
Australia	slight	42	30
	moderate	46	33
	severe	12	9
		100	72
North America	slight	2	0
	moderate	61	13
	severe	37	8
		100	21
South America	slight	4	1
	moderate	87	15
	severe	9	1
		100	17
Europe (Spain) only	moderate	80	42 (Spain)
	severe	20	11 ,,
		100	53
All continents	slight	18	
	moderate	54	
	severe	29	
		100	

DESERTIFICATION IN TANZANIA

(from an article by N. B. K. Darkoh in *Geography*, vol. 67, 1982, pp. 320–330).

Rough estimates indicate that between 45 and 75% of Tanzania receiving a mean annual rainfall of 200–800 mm is liable to desertification. There are two major types of environment at a very high risk. Firstly the semi-arid plains with their unreliable rainfall, repeated water shortages, periodic famines and high pressure of overgrazing and secondly, of dryland cultivation of marginal areas with highly populated, humid mountain slopes, with more reliable rainfall and perennial streams, but which are undergoing rapid deforestation.

The area with very severe degradation, in which desertification may be said to have reached an advanced stage, straddles an oval-shaped corridor extending from Npwapwa to Babati (Fig. 5.19; the heavily shaded area). In particular, in the Kondoa-Irangi district, some 60 km north of Dodoma, soil erosion has reduced the land to completely unproductive status. The district represents the topography of "badlands", with innumerable gullies and sand-choked rivers criss-crossing newly cultivated fields. In the years 1968–1972, a research team carried out pilot studies of soil erosion and sedimentation in four reservoirs in the Dodoma region.

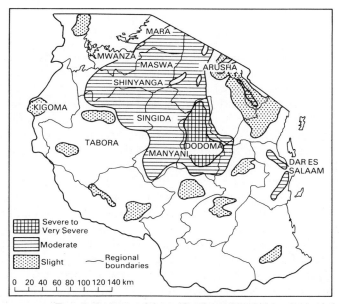

FIG. 5.19. Areas of desertification in Tanzania.

By periodic re-levelling of profiles on the floors of the reservoirs, the team recorded sediment yields of 195 cubic metres per square kilometre per year at Nsalatu, 406 at Imagi, 601 at Matumbulu and 729 at Ikowa. They also observed that because of the high rates of sedimentation two of the reservoirs, the Ikowa and Matumbulu, have very short expected total life lengths of 30 years and still shorter economic life lengths. Observation and mapping of erosion types in these catchments revealed intense gully and rill erosion on the upper slopes. Sheet erosion was found to occur over large areas of the lower slopes, and is thought to be the main cause of sedimentation of the reservoirs. The worst cases of soil erosion in the Dodoma District are in the southern part where there is greater aridity, higher livestock density and greater population pressure. In an investigation of the feasibility of mapping erosion types in the same region it was found that gullies and eroded termite mounds were the only erosion types which could be directly observed. Sheetwash, often the most important type in terms of the volume of soil displaced and its widespread occurrence in cultivated areas, could frequently be inferred only from other environmental information and confirmed by field investigation. An analysis of the food situation in the region covering the years 1923–1969 showed that nearly 13% of all the years were famine years, with loss of animals and human life by starvation. Another 34% had "local shortages" and "appreciable shortages" to the extent that food had to be imported. Only 6.4% had "ample food availability".

The human factor in desertification

Desertification in Tanzania appears to be primarily caused by man: it is not the result of the changes to a drier climate. The Government of Tanzania notes that "since rainfall records have been kept, there has been no marked trend towards dryness and the rainfall pattern has been consistently erratic". It concludes that "although many people think that the rainfall has decreased, the truth is that the same amount of rainfall is, due to man's abuse of the land, less effective than it used to be".

Perhaps the most important factor accounting for desertification in Tanzania is the pressure of population upon land use and management. The overall picture portrayed is of rapidly increasing population. Allowing for the effects which migration to towns, such as Dar es Salaam, Tanga, Moshi, Arusha, Bukoba and Mwanza, must have had on population increase in the country in general, there is ample evidence to suggest that during this century the arid and semi-arid areas of Tanzania have represented the last great frontier into which people have expanded under the pressure of rapid population growth. Nowhere, perhaps, is the effect of this population expansion and pressure so pronounced as in the Gogo country.

Dodoma and the Gogo people

Population increase among the Gogo people of the Dodoma district has led to an increase in cattle-keeping cultivators. This has brought under pressure areas used in the past only for nomadic grazing. Nomadism is transitory and does not necessarily result in overgrazing; but because modern science has enabled population, both human and animal, to increase rapidly in the area, the previously satisfactory system of animal husbandry has broken down. The traditional mobile bush-farming methods, which ensured a sustained yield, have had to give way to a more settled agriculture for which sustained yield farming systems have not yet been evolved. In parts of the Dodoma district the situation is alarming. Previously uninhabited areas of bush have disappeared and given way to human dwellings and cultivation. The cattle population explosion has brought with it problems of inadequate grazing (especially during the dry season), over-browsing, and trampling. Driven from the exhausted flat lands, people are now cultivating the rock hillsides and upper slopes. Short length of fallow between cultivation periods has led to the impoverishment of land whilst cattle grazing has removed the remaining vegetation cover. Estimates for the cattle population of the Gogo territory approximate to the one million mark. The cattle population density averages 1.9 hectares per livestock unit. A United Nations livestock project in Dodoma uses an average of 2.5 hectares per livestock unit as a minimum safe density. It is evident by this measure that Gogo territory is over-stocked.

Firewood and related problems

Desertification in Tanzania is not only caused by population pressure, overcultivation, overgrazing and poor land management. It is also caused by excessive collection of wood for firewood and charcoal, for construction and for other domestic and industrial uses. Another dangerous factor of environmental degradation in Tanzania is the periodic firing of forests and grasslands. Some of the fires, like the one which destroyed some 10,000 to 20,000 hectares on the slopes of Mount Kilimanjaro in October 1979 are believed to be accidentally caused by honey gatherers who roam around the countryside smoking out bees before raiding their hives. More often these fires are deliberately triggered off by local herdsmen, who burn dry grass so that fresh new grass will shoot up in the ashes, providing pasture for their cattle, and who also do this at times to cover their tracks when stealing cattle. There are three other sources of bushfires in the rural areas of Tanzania. These are farm fires lit for the purpose of clearing the land for cultivation; defensive (protective) fires which are lit by the villagers in order to keep out tsetse, snakes and wild animals and protect domestic animals and poultry; and hunting fires which are lit for the purpose of trapping game. It is estimated that more than 65,000 hectares of forest and bushland is burnt annually in Tanzania through these various firing practices. The threat posed by excessive collection of wood for charcoal and firewood is becoming very serious. Between 1959 and 1970, for example, the total fuelwood consumption in the country increased by 35% and it is estimated that charcoal consumption alone will increase at an alarming 1120% from the 1970 levels of 0.5 million cubic metres to some 5.6 million cubic metres a year by the end of the century. In 1972 Tanzania exported 188 tons of charcoal, mostly to Kuwait, and it was expected that exports would rise to over 30,000 tons in the near future. Recently, the Director of Forestry was quoted as saying that charcoal consumption in Tanzania has increased five times. It has also been estimated that there is now twice as much tree felling as there was 50 years ago. The per capita fuel wood consumption in the country at present is roughly 2.3 cubic metres a year; most comes from poorly stocked natural forests which are dwindling at a very fast rate. In absolute terms, Tanzania is only marginally forested (in fact only 15%, i.e. 13 million hectares of the total land area, is covered by permanent forest). Thus the felling of trees could easily cause the forest and woodland to disappear and eventually give rise to Sahelian conditions over large parts of the country. Fuelwood demand had already reached a crisis point in such semi-arid districts as Maswa, Tobora, Dodoma, Mpwapwa, Singida, Manyoni and Shinyanga (Fig. 5.19).

Some estimates put the number of man-days per year spent on the fruitless search for firewood in these districts at 200 to 300. Fuelwood shortages have also hit large areas in the more humid Coast Region, where charcoal production has led to the extinction of certain tree species. The Director of Forestry estimates that for each hectare of tobacco cultivated some 50 cubic metres of fuelwood are needed annually. Tanzania's rural population of nearly 8,000 planned villages is said to require a forest reserve of 75 hectares of consolidated forest per village if the fuelwood used is to be replenished. These figures give a rough idea of the size of the problem, and the enormity of the task facing the government and people. They are trying to stem the current tide of deforestation and the general problem of desertification and environmental degradation of the country.

Measures being adopted against desertification

Attempts have been made in some parts of Tanzania to halt desertification. But the government and people have yet to plan and carry out a co-ordinated programme of development in the degraded semi-arid areas as a whole. In some districts there has been a notable interest among local people in establishing village woodlots or small tree shambas. However, the production and swift distribution of seedlings, periodic outbreaks of bush fires, illegal poaching for fuelwood, and unrestricted grazing and browsing by domestic animals have been problems. The Ministry of Animal Production and Natural Resources has established tree seedling nurseries in many parts of the country and has distributed hundreds of thousands of various species for planting to the villages. In co-operation with the Institute of Adult Education, it has recently mounted a campaign in eight regions to educate people on the dangers of desertification and the importance of afforestation. These regions include Mara, Shinyanga, Tabora, Singidia, Dodoma, Arusha and Kigoma (Fig. 5.19). In May 1981, the *Daily News* of Tanzania reported that information so far received from five campaign regions showed that the total number of seedlings planted in Shinyanga, Tabora, Singidia, Dodoma and Mwanza was 8,485,906 covering an area of 7,657 hectares. The target for the five regions was 11,484,834 seedlings expected to cover an area ambitious conservation programme called HADO, 'Hifadhi ya Ardhi Dodoma", in the Dodoma region. To date, under this programme, some 7,500 hectares of denuded land have been reclaimed in Kondau, Mpwapwa and Dodoma districts through a special tree planting and terracing programme.

Action planned at the national level to arrest desertification includes the formulation of a national human settlements and land policy; carrying out land capability studies; preparation of regional and physical land use plans; reduction of fuelwood consumption by using alternative sources of energy, especially coal, natural gas, solar and wind power; training of environmental managers; and, encouragement of research. There is also the need to develop scientific methods to help understand the environmental impact of desertification. Finally, the simple tree planting remedial measure, and the uncoordinated approach being applied to the solution of the whole problem of desertification in the country at present, should give way to a more concerted, comprehensive and integrated approach. Development and management of traditional resource systems in marginal lands needs careful planning.

Climatic Statistics for Dodoma												
Height 1120 metres Latitude 6 degrees South												
	J	F	M	A	M	J	J	A	S	O	N	D
Temp (°C)	24	23	23	23	22	21	19	20	22	23	24	24
Rainfall (mm)	152	109	137	48	5	0	0	0	0	5	23	91

(iii) What factors may lead to desertification in Tanzania (a) physical, (b) social and economic, (c) political, (d) technological?
    (Physical – intense rainstorms, periodic droughts, light sandy or volcanic ash soils, deeply weathered soils, no or abandoned conservation measures.
    Social and economic – increased human and animal population migrations to unsuitable areas, sedentary agriculture, bad land management including overcultivation, short fallowing, bad

cropping and husbandry practices, gathering of wood for firewood and charcoal, domestic and industrial uses of wood, uses of wood for construction, periodic firing of forests and grasslands by honey gatherers and local herdsmen, land used for tobacco and coffee crops, control of the tsetse fly, mechanization.

Political – civil disturbances, and perhaps ujamaa villages.

Technological – veterinary services, infrastructure of water supplies, medical services and the like.)

(iv) What are the physical and socio-economic consequences of desertification?

(Physical – rill and gully erosion on slopes, ravines, sheet erosion on flat lands, eroded termite mounds, stripping of top soil, badlands topography, wind erosion, accelerated run off, sand-choked rivers, silting of reservoirs, impoverished and unproductive land, vegetation removal, disappearance of the forest and the possible spread of Sahelian conditions in Tanzania.

Socio-economic – inadequate grazing (especially in the dry season), over-stocking, over-browsing, trampling, short expected lifespans of reservoirs, food shortages.)

Many of these factors recall for the students the items mentioned above, p. 83 (iii), their mental picture of a desertified area.

(v) What are some of the proposed solutions in Tanzania?

(These are all quite clearly mentioned in the final page of Darkoh's article. Emphasize the not so obvious aspects of research, training, and education. The points concerning alternative sources of energy could lead naturally in to another topic following on from this unit – the issue of energy resources.)

(vi) What are, and are likely to be, some of the problems encountered in carrying out these proposals?

(Some problems are clearly identified at the end of the article, but students should be encouraged to think of problems beyond those mentioned in the article, e.g. finance, lack of personnel, slow adoption of suggested solutions, resistance of some people to changes etc.)

(vii) Draw a flow chart to illustrate how the use of modern science has led to population increase and desertification in the Gogo area.

Students turn to their local environment:

(i) Think of the local environment. Is there deterioration, soil erosion or desertification? If so are you able to identify different grades of deterioration? Draw a map of the slight, moderate and severe areas? What does your map tell you? Why are some areas more eroded than others?

(ii) How much effort is being put in to arrest erosion or to reclaim eroded areas? To what extent are schemes of prevention similar to those of Tanzania?

Land use choice in a marginal semi-arid environment
PHILIP STIMPSON

This is a unit for 16–19-year-old students. It uses a decision-making strategy within an overall enquiry framework. The enquiry raises questions, firstly, of the scientific principles needed to understand the environmental situation and, secondly, of the ethics which are implied by a particular interpretation. The enquiry framework is centred on finding answers to a set of guiding questions using the data provided. This provides students with necessary understanding to complete the decision-making exercise.

Environmental – land use decision-making

Alternative approaches and uses include:

1. Independent investigation. Here the students would be given only the data and the instructions. They would exercise their own judgement as the need to assess the land use options. Such a method assumes that students have prior training in independent enquiry.
2. An evaluation unit. The decision-making exercise would be used as an examination test question as a part of summative evaluation.
3. Role play. This could replace the decision-making exercise, or be used in conjunction with it. Role cards would be required setting out the characteristic of people involved in the decision-making process (e.g. businessman, a local farmer, a conservationist).

Strategy

Introduction

The unit uses an example of land evaluation from the Province of Murcia in south-east Spain.

Economic development has resulted in a shortage of high quality farmland, consequently there is pressure to develop marginal land which suffers from the problems of aridity and soil erosion. The problem arises as to the nature of the optional land use in the short term and, more importantly, in the longer term. Students are given information and a conceptual framework so that they can evaluate some of the issues, and make a rational choice between land use options. The focus is on land as a physical system, but students are asked to consider socio-economic factors.

Aims

To provide an understanding of

(i) the balance between ecocentric and technocentric views towards land use,
(ii) the way in which the application of scientific knowledge is vital to the understanding of (i),
(iii) the nature and causes of environmental problems which arise from land development, and
(iv) the way in which methods of farming must be adapted to the environment in order to maintain long-term stability.

Key ideas

Development or marginal land,
Environmental interaction,
Ecocentricity,
Technocentricity,
Environmental maintenance.

Procedure

The unit is based around seven guiding questions which form seven stages of its procedure questions. Questions 1 to 4 should take one to two lessons and the decision-making exercise a further two lessons. Questions 6 and 7 could be used as homework to consolidate learning.

Question 1. What issues are raised by the present patterns of agricultural land use in S.E. Spain and what attitudes do these reflect?

Read Section: The Problem

Murcia is a province in S.E. Spain (Fig. 5.20). The alluvial lowlands, near the coast, form an area which is known as the Huerta. These lands are irrigated and are a major market gardening area. Crops are sent to many parts of Western Europe and, with Spain a member of the E.E.C., the sales will grow. However, the high quality farmland of the Huerta is in short supply and has become expensive. As a result businessmen are seeking other land to develop.

In Murcia, there is a great contrast between the irrigated Huerta and the remainder of the province. Apart from the lowlands there are mountains, which are of little agricultural value, and dry scarplands. The latter were previously used for cereals, livestock and pasture. They are now viewed as having developmental potential.

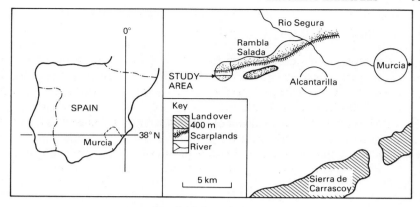

FIG. 5.20. Location.

The problem arises as to the types of activity which are feasible in the area, and which activity, in particular, is most suited to the environment. The purpose of this exercise is to assess how the scarplands could be developed. In order to do this, we need to know:

1. what the environment is like and the nature of any hazards, and
2. the nature of the different land use options which are possible.

Summary: Economic development, political decision-making, land shortage, expansion into marginal land, optimal/appropriate land use in development, technocentricity.

What are the environmental problems which hinder agricultural development and what attitudes do they reflect?

Read Section: The Scarpland Environment

The scarplands rise to 200 m above sea level, and are cut by deep narrow valleys (Fig. 5.21). The sides of the valleys are steep, 20° to 30°, and hill crests are narrow, consequently the land mainly comprises valley sides and

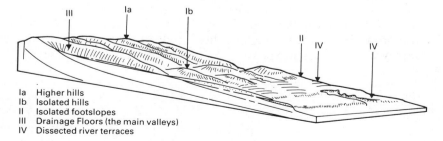

Ia Higher hills
Ib Isolated hills
II Isolated footslopes
III Drainage Floors (the main valleys)
IV Dissected river terraces

FIG. 5.21. Terrain types in the scarplands.

valley bottoms. The climate is dry and there are no permanent streams. When there is rain, it is often heavy and can cause soil erosion.

Much of the land is now abandoned. In the past, hills were used as sheep and goat pasture by herds from the nearby villages. On the valley floors, small terraces have been built and are used for tree crops (olive, fig and carob); in years when there is rain, cereals are grown.

Climate: The climate has a marked seasonality with warm wet winters and hot dry summers. It is a dry variant of the Mediterranean type. The aridity is caused by its location in the rain shadow of the Spanish Massif. The climate is semi-arid and has a mean annual rainfall of 264 mm per year (Fig. 5.22).

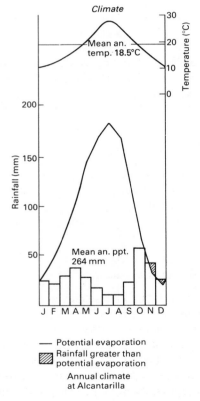

FIG. 5.22. Climate.

The mean annual temperature at Murcia is 18.5°C and ranges from a minimum of 11.0°C (Jan) to a maximum of 27.0°C (Aug). In winter there is little risk of frost. In summer short spells of hot weather associated with winds from the African landmass are not uncommon, and temperatures may reach 38.0°C. In the scarplands minimum temperatures are not limiting but maximum temperatures may restrict plant development through their effect on moisture supply (see Fig. 5.22).

Overall there is a low rainfall all year, although there is slight maxima in autumn and spring. In the autumn, high ground temperatures increase instability in the atmosphere and heavy thunderstorms result. In July and August rainfall amounts are imperceptible and the problem is exacerbated by high evapo-transpiration. Potential evapo-transpiration is high for most of the year and in most months there is a rainfall deficit.

Annual rainfall is highly variable from year to year (Fig. 5.23). The mean annual rainfall in the period 1952 to 1971 is lower than that for the period 1862–1971. At present Murcia seems to be experiencing a period of particular aridity.

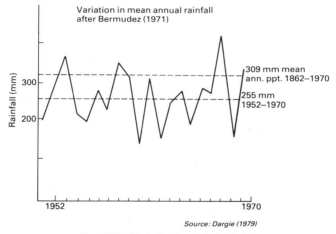

Source: Dargie (1979)

FIG. 5.23. Variation in annual rainfall.

Soils

Soil development is poor and often there is no distinctive soil profile. The soil on the hills is thin and stony with a high pH of around 8.6. Organic content is low. On the slopes there is often very little soil development at all. The finer material from the slopes accumulates on the valley floors and consequently these valleys contain deeper silty soils with less stone. This change in soil character with position on slope is commonly found and represents a catenary structure (Fig. 5.24).

The soils are developed from sandy conglomerates which in places contain gypsum (calcium sulphate). As a result salinity levels are high where gypsum bearing rocks are exposed or where gypsum debris accumulates. Salinity levels are such that plants exhibit specific adaptations or are dwarfed. Rarely however are the levels high enough to restrict growth completely. This will

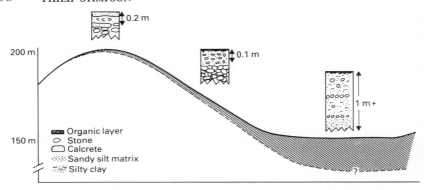

FIG. 5.24. Soils of the scarplands.

only occur where the salinity concentrations in the soil water solution are high enough for water to move from the plant tissue and will cause a break-down of plant material.

Vegetation

The vegetation pattern forms a complex mosaic with the changing influence of the natural environment and people. The vegetation is adapted to dry land conditions, the climax vegetation is oak woodland or dwarf palm in the drier areas. However, both are rare because of the long history of clearance and grazing.

The vegetation shows stages in a regeneration/degeneration sequence. Vegetation cover is usually less than 50% and is often below 10%. The main vegetation is either garrigue or tomillar. Garrigue is a scrub of rosemary and thyme, whilst tomillar is a more degraded form made up of thyme and grasses.

Summary: aridity, high rainfall deficit, variability, heavy storms, steep slopes, poor soils and hills, saline soils, erosion, ecocentricity.

Why are dry-land agricultural methods needed?

Read section: Dryland farming

Where land is marginal, returns are usually low and variable year to year. Thus the large scale investment needed for irrigation is often not available. The alternative is to use farming methods which conserve water and to cultivate crops, or rear livestock which can survive in arid conditions.

Soil water is usefully viewed as an INPUT–STORE–OUTPUT system. The aim of dryland agriculture is to minimize the output to increase the amount in store which can be used for plant growth. The main inputs are from rainfall and from water running on from up slope. Outputs, or losses, are from evaporation, runoff, shallow sub-surface flow and downward percolation.

The main losses are from evaporation and the main aim of dryland farming is its reduction. The fields are regularly ploughed; this breaks up capillary tracts up which water can move to the surface and removes weeds which take up moisture. However, this action also produces a friable soil which is easily eroded by wind or water.

Runoff losses after infrequent rainstorms are reduced by building barriers across drainage lines. In areas of gentle slopes, banks are built across the valleys to trap water; these are called bunds. On steeper ground the land is terraced; a bench is made by excavating on the upslope side and depositing the material on the downslope margin. Such building work inevitably exposes land surfaces to increased erosion risk. On a more restriced scale, pits are dug into which water will drain and where trees can be planted.

Dryland farming requires both water conservation and soil protection measures. The shape of land, the soils, the water availability and the plant and animal life the land will support are all related in a bio-physical system. A change in one part invariably results in changes elsewhere. Thus water or soil conservation should not be looked on in isolation but as a part of "land conservation".

Summary: Lack of available soil moisture, conservation by ploughing and weeding and by terracing.

What are the advantages and disadvantages of the land use possibilities suggested for the area?

Read section: Land use options

Land use options for the Scarplands of Murcia

A. *Grazing.* This is the traditional land use in the hills, and on the lowlands when it is too dry for crops. However, the returns are generally low. Flocks of a few hundred sheep and goats are grazed in an extensive manner. The quality of the semi-natural grazing is poor. Many of the plants have adaptations to minimize water loss which makes them unsuitable for grazing. For example plants often have leathery or spiky leaves which sheep find unpalatable. The herdsmen drive the flocks over large areas to find favoured grazing. Where there is overgrazing, trampling and loss of plant cover can increase the risk of erosion.

B. *Cereals and olive.* This is the traditional use of the valley floors which are terraced or bunded to increase water availability. The potential tree density for olive is low as are the returns, especially given the olive oil surplus in the

E.E.C. In years of higher rainfall cereals are planted out: this occurs infrequently. The low returns cannot support a family and farming is usually a weekend recreational activity in a social environment where land ownership is prized.

C. *Recreation.* Hunting for small birds, rabbits and foxes is popular. Abandoned farmhouses have potential as weekend and holiday retreats for people from nearby towns. The hill lands have a distinct flora and fauna which, although widespread at present, is shrinking under agricultural pressure. Few areas of the oak woodland or dwarf palm climax communities remain. Consequently some places might be developed as country parks although funding could be a problem.

D. *Almond.* The highest returns are from growing almonds which are in great demand. This tree crop is suited to a semi-arid environment where there are water conservation measures. The trees must be regularly sprayed against pests. This, with the water conservation requirements, demands greater capital investment. Consequently almond cultivation is a relatively large scale operation. For example, heavy machinery is used to construct large terraces upon which a high tree density can be supported. The environmental impact is thus greater than with other land use options.

Summary: Grazing, low returns on hill environment, cereals and olive, low returns, on valley floors, almond, maximum returns with soil erosion risk, recreation/conservation, minimum returns.

What land uses are best suited to the different parts of the area and what values are reflected in your choice?

Now do the following exercise

Land use Allocation Exercise

The typical scarpland landscape is showing the block diagram (Fig. 5.21). Erosion of the hills has left narrow steep ridges (Ia) and isolated hills (Ib). Between the ridges are the valley floors (III) which widen out into dissected river terraces (IV).

The steeper land between the hills (I) and the lower land (III and IV) form foot slopes. These five form the main terrain types. Fig. 5.25 is an evaluation of the terrain types according to their potential for agriculture. A six-fold classification is used ranging from 1 (very good land) to 6 (of little agricultural value). The land in the scarplands being marginal belongs to 3, 4, 5, and 6, the meaning of which is explained in the key. Particular problems for agriculture are shown by a subscript if needed; for example r = rooting problem.

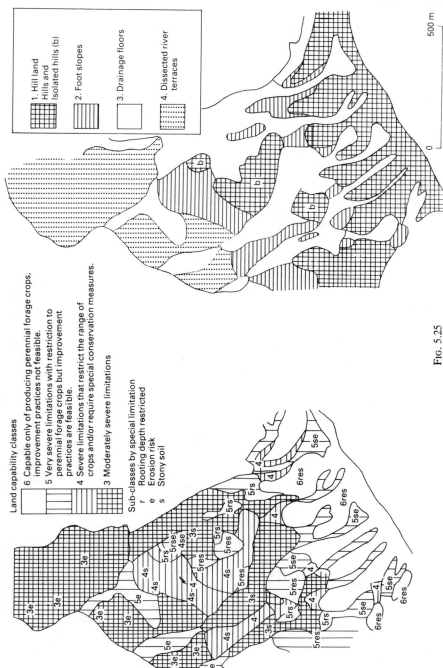

FIG. 5.25

The task

Examine the information in the maps along with the data on soil and land use options. Use them to prepare a land use plan. You may wish to adopt just one farming type or you may feel that a combination of types would be better. Think carefully about the short and longer term impact of any decision.

Prepare a report justifying your plan outlining the advantages and disadvantages (if any) of your choice.

What other factors (socio-economic) would you need to consider (e.g. social structure, attitudes and education, land tenure, crop price, new technology transport, government action).

Read Section: What has actually happened?

What has actually happened?

Only the land in the lower part of the valley (II, III, IV) has been developed. Large terraces were built for almond cultivation and the land now supports a relatively high tree density. The silty soils are regularly ploughed to reduce evaporation but this has led to wind erosion and to water erosion on the higher foot slopes.

Development of the hills has been piecemeal. The narrow valley heads have been abandoned. Some of the steep hill slopes have been terraced using heavy machinery and are used for almond growing. Similarly almond is grown on some hill crests in shallow pits.

Soil erosion in these areas is a problem and the success rate in growing almond is low. Much of the land in the hills has been left as scrub. It is still used by herdsmen and weekend hunting parties. In the valley families continue to tend olive trees in their recreation time. As yet there have been no initiatives to develop a country park.

What are the similarities and differences between your plan and what actually happened? Suggest reasons for the differences.

Urban planning in Bombay – an exemplar unit in role play

ELEANOR RAWLING

This is a unit for 16–19-year-old students. It uses a role playing strategy within an overall enquiry framework and would probably require two lessons and home work. The enquiry exercises should make it clear to students that there are no right or wrong answers in urban planning which are applicable to all people. In this exercise the plans for a new city, New Bombay, are examined from the various points of view of people living in the area. Ideas gained from the study can be used to raise more general questions about appropriate urban planning strategies for a Third World city. At the same time students are provided with the opportunity to practise a range of intellectual skills (interpretation and analysis), social skills and communication skills. Some preliminary work on Bombay will be required, covering the size of the city (around 9 million people in 1985), its rate of growth (a narrow peninsular site which acts as a restriction on its physical growth, Fig. 5.26), and the fact that a major element in the planning strategy adopted is a new large sister city to be known as New Bombay.

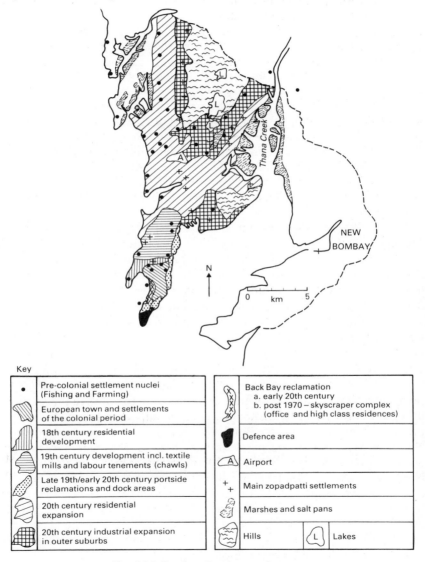

Key			
•	Pre-colonial settlement nuclei (Fishing and Farming)		Back Bay reclamation a. early 20th century b. post 1970 – skyscraper complex (office and high class residences)
	European town and settlements of the colonial period		Defence area
	18th century residential development		Airport
	19th century development incl. textile mills and labour tenements (chawls)	+ + +	Main zopadpatti settlements
	Late 19th/early 20th century portside reclamations and dock areas		Marshes and salt pans
	20th century residential expansion		Hills Lakes
	20th century industrial expansion in outer suburbs		

Fig. 5.26. Bombay: Land use and structure.

An alternative strategy

Other teachers might prefer to use a simulation exercise. As before, students, would require some preliminary work on Bombay, and also an understanding of the principles used in urban planning. Students are then provided with a base map of the Bombay area which they use to prepare their own plan for a new city. Then maps are compared with the actual plan for the new city leading to a discussion of reasons for the new city, and similarities and differences when compared to the existing city.

The exercise

The idea for a New Bombay was first proposed in the early years of the 20th century. It was not until 1973, however, that it was incorporated in the official Regional Plan for the Bombay area. In order to ensure that the plans were implemented, a new development authority – the City and Industrial Development Corporation (CIDCO) was established and given full powers over land acquisition, land use zoning and building development. Initially CIDCO carried out a survey of the proposed site leading eventually to detailed plans. A limited public consultation exercise was conducted and finally the plans were given approval in 1979. Since that date construction has been in progress.

The site chosen is the mainland area to the east of Greater Bombay across Thana Creek. The area is low lying land, surrounding both the Thana and Panvel Creeks. A new bridge was built in 1972 to join the site to the existing Bombay urban area, whilst the Thana-Pune road effectively delimits the site to the north-east. In the south, the new city boundaries take in the already developing Uran/Nhava Sheva port and industrial complex.

Before any development by CIDCO, this area contained a sizeable rural village population (about 95 villages) and a rapidly growing industrial population of about 25,000 workers. The total pre-Plan population was estimated at 117,000. CIDCO suggested that, as a result of the existing situation, some kind of further mainland development was inevitable. The plans for a New Bombay indicate a determination to improve the quality of urban life throughout the Bombay region as well as to reduce the intense pressure for growth within the Bombay peninsula. However, elsewhere in the New Bombay report, it became clear that the city is seen as far more than just an eastward extension to Bombay. The report gives high priority to making New Bombay independent of the old city. It should have its own administrative, commercial, industrial and residential sectors, and it should be large enough to act as a counter magnet to the existing Bombay city. It is even suggested that part of Bombay's state capital functions should be transferred to New Bombay. "Only if the new city has this independent character will it become a real alternative to the City of Bombay". The broad plan objectives set by CIDCO reflect this image of a significant new growth centre in its own right. Reference to an intention to "reduce disparities" and to enable citizens "to live fuller and richer lives" also indicates that the planners have social as well as economic objective.

The procedure

The success of the project depends on people and activities being prepared to move. The question is "are they?".

The exercise starts from information, presented in the form of "decision profiles" about different people living in Bombay, or interested in its future growth. Six decision profiles are required as indicated below. A brief example of six profiles follows.

* Should Rajiv Gupta advise his firm to move their offices to New Bombay?
* How should William D. Hartburg advise Onoco International?
* Will Kala Gupta find New Bombay attractive?
* Should Nerita Chowdhury advise the Maharashtra State Road Corporation to relocate in New Bombay?
* Should Ravinder Kumar establish his flourishing electronics industry in New Bombay?
* Should Vijaya Subaiah approve a World Bank loan for New Bombay.

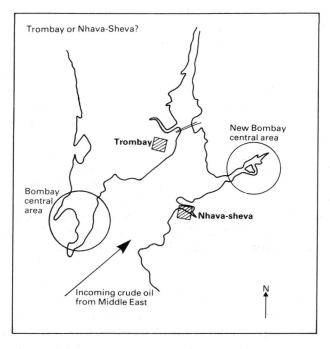

Fig. 5.27

DECISION PROFILE 1

Should Rajiv Gupta advise his firm to move their offices to New Bombay?

Rajiv Gupta, senior executive with Remco, a large multi-national firm mainly concerned with food processing, has been asked to advise the firm whether to move to New Bombay. Office space is available in Belapur at cheaper rates than in Central Bombay and housing is likely to be cheaper and easier to obtain for office staff. Remco needs immediate contact with other firms and with banking/insurance facilities, plus a well-established network of communications abroad. Also important are links with its Bombay factories in the outer Western suburbs (Santa Cruz), ½ hour drive from Central Bombay, but a good hour from New Bombay. Access to government offices may be important.

A Business Guide to Central Bombay

Government Offices	Banks	Hotels
Central	40 commercial banks	50 Hotels including the
13 including:	including:	worldrenowned:
All India Radio	Bank of America	Taj Mahal
Central Railway	Bank of Maharashtra	Intercontinental
Collectorate of	Bank of Tokyo	Oberoi Sheraton
Customs	Banque Nationale	
Income Tax	de Paris	*Clubs*
Department	Hong Kong and	16 including the
Meterological	Shanghai	prestigious:
Department	Indian Overseas	
	State Bank of India	Bombay Gymkhana
State		Royal Bombay Yacht
15 including:	*Shipping Companies*	Royal West India Turf
Director of Tourism	10 including several	
Maharashtra State	international lines	*Airline Offices*
Road		27 including those of
Transport	*Telegraph Offices*	major world airlines
Corporation	10	and Air India
Commission of Police		(international) and
Regional Transport		Indian Airlines
Office		(internal)

(from Directorate of Tourism, Government of Maharashtra)

DECISION PROFILE 2

How should William D. Hartburg advise Onoco International?

William D. Hartburg is a representative from Onoco International, a petro-chemical firm looking for a site for the Company's Indian operations. The choice of the Bombay area has already been made, because of the existence of port facilities and experience with oil imports and oil refining. However, the firm has not decided on the site. An extension to the Trombay petro-chemical area has been considered; but the firm have also heard about the Nhava-Sheva complex and are anxious to see what the opportunities are like here. Housing for workers needs to be considered and various subsidized schemes exist in the new city's residential nodes (Fig. 5.27).

Proposal from New Bombay Plans Development of Nhava-Sheva Port
To meet the growing needs of overseas trade particularly for handling bulk and containerized traffic, a deep water port is proposed to be developed at Nhava-Sheva. In addition, facilities will be established for a variety of port-based industries, including petro-chemicals. Nhava-Sheva will have its own Export Processing Zone where processing of certain imported materials can take place without payment of duty, as long as the goods are re-exported.

Situation so far, 1982
The setting up of the deep water port has been cleared by the Government of India, and it is hoped that the project will be completed by 1986–87. However, so far there has been little progress and there are no amenities and no housing units available. Two authorities which are likely to take up sites here are both state run, and include the offshore natural gas project, ONGC.

– extract from an article in the *Economic Times* (India) 5.12.82 special feature on Metropolises Under Stress . . .

One maverick public agency that has managed to defy the Regional Planning authority's directive is the Rashtriya Chemicals and Fertilizers firm. When the RCF approached the Bombay Municipal Corporation for permission to expand the fifth stage of its Trombay fertilizer plant, its request was turned down. Yet it still went ahead with the project in 1978 . . .

DECISION PROFILE 3

Will Kala Gupta find New Bombay attractive?

Bombay for the "Jet Set"

Kala Gupta, Rajiv's wife, has been asked by her husband to advise him. If the headquarters of her husband's firm, Remco, moves to New Bombay, should the family move to new accommodation. At present they occupy a luxury apartment in Colaba subsidized by the firm. Subsidies would be available on new accommodation in Belapur, but there are no high rise luxury apartment blocks being planned in New Bombay. The family would also lose its close links with friends, social activities and cultural amenities in Central Bombay. Mrs Gupta is a lively member of the Bombay "jet set", enjoying the easy access to bazaars, boutiques, clubs and beaches. She is also involved with voluntary social work in the city.

Boutiques and bazaars

Bombay is an exciting place to shop. Browse around in its smart boutiques and emporia hunting for bargains in printed silks and handicrafts, clothes and leatherware. One day, for a change of scene, wander through the city's old bazaars – Jhaveri Bazaar; the traditional Jeweller's Market, where you might recline against soft bolsters on the floor, letting the exquisite gold or enamelled jewellery drip through your fingers . . . Chor Bazaar, the so-called "Thieves Market", where, if you're adventurous, you can haggle over anything from a 19th century Russian chandelier to a gaily painted, hand-cranked gramophone that still works! In the crowded little shops of Bhuleshwar, you find a bewildering array of colourful glass bangles, embroidered saris, vivid pink-and-green sweetmeats, inexpensive silver jewellery. The shopkeeper, your host for the moment, insists you have a soft drink. Or tea perhaps? Coffee? He won't take "no" for an answer.

Beaches and, unexpectedly, fishing villages

Bombay has some fine beaches. Juhu, being the most popular, is sometimes crowded, but at Versova, Madh, Marve and Manori, all you find are broad sandy beaches, warm, lapping surf, swaying palms . . . tranquility . . .

Nearby, you may discover the simple little villages of the Koli fisherfolk, Bombay's original inhabitants. They are unspoilt by the big city that lies perhaps 20 kilometres away.

from: Bombay tourist brochure

DECISION PROFILE 4

Should Nerita Chowdhury advise the Maharashtra State Road Transport Corporation to relocate in New Bombay?

Nerita Chowdhury is a senior official with the Maharashtra State Road Transport Corporation. The MSRTC has come under pressure from the State Government to move its offices from old Bombay to the new city. Nerita has been asked to make a recommendation to the MSRTC Board. The State Government provides most of MSRTC's funding; in addition it is likely to bring in a special tax on businesses continuing to occupy land in Central Bombay. The New Bombay CBD zones offer office accommodation at low rents, although at present the infrastructure and basic services are poorly developed. In making a recommendation, Nerita needs to consider how far MSRTC's staff would follow the move. Since employment in a State run body is secure and promotion incentives could be offered, a high percentage of staff are likely to accompany the Corporation. However, not all Central and State Government departments have taken the advice to relocate in New Bombay . . .

No more soft options

by Rajiv Shankar

"While debating on the means for decongesting the city or who should be made to shift out, little is ever said about public sector or government agencies and the tremendous strain they create on the civic infrastructure.

"Bombay has several such agencies, which though do not have any activities in the metropolitan region insist on setting up their head offices and residential premise often in blatant disregard to the detriment of the public. They should immediately be compelled to shift outside the region in proximity to wherever their activities are concentrated. Currently, the biggest violation of the policies laid by the Government are the Central and State Government departments and agencies.

"For instance, the Maharashtra State Electricity Board which has no customers and generated no electricity in Bombay and deals with the entire state of Maharashtra barring this metropolis was almost on the verge of locating its headquarters at Backbay! But finally it was compelled to move over to the Bandra-Kurla complex, which though not good enough was, still, an improvement over being located at Backbay.

"Similarly, the headquarters of the ONCG's 'Bombay Offshore Project' (for employing 1400 people) is going to be located at the Bandra-Kurla complex. In fact it would be logical of them to set up their complex at New Bombay's Belapur or Panvel where a large ONGC resident colony is coming up and which is in close proximity to their bases on Nhava island and Uran and, moreover they would have saved several crores of the tax payers' money. The land cost at the Bandra office complex for per sq. metre cost Rs. 98 lakh[1] while the same land at Belapur was being offered to ONGC by the CIDCO at only Rs. 250 per sq. metre, i.e., a total of Rs. 17.50 lakhs only! Consequently, if ONGC had agreed to move to New Bombay it would have saved at least Rs.80.50 lakh."

from *The Economic Times* (India) 5.12.82.
special feature on Metropolises Under Stress

[1 one lakh = 100,000]

DECISION PROFILE 5

Should Ravinder Kumar establish his flourishing electronics firm in New Bombay?

Ravinder Kumar is the managing director of a small firm (Kumatron) which assembles electronic equipment, mainly for sales to South East Asian countries. The firm has been built up by Ravinder himself, working initially with five employees in an old warehouse unit in the Mazagaon area of central Bombay. In many ways this site has been ideal providing nearness to central services, to the docks and to Ravinder's home in the inner suburbs. However, due to Kumatron's success, Ravinder now wishes to expand. There is no room in the existing warehouse. Ravinder has heard that there will be small industrial sites available in the new port area of Nhava-Sheva, attractive because of their low rents. He has also heard of a new electronics export processing zone (the Santa Cruz E.E.P.) in the outer suburbs . . .

DECISION PROFILE 6

Should Vijay Subbiah approve a World Bank loan for New Bombay?

Vijay Subbiah works for the World Bank. The Bank is giving consideration to a request from the Bombay Mertropolitan Regional Development Authority. BMRDA is already receiving loans worth over 6000 million rupees from the World Bank to cover schemes concerned with urban transport projects. The proposals now under consideration include several projects which form part of the New Bombay scheme, particularly office development at Belapur, the steel dockyards at Kalamboli and some village improvement schemes. Vijay must advise the World Bank whether to approve all or part of the loan – bearing in mind World Bank aims to fund projects which are likely to be effective and also to improve conditions for as many people as possible. The Bank would be unwilling to make more than 5000 million rupees available at one time.

WORLD BANK   *Memo:*

Schemes in the Bombay Metropolitan Region already funded by World Bank	*million rupees*
Bombay Urban Transport Project	425
East Island Tollway Project	435
Bombay Water and Sewerage Scheme	5580
Bombay Waste Disposal Scheme and Urban Health Project	800
TOTAL FUNDED	7240

Schemes requested for funding by World Bank

Thana Creek Waterway Project		
Rail Extension		
Nhava-Sheva Port		
Public Bus Services	all	
Roads and Bridges	for	4500
Village Improvement	New	
Office Complex	Bombay	
Markets/Stockyards at Kalamboli and Turbhe		
Water Supply Schemes		
House Repair/Reconstruction	for Greater	
Zopadpatti Improvement	Bombay	2850
Water Resource Development		800
Irrigation		
Environmental Protection		10
TOTAL REQUESTED		8160

Extract from World Bank Staff Working Paper No 347

   "National Urbanization Policies in Developing Countries". . .

   New towns are a very poor way to attempt a better 'balance' among various cities in order to alleviate congestion in old urban centres. They have problems, whether they are intended to be industrial new towns, residential new towns or new capital cities. While being particularly fascinating to urban designers and architects, new towns frequently represent a fundamental misunderstanding of urbanization and play on the desires of the upper income groups to cut themselves off from urban pollution and congestion by creating fully planned, well designed "garden cities". The construction of new towns raises questions of urbanization rationale, costs, methods of financing, economies of scale, localization, and of manpower and planning capabilities.

One of the two initial reasons for avoiding new towns programmes in developing countries is that new towns have never lived up to the claims that they were a particularly good way of absorbing urban population increments. Even on the largest scale, they will never absorb more than a very small percentage of the total annual increment of the national urban population.

The second critical reason for avoiding new towns in developing countries is that they constitute the most expensive ways of financing urban development. The universal experience with new towns is that they are capital-intensive experiments where the cost of living tends to be significantly higher than in existing cities. They have the additional undeniable feature of developing countries: in the shadow of the planned, highly serviced new towns with their high income populations, will grow a separate town, unplanned, poorly serviced and with a very low-income population.

New towns in developing countries are not consistent with the general country context of pronounced scarcity of resources. At a time when many existing cities lack adequate water supply, drainage, sewerage, public transport and low-income housing, new towns compete with old cities for central government funds. High standards, high costs, low economic returns and high maintenance costs make new towns inaccessible to most of the population and are inconsistent with prevailing urban income levels.

1. *CONSIDERING THE DECISION PROFILES (Work in pairs)*

In order to make use of all this information, it is best to work in pairs. Two students will need background information about New Bombay, in particular a diagram on the New Bombay Structure, and the New Bombay progress report. The aim is to use the information on the decision profile plus any other useful material, to decide how each person is likely to view New Bombay. In effect, the New City proposals are considered through the eyes of people affected by them. A New Bombay Appraisal Sheet will help organize the work and to record final ideas. For each person those aspects of the New City which may seem favourable or unfavourable are noted.

2. *DISCUSSION OF THE DECISIONS*

Students should now be ready to discuss new findings with other members of the class, one of whom should act as Chairperson. The Chairperson should organize the proceedings so that each pair of students, in turn, to present their findings relating to the six decision profiles. Comment and discussion should be allowed after each presentation. Students find that they change their minds about some of the people in the decision profile after listening to other views.

Finally, the Chairperson should lead a general discussion covering:

1. What kinds of people and activities are likely to support the new scheme? Why?
2. What kinds of people and activities are unlikely to support the new scheme? Why?
3. How do you rate the overall chances of success for the scheme as set out in the New Bombay proposals.

Soils and land activity module for primary level

SASH MATTIGOD

Introduction

Soils as part of land based ecosystems play a vital role in human activities such as agriculture, engineering and disposal of wastes. The burgeoning human population demands increasing food and fibre production and shelter. These in turn generate ever-increasing quantities of wastes that need to be disposed of. It is recognized that all these human activities are causing increasingly deleterious effects on world soil resources. Therefore, in 1981 a World Soils Policy was drafted under the auspices of several agencies such as FAO, UNESCO and UNEP with the leading principle that: "Among the major resources available to man is land, comprising soil, water and associated plants and animals, the use of these resources should not cause their degradation or destruction because man's existence depends on their continued productivity".

Traditionally topics such as Soils and Land have not been taught at pre-college levels. However, during the last few years, science educators especially in developing nations have expressed a need to teach these topics beginning at the primary level. Many pupils attend rural schools and these schools have few resources. However, soil is usually abundant locally and may be used as a teaching resource for science education.

Activity module

The module has been designed to teach certain important concepts about soils. Inexpensive and locally available materials can be used to conduct all the activities suggested in this module. There are three activities with suggestions for extending the activities to observations of soils, land and land use in the pupils' environment. The suggested activities are designed for 40 minute periods and can be conducted individually or in groups. The suggested outdoor activities can also be assigned as homework, if the teacher thinks that the pupils are capable of handling such an assignment.

These activities involve only qualitative observations. However, the teacher can encourage upper primary students to quantify their observations. The module is designed to develop scientific skills and formalize observations about soils and landscape. Therefore the teacher should encourage the pupils to record their activities in a format resembling scientific experiments. These activities can be part of the course; in geography, environmental science and agriculture.

Activity 1. Rocks and soils

Objectives	1. Soils are derived from rocks
	2. Soil contains particles of varying sizes, shapes and colour.
Materials	1. Collect pieces of rocks and samples of soils from various parts of surrounding landscape.
	2. Clear glass or transparent plastic wide mouth bottles of 1 litre capacity.
	3. Optional: Magnifying glass or microscope.
Methods	1. Pulverize pieces of rock. Pour approximately 50 gm each of pulverized rock and soil samples into each of the bottles.
	2. Mark a line 2 cm from the top of each bottle and fill the bottles with water to the mark.
	3. Stir vigorously to suspend the soil particles.
	4. Allow particles to settle for 8–10 hours.
Observations and conclusions	Observe that the largest soil particles (sand and gravel) have settled first, followed by medium size particles (silt), and at the top fine particles (clay). In some cases extremely small particles (very fine clay) may still be suspended in water. Note that the organic particles are floating on the surface of water, including worms and insects. Observe that different soils contain varying proportions of sand, silt and clay particles as well as varying amounts of organic particles.
	Soils have different textures characterized as sandy, silty or clayey depending on the dominant particles size that constitutes the soil. If none of the particle sizes is dominant, the soil is loamy.

Classify the soils under observation into the above categories (sandy soil, silty soil, etc.). Decant the water and examine the sand, silt and clay fractions with magnifying glass and note the similarities between particles of pulverized rock and soils. Explain that the similarities are due to the fact that soils are formed by the action of water and solar energy over tens of thousands of years. Summarize the observations.

Field Observations

Encourage students to study the soils in the local area. Ask them to make a list of various soils (based on texture, sandy, silty, etc.) and different kinds of land uses. Ask them if there is any relationship between soil texture and land use.

Activity 2. Soils and plant growth

Objective

1. Soils differ in their ability to support plant growth.
2. Application of fertilizers to soils produces better plant growth.

Materials

1. Collect 3 kg each of sandy, silty, clayey and loamy soil.
2. Pots (clay, plastic or any other locally available containers to grow plants).
3. Locally available organic fertilizers such as compost or chemical fertilizer (available from a garden supply store).
4. Bean seeds (any variety).

Methods

1. Fill one set of four pots with soil samples.
2. Fill a second set of four pots with soils mixed with fertilizer. (If organic fertilizer, use 1 part fertilizer to 3 parts of soil. If chemical fertilizer, follow the directions on the fertilizer packet.)
3. Plant three bean seeds in each pot and add water.
4. Add equal quantities of water daily as needed to each pot.

Observations and conclusions

Encourage students to share the daily watering chore. Ask them to note the time of seed germination and progress in growth. Observe any lack of germination, poor growth or death of plants. At the end of 2 or 3 weeks, compare the growth of bean plants in pots that do not contain added fertilizer. Measure and compare the heights of plants. Identify the soils that support the best and worst growth. Make similar observations about the plants growing in fertilized pots. Observe whether fertilization improves plant growth and identify the soils and note whether they have received any fertilizer. Observe any relationship between soil texture, fertilizer addition and plant growth. Summarize the observations.

Field Observations

Ask the students to observe the relationship between soil texture and the kinds of crops grown on the surrounding lands. Ask them to list the kind of fertilizers used locally. Help them to make a soil map and agricultural crop map showing various crops grown.

Activity 3. Soil Erosion

Objectives

1. Soil resources can be lost through denuding of soil surface.
2. Soils can be conserved by protecting the soil surface from the impact and flow of water.

Materials

1. Two (approximately $60 \times 60 \times 15$ cm) pans.
2. A local soil.
3. Dry straw, wood chips, grass clippings.
4. Sprinkler attachment to a garden hose or a watering can with a sprinkler attachment.

Methods

1. Pack the soil firmly into the pans.
2. Prop them at an angle (approximately 15°).
3. Protect the soil surface in one pan with dry straw, woodchips etc.
4. Sprinkle water on the soils in the pans from a height of approximately 100 cm for period of 2–3 minutes.
5. Repeat the activity with the soil pans at increasing angles.

Observations and conclusions

Observe that more soil is detached and removed from the unprotected soil surface by the impact and flow of water. Protection of soil surface by plant materials prevents excessive loss of soil. Also observe that as the slope of the pan increases, increasing amounts of soil are lost through erosion. Summarize the observations.

Field Observations

Ask the students to observe the relationship between slopes and erosion in the local landscape. Help them prepare an "erosion map" of the local area using categories such as severe, moderate and slight. Observe and note any relationship between any particular type of land use and severe erosion.

Laying foundations for appropriate use of land through experiential learning in primary schools

JULIE N. OKPALA

Introduction

Inappropriate use of land is an environmental problem which can result in immeasurable loss of resources, property and lives. Therefore, the foundation for this value should be laid from the primary level of education.

Examples of inappropriate use of land include urinating, defecating and disposing refuse in inappropriate places, creating routes in wrong places, uncontrolled excavation by construction firms, and setting up semi-permanent or permanent structures in unauthorized and disadvantageous locations. The degrees of inappropriateness in use of land vary from country to country and often reflect the physical and cultural aspects of the environment. Nigeria is given as an example of inappropriate use of land in its cultural perspective.

Southern Nigeria is an area of high-land pressure, high land cost and sentiment about the land. Two factors which contribute to the land problem are competition for different uses and the land ownership system. The finite land resource has to accommodate the increasing population's need for invaluable farmlands and for industrial expansion.

This pressure creates a problem of availability of land which is worsened by the traditional land-ownership system.While land is inequitably accessible to the population, the land ownership system, in which land is regarded as inalienable and is handed down to members of the family, makes land inaccessible to others who need it. Land cost and speculation increase at an unprecedented rate. Encroachment into private and public land is rampant. The former has led to squabbles over boundaries and has resulted in loss of lives. It has resulted in natural disasters as exemplified by the Ogunpa stream flood disaster of 1979 in Ibadan.

Although flooding is a physical phenomenon, the encroachment into the Ogunpa flood plain aggravated the level of damage to property and lives. Igbozurike (1981) observes that the painful episode seems to have been forgotten in Ibadan as human occupance and adverse land uses have started creeping back to the lower sections of the flood plain. He warns that the catastrophy will be repeated. In order to reduce the incidence and intensity of hazards aggravated by misuse of land as exemplified by the Ogunpa flood, feeling for appropriate use of space should be inculcated in learners at all educational stages. The crucial foundation is in the primary stage.

Need for foundation at the primary level

The primary level is the child's first contact with the deliberately structured learning experiences. The experiences he is exposed to at school at this stage leave lasting impressions on him. The values which are inculcated at this stage help him to modify his existing values and to assimilate new ones in the future. Deliberations on appropriate use of land at this level will not only provide direction but will facilitate in solidifying values as he moves into higher educational stages and into the society.

A fundamental attitude which should be laid at this level is that of a sense of place. This is a feeling of identity, purpose and belonging in his interaction with the environment. This is linked up with a feeling of attachment to a place and the understanding that he is responsible for and capable of improving the quality of life and environment. It is contended that the type and degree of meaning one makes of a place determines one's level of commitment to improving the place. The child of today who is the adult of tomorrow therefore needs to develop sense of the responsibility for appropriate land use. Inculcating sense of place requires that the child observes his environment and expresses opinions and feelings about it.

The experiential approach

The experiential approach involves combining observed information and expressed opinions and feelings in deliberating on use of land. Observation of the situation is the starting point and provides raw material for interpreting, criticizing and evaluating the phenomenon under study. This approach is activity and pupil oriented. Pupils are guided into realizing the quality of their environment as they identify areas needing change, the nature of the changes that are necessary and suggest steps for action. A prerequisite for using the experiential approach is that the child deals with a situation which is within his experience in the expanding horizon and which directly affects his life. This is essential if he is to be an active participant in the lessons. At the primary level issues on the appropriate use of land could be featured under Geography, Social Science, Integrated Science or Agriculture.

An example of content of land use issues suitable for Primary Social Studies is given below:

Year	Content
6	Use of place at home and class (e.g. wall, wash area, sitting area, aisle waste paper basket, seats and desks).
7	Use of places in school compound (e.g. lawns and paths, playground, rubbish dump, toilets).
8	Use of community facilities near the school (e.g. roads, rubbish dump, public toilets, parks).
9	Use of land for economic activities near school (e.g. market).
10	Use of land for primary economic activities of the area near the school (e.g. farming).
11	Other uses of land in the area for economic activity (e.g. by industries, by crafts and by workshops).

Whatever the content area the strategies that need to be involved in the experiential approach include:

1. Observation (direct)
2. Expression of values and feelings
3. Statement of facts
4. Suggesting reasons for alternative or varying situations observed from both the physical and human viewpoints.
5. Suggestions for future actions.

Samples of teaching procedure

A sample of how primary school pupils could be sensitized into developing awareness for appropriate use of land through use of the experiential approach is given below.

Lesson plan

Topic	Use of lawn in the school compound
Time	Two periods of 25 minutes each
Class	Primary two
Objective	The pupils should be able to:
	— identify the function of the lawn
	— identify reasons why some people use lawns; when they should use paths
	— express opinions about the paths on the lawn, identify human and physical problems which might arise due to people walking on the lawn
	— suggest through art expression the type of lawn they would like to see there.

Instructional Materials: A lawn on the school compound dissected by footpaths.

Entering Behaviour: Pupils have been introduced to the concept of "doing the right thing at the right place in Primary School".

Teaching procedure

Objectives	Teacher Behaviour	Pupil Activities	Instructional Strategies
1. Introduction	1. Teacher instructs pupils on meeting point for the lesson at the other side of the lawn beforehand 2. Teacher gets to the location first 3. Observe the routes taken by pupils	Pupils congreate at the location for the lesson	Observation
2. Identify reasons why some people use lawns when they should use paths	Ask pupils the route they took to the meeting point and why (Direct questions about diverse routes. – along paths – across lawn)	Explanation and reasons for routes taken	Discussion Questions and Answers
3. Identify the function of the lawn (e.g. protect soil, pleasant to look at).	Take pupils to the lawn. Pose questions e.g. – What can you observe that makes a lawn	Pupils observe nature of the lawn and talk about what they can observe.	Discussion Asking and answering questions.

Objectives	Teacher Behaviour	Pupil Activities	Instructional Strategies
	– Why is it grassed? – Why are stones lined at the outer edge? – How do you feel about the flowers? – Do you think they are useful?		
4. Express their feelings about the footpaths on the lawn	Draw pupils attention to the paths on the lawn	Pupils express their feelings	Discussion
5. Identify physical and human problems which might arise due to people walking on the lawn	Pose questions. Do you think that there is any problem in people walking on the lawn? Direct questions. Follow up to – – erosion – unsightly	Observe and express opinions	Discussion
6. Through art expression show the type of lawn you would like to see on the school compound	Instruct pupils to produce art expression in groups	Art expression	Group work, group presentation and class discussion of art work

Conclusion

JAGAR DORGI AND W. F. MOYO

The materials produced in the land use section of the book are designed so that teachers at all levels in education (primary, secondary and tertiary) and in varying circumstances may use them. There are lesson modules, teachers' guides, and sources of content which teachers may adapt and develop for their own individual teaching. It is accepted here that no single teaching strategy can suit all possible circumstances even within one classroom at different times, let alone in different schools all over the world. Teaching strategies are affected by various factors such as students' ages, their skills and range of abilities and their family backgrounds; teachers have different levels of inventiveness, different motivations and different resources. Other factors such as culture and even political ideologies affect what and how teachers teach. In view of these variables, it is not only difficult but impossible to provide a definite set of teaching materials to benefit all teachers in all schools. In a volume of this size and scope one cannot discuss all aspects of land and land use studies. For example the following aspects were not treated at all: the use of mountains, and oceans, marine flora and coastal environments. Therefore, it is expected that teachers need to look on the content of this section as a springboard for developing their own curricula.

The central viewpoint of the authors is that land is a finite resource and can be treated within the framework of an ecosystem. The activities of human beings and indeed our very existence and future livelihood and that of the other organisms depend upon our taking a responsible attitude towards land resources. Land must be conserved for future development so that future generations may also benefit. The best tool that can be used in achieving this objective is education viewed in its widest sense whether formal or non-formal. The emphasis must be made on sustainable and optimal utilization of land. This must be the guiding principle whether making decisions in the political, demographic, economic, technological, cultural or aesthetic dimension.

One may pose a question as to how the awareness of optimal and sustainable utilization of land can be developed in the classroom. There is no one answer, but the authors in section two of this publication have offered the following strategies.

1. Identification of the problems and needs of land use studies.

2. Presentation of illustrative case studies rich in content material and supportive data drawn from different regions of the world.

3. Development of teaching strategies by:
   (a) formulating teaching units;
   (b) stating objectives for each module; and

(c) presenting teaching methodology geared towards the maximum exploration of the cognitive, affective, perceptual, experiential and manipulative aspects of learning relevant to the students.

4. Suggestions of experimental procedures and field work.

5. Suggestions of apparatus for use ranging from low cost materials which a teacher can improvize in his/her local environment, to sophisticated technologies such as satellite images for remote sensing.

The authors have, in their papers, also highlighted the educational implications of land use in relation to science, technology, social and cultural aspects, while keeping in view the level of comprehension of students at different stages. It is apparent in these papers that the strategies are pupil centred. Hence, areas of experimentation such as soil testing and studies of social and economic impact on the environment and interaction between land, water and mineral resources and people are encouraged. Emphasis on using local resources is made to help develop concepts and ideas in different subject areas such as pedology, land use, geology and so on.

Another medium which can be used in land use studies is remote sensing through satellite images. While this is considered as a potential for future use, the posters and photographs of both local and distant areas may be thought of as skills which serve as stepping stones towards the use of remote sensing in the future.

The most important point here is that an education system needs to provide skills for development. Science particularly, taking a holistic view, can provide the strategies to meet present and future human needs. It becomes the task of teachers and educators, therefore, not only to provide the skills but to inform humanity of its possible future.

Supplementary references

Soils:

International Soil Resource and Information, Centre PO Box 353, 4700 A. J. Wageningen, Netherlands, Registry of Post Graduate courses in various aspects of land use are available for developing nations.

Tropical Forests, Marginal lands, Cities, Conservation:

Ecology in Action from Heinemann. A schools' resource pack on the environment and its relation to human activity.
Population and Urbanization, Brian Greaseley and Michael Younger (1982), Thomas Nelson and Sons Ltd (ISBN-0-245-53698-1).

Agriculture and rural development, Brian Greaseley and Michael Younger (1985), Thomas Nelson and Sons Ltd. (ISBN-0-17-444231-I), Nelson House, Mayfield Road, Walton-on-Thames, Surrey KT12 SPL, United Kingdom.

General:

The Biosphere Catalogue, The Synergetic Press, 24 Old Gloucester St., London, WC1 U.K.

PART III

Water Resources

Team leader: HANS VAN AALST.

6

Water Resources

HANS VAN AALST
*President of the State Advisory Board for Innovation in Secondary Education
in the Netherlands*

Problems and needs

Water as a resource

The need for water

Water is a resource with a large number of uses. It is essential for all living organisms.

The human body, which contains over 60% of water must get about 2.5 to 3 litres of pure water each day to remain healthy. A typical human in and output balance is given in Table 6.1.

Plants will not grow without an adequate supply of water. The initial stage of germination of seeds is the absorption of water. Water which is absorbed by the roots of plants is used in many ways for the growing processes of plants, but an astonishing amount of it is evaporated from the leaves. To grow 1 kg of wheat needs about 1500 kg of water. Water is also needed for numerous domestic and industrial uses. Other uses include transport, recreation, electricity-generation and fishing.

TABLE 6.1

Intake	Output
50% drunk as liquid	15% breathed out as water vapour
40% from solid food	20–25% perspiration
10% from chemical processes in the body	50–65% excreted in urine and faeces

The world's water inventory

There is a lot of water in, on, and around the earth. The hydrological cycle deals with circulation of water masses. This cycle is an interesting and complex part of our biosphere. Plants and animals transpire and water vapour goes into the air. Seas and lakes evaporate. Under certain conditions

127

clouds are formed. The clouds give rain or snow. The rain water drains out through streams, rivulets or rivers or forms lakes.

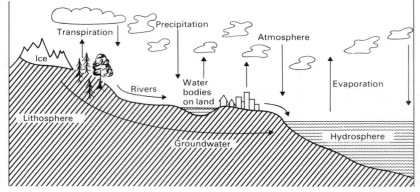

FIG. 6.1. Water cycle.

Most of this amount is unsuitable for human consumption. Less than half of the extractable fresh water is on the surface, in rivers and lakes, the rest lies trapped underground (Table 6.2).

TABLE 6.2. *Distribution of the Earth's Waters*

Water on Earth	% of Total Amount of Water on Earth
Marine Water	
Oceans, seas, gulfs, bays, straits and channels	97·20699
Inland Water	—
Surface water	
Lakes —	0·017
Rivers and streams —	0·000
Subsurface water	
Soil moisture —	0·005
Ground water —	0·62
Ice caps and Glaciers —	2·15
Atmosphere —	0·00101
TOTAL	100·0000

97.2%
2.8%

There is nevertheless sufficient for mankind's forseeable needs even if one includes increases of population.

(The Open University Unit "Water Resources" includes a nice exercise to control this statement.)

The problem of development of water resources:

Most of the human population settles down where water is available. The problem of the development of water resources is that water is not always available when and how it is wanted, or its quantity falls short the demand. If fresh water is available, problems of depletion, pollution or even flooding may arise.

Depletion of available fresh water supply can result from:
– overgrazing and deforestation,

– excessive withdrawal of ground water and consequent lowering of the watertable,
– evaporation and transpiration from plants.

Pollution can result from:

– agricultural runoff. This runoff may contain herbicides, pesticides fungicides and drainage from barns, stables and feed lots,
– discharge of raw residential effluent and industrial waste into waterways.

The development of water resources does not just include the development and operation of new resources but also the conservation of available clean water, the elimination of waste, and recycling of water used.

In many countries, there is a growing concern at the supply-and-demand situation for pure water in the future. One factor involved is economics.

It can be argued that fresh water can always be made available, but at a price. The public, however, is only prepared to pay a low price for handling and purifying water.

Traditionally water has been counted as a gift of nature. It has been free, because it could be collected by anyone as rain, or river water. Michael Overman, a journalist in technical subjects, notes in his book on water: "What are we to choose? Inadequate supplies at the price the uninformed public considers fair; or plentiful water at an economic price?"

Is water a resource, to be provided on an economic supply-and-demand basis, like gasoline or whisky?

Inset 1

WATER ON A SUPPLY-AND-DEMAND-BASIS?

A University of New Mexico study has estimated that the economy of the American Southwest profits by approximately 4 cents/m^3 of water used in irrigation. This is substantially less than the cost of bringing water in from the north. The same study has shown, however, that the development of industry in this region brings in a profit of not less than $2.50/m^3 of water utilized.

Would it be a reasonable decision to augment supplies in this area, to put up the price of water, and in order to meet it, to shift the emphasis of the economy from agriculture to industry?

Data from: Michael Overman: *Water* (The Open University, 1976)

Water supply for development

The need for action

The WHO (World Health Organization) estimates that about half of the worlds' people do not have access to a safe supply of drinking water (1980).

There really is a need for action for better water-supply! But the extent of the problem is enormous.

The UN estimates that worldwide, no less than 6 or 7 million hand-pumps and water-taps have to be provided for as many rural villages, to provide safe drinking water for people in rural areas.

Inset 2

WATER FOR ALL: THE CASE OF INDIA

According to India's Sixth Plan (1980–85), 57,000 problem villages have yet to be provided with safe and assured water supply. The Government has ruled that one water source, usually a hand-pump, is to be provided for every 250 to 300 people. An additional source is to be provided in areas inhabited by socially and economically backward classes. India counts 550,000 villages at present.

Data from: U.N., *World Health*,
August/September 1983.

The need for clean water in countries of the Third World is primarily seen in terms of *food production* and *health*.

Food production

Can be improved by irrigation. Irrigation can not only increase crop yields but also increase frequency and variety of crops. The effect of irrigation-schemes, may be that the population can not only feed itself but also earns a small profit on surplus produce.

The relation to *health* is largely because of the large number of water-related diseases, and because of the continued high rates of infant-mortality from this cause. Improved health and life-expectation will likely result in smaller families. Better health might also stimulate productivity. In India alone, water-borne diseases claim 73 million work-days every year.

Better water supply would also *save the time* and effort for women, one of whose main tasks has hitherto been to transport water every day. Women in some rural areas in the Third World spend up to 3 hours a day, fetching and carrying heavy watercans (to get water which is often of dubious quality) many miles for the home.

However, it would be a mistake to suggest that more clean water would just mean better health, or more crops. It is certainly a condition, but it is not the sufficient one.

Water and health

The WHO estimates that four out of every five illnesses in the world are linked to poor water-supplies or poor sanitation. This includes the effects of drinking-water that is contaminated by such diseases as cholera, hepatitis, typhoid fever and amoebiasis. Water acts as a breeding ground for disease-carriers like mosquitoes, and diseases caused by people not washing themselves well enough.

Nearly 30,000 people, mainly young children, die in the Third World every day because of inadequate water.

Improving water supply on its own is not sufficient in eliminating disease. Even when clean water is provided, it is often polluted during storage.

Static pools of water in the fields or around a pump may become breeding-grounds for insects and so become a means of water-related disease.

One study reports: "villagers do not know that walking in bare feet on moist soil gives them hookworms, and most cannot afford slippers. There are government subsidies to help villagers build latrines, but none to buy footwear" (Waterlog 7, May 1983).

If better water supply is not linked with better sanitation, human waste, scattered over the fields and in the bush will severely pollute underground reservoirs, as it does already. In 1980, the WHO estimated that only 13% of the developing world's rural population (exclusive of China) had access to adequate excreta disposal facilities. For urban areas the figure was 53%.

Also, people will not necessarily practise good personal and domestic hygiene as clean water supply becomes available. Safe storage of water in the home is one factor.

Inset 3

A study to assess the effects of improved water supply was carried out in Malawi. The water was taken from a protected catchment in an uninhabited mountain area. The water was led in pipes through gravity from the mountains to the lower lying areas. Traditional water sources and the improved piped water as well as water in household storage container was analysed for indicator bacteria, i.e. fecal coliforms and fecal streptocci (see Table 6.3).

TABLE 6.3.

	Fecal coliforms/100 ml		Fecal streptocci/100 ml
	sample size	mean	mean
Before intervention:			
Dry season: non-protected			
water-sources	106	820	470
Dry season: households	62	1800	1700
After intervention:			
Dry season: piped water	39	85	118
Dry season: households	198	1100	950
Wet season: piped water	10	330	630
Wet season: households	48	⌐200	3680

Thus the non-protected water sources were rather contaminated compared to the WHO standard of 0 coliforms/100 for drinking water and the water quality got worse during storage in the house. The piped water was a big improvement although it was not as good as the WHO standard. However, most of the household water was still highly contaminated.

During the wet season the increase in contamination was still higher. There must therefore be other factors than the quality of the water at the source which influence the household water quality. It was found that conditions of storage was a main factor here. Such conditions include:

– Careful cleaning of water containers every time they are filled.
– Use of a cup with a long handle so that fingers do not touch the water when water is scooped out of the container.
– Hands should be washed whenever dirty.
– Animals should be kept away otherwise they could contaminate the water.

Data from: P. A. Lindskog and R. U. M. Lindskog, The importance of hygiene education in obtaining a health impact through improved water supply and sanitation with examples from Malawi. Address for copies.

P. Lindskog, Department of Water, Tema, Linköping University, S-56183 Linköping, Sweden.

A UNESCO study in Bangladesh found that even in villages where clean tubewell water was available, individuals were still using the traditional contaminated water source for bathing, cooking and washing utensils.

Indeed, as the "Earthscan" document concludes: "The Provision of water supply, sanitation facilities and health education must go together. If each component is implemented separately, much of the health benefit may be lost."

The UN launched the International Drinking Water Supply and Sanitation Decade 1981–1990. The goal is clean water and adequate sanitation for all by 1990. The programme includes the stimulation of education for hygiene.

Water and agriculture

A second main reason for improving water supply in developing countries is the use of water for irrigation purposes, needed to supply a growing population with food.

The recent problems in Mid-Africa only underline the absolute need for water for food production.

Irrigation can increase crop yields, frequency and variety. This is illustrated by the case study of the Periyar-Vaigai-Project, Madurai, India.

Inset 4

THE PROFITS OF IRRIGATION-SCHEMES

(The case of the Periyar-Vaigai project, India)

Rainfall data for Madurai show marked variations, which stem from four vagaries of monsoon-rains:
- Delay in the commencement,
- Prolonged break during the season,
- Premature cessation,
- Concentration in one part of the region. (see p. 162)

The seasonal variation over a 30-year period seldom followed a regular pattern.

The "Periyar-Vaigai" project which diverted water from one catchment area and used it for the irrigation of arid tracts elsewhere, has had a notable effect:

1. The Suruliyar and Vaigai-rivers, formerly reached flood stage for a week or two and then being nearly dry for almost the rest of the year. They have now a nearly constant flow of water most of the year.
2. As a result, irrigation has been extended to a larger area; the average area cultivated has increased by 22%.
3. Even more important is that there is an assured supply of water for a greatly expanded wet crop land use. A little over 60% of the dry land has been converted into wet land. This regular supply of water for the wet lands assures successful raising of one crop per year; in the pre-project days the wet crop was precarious. The expansion of wet lands allows for two crops: a wet (rice) and dry one (ground-nuts or any millet). For the average farmer this means that he is now able to produce more than his family needs and the tenant farmer paying the landlord's share, is able to feed his family and even earn a small profit on his surplus produce.

> Data from: E. G. Vedanayagam's
> *Case study of the Periyar-Vaigai project*

Irrigation has its undoubted benefit. But there are problems as well. Such problems can be listed as follows:

- wastage of scarce water,
- waterlogging and salination of fertile land,
- erosion,
- increase of water-based diseases, such as Bilharzia,
- people may be unwilling to move to the irrigated areas and farmers may not easily change over to better farming habits.
- loss of soil-fertility by washing.

Wastage of scarce water

Agricultural water consumption is immense. To grow 1 kg of rice requires 4,500 kg of water. The production of 1 kg of cotton requires more than 10,000 kg of water.

Less than half the water that does reach the field is actually used in the life processes of plants. The remainder percolates down through the soil or is lost to the atmosphere by evaporation from the soil-surface. Because of the very considerable volume of water used for irrigation, reduction of wastage in irrigational usage of water should be considered.

The steps that may be taken to effect maximum savings is an area in which research is still required. Some of the options are:

– Cheap means of rendering water channels impervious.
– New mulching methods to reduce evaporation from the soil surface.
– Modification of water requirements of the crops themselves.
– Reduction of evaporation from open tanks by covering the water by thin layers of chemical emulsion such as ethyl alcohol.

Waterlogging and salination

A very disturbing consequence of irrigation is the ruination of fertile cropland by waterlogging and salination.

Heavy irrigation serves to raise the water-table level, and this often results in the land becoming waterlogged. The plant roots have no access to air and the crops fail, due to lack of oxygen. Irrigation in hot dry areas results in very considerable evaporation; the proportion of dissolved mineral salts in the unevaporated water increases slowly but steadily, until the concentration of salts in the transition zone from which the crops draw their water becomes higher than the crops can tolerate.

It has been estimated that the area of crop-land lost because of waterlogging and/or salination is as big as the area of crop-land gained by new irrigation-schemes.

The effect of waterlogging and salination can be evaded by better control of water-inlet, efficient drainage and pumping to lower the water-table. But this demands better education of local farmers and more expensive equipment.

Erosion

Irrigation channels are enlarged by the flow of water through them, and this may cause considerable erosion. Of course concrete channels may help. Also sprinklers may be used. However, when they are used evaporation rates are higher, and sprinklers mean more outlay on equipment.

Water-based diseases

It is a tragic irony that in many parts of the world irrigation schemes constructed with the aim of improving the standard of living have had the effect of undermining the health of the areas they serve.

With the completion of irrigation schemes in the tropical world there has been a commensurate increase in Bilharzia. Bilharzia (or schistosomiasis or Snail-fever) has been called the "disease of development" (Inset 5).

Inset 5

BILHARZIA: THE DISEASE OF DEVELOPMENT

The Sennar dam built on the Blue Nile converted 360,000 hectares of dry savanna to the fertile Gezira cotton growing area. But within 3 years Bilharzia had spread widely amongst the farmers and their families. A much smaller scheme to utilize the river Niger for irrigated sugar cane growing at Bacita in Nigeria had similar consequences. Before the introduction of the scheme 6% had Bilharzia, at the end of the first year of irrigation the figure had risen to over 20%.

Medicine to heal individuals from Bilharzia is still under development. Available drugs are expensive and inefficient.

Another approach to fight this disease is to tackle the snails who carry the parasite during one phase of their life-cycle.

Finally, people can be trained not to go into water with bare feet or hands.

Change of living and working conditions

Many irrigation schemes ask people to move in the newly irrigated land. But they may be unwilling to do so (Inset 6).

Inset 6

MOVE THE PEOPLE OR THE WATER?

The case of Sarir and Kufra (Libya)

In recent years several hundred wells have been dug into the aquifers at Sarir and Kufra in Libya, to feed isolated irrigation schemes in the desert. These irrigation projects have not been a great success because Libyans have been unwilling to move into the desert to grow alfalfa on the newly fertile land. Kufra is now virtually abandoned as an agriculture scheme. Because of this, the idea now is to bring water to the people instead.

Data from: *New Scientist*,
6 September 1984.

Irrigated land demands different methods of farming, different crops to grow. Irrigation schemes therefore include educational programmes, but no immediate effect is expected. It may take 10–15 years. This is considerably longer than the time most projects are planned for (Inset 7).

Inset 7

ARE THE FARMERS LIKELY TO CHANGE?

The case of the Mahaweli-Project, Sri Lanka

Two large-scale irrigation schemes were initiated in Sri Lanka in the sixties. One of these, the Uda Walawa scheme, is at present troubled by the failure of farmers to change their farming habits immediately. The newly irrigated land was known to be very permeable and was therefore unsuitable for paddy cultivation. The farmers who moved in were told to grow crops like chillies, onions, pulses, etc. But they nonetheless started to grow paddy because this was the crop with which they were familiar.

Consequently, they used much more than the planned amount of water, and the land lower down the main irrigation channel remains deficient of water. The Mahaweli-project, more recently, has instituted education programmes for the farmers who are to be settled in the new areas. Officials, however, reported that the achievement of the desired diversification of crop production will inevitably be a slow process, taking 10 to 15 years.

Data from: F. R. McKim: *Using more water*, p. 69.

To conclude

Irrigation is a good use of water resources. But the potential problems should be properly assessed and measures taken to minimize them.

Urban and rural supply

On a world scale, access to clean water is a larger problem in rural areas than it is in urban areas. The WHO estimates that 78% of the poor world's rural population (excluding China) is without access to clean water. Of the urban population the figure is 23% (1980). The difference is partially because of government neglect of the rural regions. Governments tend to favour supplying clean water to the towns rather than the rural areas because:

– It is more convenient and cheap to supply densely populated urban areas.
– It is less dangerous to drink from standing water or wells in the country and it is more important to provide sanitation for cities where water-borne diseases can quickly infect thousands of people.

The urban areas have more political clout.

Urban supply

Urban demand per person is considerably larger than rural demand.

In East Africa a study revealed that city dwellers use 14–40% more water than rural households.

Urban demand grows faster than population increases. This presents special problems, since not only does an increased supply of water have to be collected from further and further afield as existing sources fall short of demand, but all this water has to be channelled into a restricted area that is growing more and more congested.

Urban supply does not end with the construction of a dam, of a ground water pumping station, or a desalination station. It also involves the problem of transporting storing locally, and distributing the water; and ultimately, of disposing of it when it reappears, polluted.

For urban areas the conservation of water is specially important (Inset 8).

Inset 8

URBAN SUPPLY: THE CURVE CANNOT GO ON RISING

The case of Teheran

The Lar River rises in the Elburz Mountains about 40 km north of Teheran. It has a sufficiently large flow for its water to have been used for sometime for irrigation. However at times of its peak flow, there is far more water than the demands of irrigation requires. The idea behind the Lar Project was to dam the river so as to retain the excess water behind the dam rather than send it uselessly down to the Caspian. The excess water could then be piped to Teheran. The whole scheme came about because of the demand by Teheran for more and more water.

But, as can be seen from Fig. 6.2, it would not solve Teheran's water problem for long. Within 5 years after finishing the project, another equally big scheme will be needed, unless a significant lowering of the rate of population growth and a better use of water can be realized. The inhabitants of Teheran are not unduly extravagant in their use of water. On the other hand, it is the usual practice throughout Iran to wash under running tap (or in a running stream, etc.) rather than in a bowl, basin or bath of water. Yet while a change of habit to washing in a definite amount of water rather than in running water, would undoubtedly save water, it would require a great social upheaval. For non-flowing water is "unclean" to the Iranian Muslim, and any attempt to enforce a change in washing habits would run across this religious taboo. However, something will have to happen. The curve in Fig. 6.2 cannot go rising indefinitely.

Even if the country could find even more water, it would eventually run out of the means of supplying it.

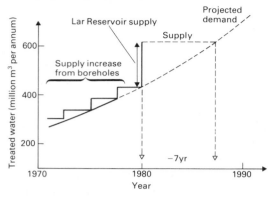

The supply and demand situation for
water in Tehran (actual and
projected figures in 1976)

FIG. 6.2. Data from: F. R. McKim, *Using More Water*.

Rural supply

For several reasons, centralized schemes with big dams, are not the main
nor the most urgent priority from the point of view of the development of a
rural supply.

In rural areas the focus of attention is on the conservation of water at the
village-level, both for drinking and for cultivation, with the help of wells and
boreholes, pumps and small dams. The need is for the development of
practical low cost and easily maintained hardware that is acceptable in the
communities for which it is intended. The involvement of local people in
simple skills in hygiene, nutrition and, for some of them, the maintenance of
hardware is seen as crucial.

Attention has been concentrated on ground water supplies. Rainfall in
Third World countries is often unreliable as a permanent source of drinking
water and streams are subject to pollution.

Ground water is cleaner than surface supplies, but the main problem is
getting it to the surface.

Shallow, uncovered wells are subject to pollution and to drying up; deeper
wells are more expensive to build and maintain. Both need pumps for
maximum easy use.

New hand pumps are now being tested to field condition in many
developing countries. (For example: see IRC-Book: Handpumps for use in
drinking water supplies in developing countries, and more up to date
manuals.)

Solar technology and wind-energy are expected to make a small
contribution in the future.

The pumps may not always last for long. In some areas the technology used is inappropriate to the local circumstances. Sometimes money and equipment do not continue to be available for maintenance and repairs. In other cases the social structures do not allow proper maintenance.

The case of Tamil Nadu (India) man illustrates the point (Fig. 6.3) (Inset 9).

Inset 9

HAND PUMPS AND THEIR MAINTENANCE –
The case of Tamil Nadu

In the south Indian State of Tamil Nadu shallow wells, ponds and streams dry up in summer causing acute water shortages. Yet even by 1970 about 8000 villages in the State had no assured water supplies. The Tamil Nadu Water and Sewerage Development Board (TWAD) later installed 15,000 shallow well pumps, 15,000 deep well pumps with overhead tanks in larger villages, but due to overuse, silting and neglect of maintenance, a large number of them went out of use.

The UNICEF involvement at this state with the TWAD enabled the improvement of these facilities with the design and installation of a more robust steel pump – the India Mark II. A supple plunger, an outlet safe for children, an extra solid handle, a concrete base and gutter for efficient drainage disposal all soon rendered this design very popular and its

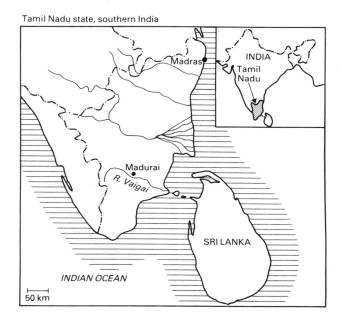

FIG. 6.3

production crossed the 100,000 a year mark. Direct involvement of village communities in the provision and maintenance of these pumps was an important aim of this collaborative project.

In the district of Salem where this programme was first set up there are six administrative units known as "Blocks" with several villages in each block. The village development implementation was located at the block headquarters. A three-tier maintenance scheme initiated to simplify the pump repairing procedures consisted of:

   i. A voluntary pump caretaker usually a teacher,
  ii. A block level mechanic/fitter for every hundred pumps and
 iii. A mobile team for every thousand pumps.

The caretaker dealt with minor repairs and informed the fitter about any break-downs.

Tirunelveli is the next district in Tamil Nadu to which these ideas were transferred; 2 years after the project began 15 out of 31 blocks were covered and 620 caretakers were trained in UNICEF camps.

The scheme has since spread to other districts in which the first tier was taken over by block officials who visited the villagers regularly and informed the fitters at the headquarters about cases of any breakdowns through messengers on bicycles.

One of the main hopes of the three-tier scheme was that the pump caretaker would also act as a primary health motivator teaching about the need for safe water and elementary hygiene. This has not been achieved in all cases; the major success was the development of the Indian Mark II pump itself.

Data from Geofile No. 39, September 1980.

Big dam schemes

Perhaps what stimulates the imagination, are the big dam undertakings. Big dam schemes have their benefits and problems.

Typical benefits

– Irrigation of new areas as well as supplementing the water-supplies for existing irrigation schemes,
– urban and industrial water supply, leading to development of new urban areas.
– Hydro-electric power,
– Flood control.

As always with technical undertaking, there are also aspects that could be qualified as negative:

– The damage and suffering from a break-down of dams is enormous.
   The engineering involved in building big dams is in principle available,

and one can have reasonable confidence in their safety. But not everything is known or under control (e.g. earthquake) and during the building process, mistakes can be made.
– Some people argue that in some cases the electricity gained is not really used for development but for cheap production of goods and minerals for western countries. Also big dam-schemes give most profit to urban areas, where some people argue that rural areas should have priority.
– Finally big schemes in general may disturb the ecological balance and socio-economic systems, and such effects have not always have been taken into account, or are really controversial (Inset 9 and 10).

Inset 10

FISHERMAN LOST THEIR INCOME AFTER THE BUILDING OF A BIG DAM

Before the Akosombo Dam was constructed in the lower Volta valley (Ghana) the flooding river brought large quantities of nutrients into the sea off the estuary between September and December. This attracted huge shoals of horse mackerel providing excellent catches for sea fishermen. With the retention of the sediment in Lake Volta the fish are no longer attracted and the fisherman have lost their income.

Data from: WDSE Bulletin 2

Conclusion

There is no doubt that a crucial contribution to development is the provision of appropriate water supplies.

Clean, safe drinking water may improve health, but it should go together with better sanitation and education for hygiene. Irrigation can increase food production, but maximum effect will only be reached after a change of farming habits. Irrigation should be controlled very carefully, to prevent waste and to avoid water-logging and salination of the soil.

Urban schemes are different from rural schemes. There has been a tendency to favour water supply to urban areas. Urban use tends to increase rapidly and there is a need for conservation.

Rural programmes concentrate the effort on easily maintained pumps, and adequate involvement of local population in terms of maintenance of systems and use of the water supplied.

Water supply schemes may have side effects, some of which are inherent to the technology used, others are consequences of the supply of water itself.

References

Open University Water Resources, London 1974; Earthscan: Water and sanitation for all, London 1983.

7

Educational Implications of Water Resource Problems

Introduction

HANS VAN AALST
President of the State Advisory Board for Innovation in Secondary Education in the Netherlands

This book is meant to contribute to "Science and Technology Education and Future Human Needs". Adequate water supply is certainly a human need. As has been shown, this need is interrelated to other needs such as health, food and agriculture, the environment, etc. Therefore, education for the area of water-supply-development does not necessarily need to take the form of specific courses, curricula or programmes on water-supply-development.

This chapter is dedicated to the educational aims, the content and activities which might set the scene for future educational efforts in the field.

Educational settings and target populations

Education can take many forms and be intended for different groups of the population. We can plan for formal or for non-formal education, for general or for vocational curricula, for young children or for adults, for a science curriculum or for social studies. Of course each country or authority or project has to decide what specific educational setting and which group of the population they want to concentrate upon for implementing certain goals.

Nevertheless, within the context of the present effort, an accent on the settings and target groups as given in Table 7.1 could be justified: Primary schools, and perhaps junior secondary schools are as far as most Third World children will go in their education. To provide a general basic science education for the large part of the population, we must turn to these levels. Most curricular for primary education have openings to include water-supply related topics, as far as they cover local context and provide children with first hand experience.

143

TABLE 7.1. *Proposed Priority for Educational Efforts*

---

1. The science curriculum in primary schools and perhaps in junior secondary schools.

2. Special training courses and information services for youth and adults, in direct connection with water-supply-development schemes.

3. Vocational (technical) education at secondary and tertiary level.

4. Special projects/modules field work connected to science/technology curricula of secondary and tertiary levels.

The science curricula for secondary level in most countries have an academic and modern-sector orientation, which is strongly held by teachers, students and parents. The vast majority drop out early. Vocational education is quite often inadequate.

The integration of water-supply-development-issues in science curricula requires the adoption of a more technologically based content, the scrapping of traditional content and the use of different examination questions. There are very few ideas that could fit quite neatly into the traditional syllabuses (e.g. static pressure-pumps; chemical analysis of water quality).

Traditional ways of teaching should be amplified by others such as project work, productive skill-training etc. to connect academic skills to practical contexts (van Aalst and Eijkelhof, 1982). Such change of curricula is certainly the ultimate aim, but cannot be reached in a short time.

In the short term, the main effect may result from links with developmental schemes. Many water development schemes include education. Together with the training of executive staff and foremen, special programmes are made available to specified groups of local people. Training courses for staff-training now occasionally offer degrees, which are officially recognized, although they did not exist earlier.

Secondary schools, curriculum centres, and teacher-training departments should be involved in such programmes. For such schools and institutes the interaction with developmental schemes would mean a direct source of information, materials and know-how. These could be used for updating formal curricula; for adding vocational courses to it or for offering special projects connected to the formal curricula.

Finally, a more predominant place for vocational education (matched by attractive career prospects) together with better general science and technology education have been advocated by many industrial project-managers as well as by water-development project-leaders (see H. Herrmann and R. Zelder, *Berufliche Bildung fur die Dritte Welt*, Koln, 1984; and UNESCO: Science and Technology Education and National Development, 1983).

General aims

Table 7.2 lists general aims for education for water-supply-development.

The need for awareness on the part of local people about the proper and controlled use of water and their own ability to interact with water supply systems has been stated in aims 1 and 2.

The training of people in engineering, planning and management of water supply system, probably applies mainly to specific vocational courses. But some aspects may be implemented in programmes for the general public or for general education in schools in order to stimulate job-seeking in such directions and to promote public understanding of water supply schemes.

Aim 4 is the training in techniques, where no. 5 and 6 really consider technologies, i.e. methods of inventing, assessing, and improving techniques for specified purposes.

Finally, the ability to evaluate schemes in terms of developmental progress seems to be appropriate to include in educational programmes, as a means of better public involvement. Of course the aim is certainly of importance for governmental leaders.

TABLE 7.2. *List of General Aims for Education for Water Supply Development*

---

1. To help local people to see the importance of safe water and proper sanitation and/or carefully controlled irrigation.

2. To help local people to become aware of water supply systems which they have at their disposal and that they are also aware of their ability and responsibility to control and improve these systems.

3. To enable young people:
   – to get a preview of the technological design process, the mastery of the instruments and techniques of productive work;
   – to get an acquaintance with men in the field; and
   – to become aware of opportunities for vocational courses leading to careers in engineering in the public and private sectors.

4. To train people to plan, build, operate and maintain low-cost water supply, sanitation and irrigation systems.

5. To train people to choose to adopt and to develop appropriate technologies for tapping, pumping, transporting, storing, purifying and delivering water and for effectively disposing of wastes.

6. To train people to locate and assess sources of safe water: – rainfall, lakes, rivers, springs, and underground reserves – which can be utilized for human consumption, irrigation or else.

7. To help people to evaluate water supply and sanitation achievements, in terms of their impact on health and well-being, and over-all development progress.

Of course all the aims listed in Table 7.2 would not apply to all circumstances. In each specific context a selection has to be made and an appropriate specification has to be drawn up.

Content areas

According to specific educational settings or target-groups special content may be selected. A starting point for selection may be the list given in Table 7.3.

TABLE 7.3. *List of* Content-areas *for Teaching Water Supply Development*

(A) *Water as a resource*
1. The hydrological cycle and its basic sub-processes.
2. Main sources:
   – ground water (aquifer, water-table, artesian wells; soil moisture).
   – Surface water (rivers, lakes, rain-water reservoirs).
   – sea-water (desalination).

(B) *The concept of water supply development*
1. Water supply and agricultural use: development of food production.
2. Water supply and human/animal use; development of health; relation with sanitation.
3. Water supply and industrial use; development of industry.
4. Economic pay-off of improved water supply system.
5. Methods to estimate future needs as a function of time (in the areas of agriculture, human living, industry) including use as function of supply.

(C) *Basic scientific principles*
1. Static pressure, water flow quantities, capillarity.
2. Chemical and biological standards for water quality.
3. Methods of locating water resources and estimating available quantities; water basin; replenishment rates of aquifers, etc.
4. Water supply and the limits of tolerance in the biosphere to the distortions of and within the hydrological cycle.

(D) *Technologies for water supply*
1. Methods of extracting water from aquifers; bore-hole/well-pumping systems;
   – local approach
   – large scale implementation approach.
2. Methods of extracting water from open reservoirs:
   – local (e.g. roof-storage),
   – large scale (e.g. river-dams),
3. Desalination.
4. Purification:
   – filtration,
   – distillation,
   – use of chemicals (chloride).
5. Piping system.

(E) *Ways of preventing water supply problems*
1. Not pumping too much from aquifers. Preventing waste. Re-cycling water.
2. Avoiding pollution (natural, from industries, from human waste).
3. Limiting increase in demand which comes with a better supply.
4. Maintenance with appropriate technologies.
5. Assessing the ecological effects of big schemes.
6. Controlling irrigation to prevent:
   – waterlogging and salination,
   – increase of water-based diseases,
   – waste of water,
   – erosion.

(F) *Planning and decision handling*
1. Decision-making between alternative techniques taking into account:
   – costs,
   – maintenance organization,
   – social cultural factors,
   – local physical conditions,
   – actual and future needs,
   – economic pay-offs and diseconomies.
2. Public participation in planning and decision-making.

3. Decision-making between alternative development strategies (e.g. total village, self-reliance, partial self-reliance, external production); welfare approach versus development approach.

(G) *Jobs and courses in water engineering*
1. Formal courses.
2. Community projects.

Matching aims and content to levels of education

HARTWIG HAUBRICH

One aspect of educational planning is certainly the appropriate matching of aims and content to levels or age-groups.

H. Haubrich (1980) suggests a curriculum-spiral for education on water which specifies:

– Objectives,   – Activities,
– Teaching Materials and Media,   – Themes/case studies.

for different levels of general education, going from kindergarten to upper secondary.

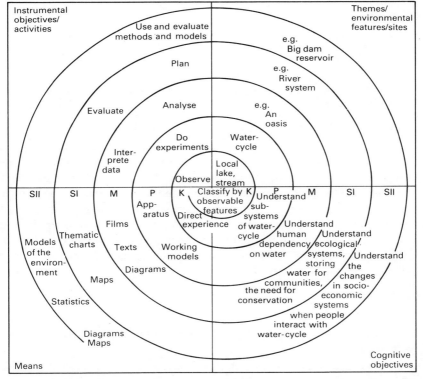

Levels: K = Kindergarten; P = Primary; M = Middle school; SI = Lower Secondary, SII = Upper Secondary.

FIG. 7.1. A water curriculum-spiral for science curricula in general education.

Alternatively, a table may be constructed to show the same thing.

TABLE 7.4

Stage:	Objectives (1)	Theme/ case study (2)	Activities (3)	Media (4)
Kindergarten (K) 5–6 yrs	1.1 to know forms, distribution and effects of water	1.2 spring river lake	1.3 to observe to play	1.4 real world
Primary School (P) 6–10 yrs	2.1 to explain subsystems of the water-cycle	2.2 hydrogolical cycle	2.3 to experiment	2.4 apparatuses models
Orientation stage (O) 10–12 yrs	3.1 to explain and value people– water relations	3.2 oasis	3.3 to analyse to interpret	3.4 film picture diagram programme
Secondary School (SI) 12–16 yrs	4.1 to evaluate the ecosystem "Rhine" and to decide upon national and international conservation measures	4.2 Rhine	4.3 to plan to evaluate to decide	4.4 thematic maps aerial and satellite photographs
Secondary School (SII) 16–19 yrs	5.1 to evaluate the impact of human activities on ecosystem	5.2 Lake Nasser	5.3 to use and to evaluate scientific methods and models	5.4 descriptive and interpretative statistics

The main emphasis in this scheme is on the understanding and proper management of water supply systems. It is not so much related to the development of supply systems. It is intended for use in western countries where most of the children go to secondary schools. Perhaps it is not quite appropriate for education in Third World countries. But it is worth thinking about it. The teacher or curriculum planner in a developing country may well be able to devise his own spiral, using for example the aims and content specified in Tables 7.2 and 7.3.

Possible activities

ROY PALLETT

Generally, the teaching practice in school and university science courses involves the following approach.

Assume ⟶ Knowledge A ⟶ Knowledge B etc.
no knowledge

Practical activity   Practical activity
based on knowledge A   based on B

In industries, crafts and families the method of instruction is likely to conform to the following approach which results in the acquisition of a "useful" skill.

1	2	3	4	5
*Primitive → skill	Demonstration → and practice	Improved → skill	Knowledge → on which skill is based	Developed or Mastered skill

The "primitive" skill stage reflects little or no familiarity with the skill required e.g. how to use pruning shears or using a calculator. Demonstration and practice is required to bring the learner to a stage of competence to operate efficiently but without necessarily understanding why the operation is being carried out or how the component parts interact, e.g. society requires that licenced drivers of cars operate at the "improved skill" level but does not require that all drivers understand the handling characteristics of cars or how the internal combustion engine works. The knowledge on which the skill is based and the mastery that enables thorough instruction of other people on the task belongs to a small percentage of the population. In looking at water resources, several practical exercises have been proposed in Chapter 8. Keeping in mind the various levels of understanding, these exercises can be arranged such as has been done in Table 7.5. The teacher is invited to develop his own scheme.

TABLE 7.5

	Science in the social historical economic context.	Science in technological context.	Science fundamentals.
Initial (primitive) skill level	– How much drinking and cooking water is used? – Household water resources – Frequency of waterborne diseases.		What happens to rain?
Improved skill level	– Quality of stream water – How can water be purified?	– Rain gauge – Simple pump – How brackish water is purified.	– Speed of ground water flow – What is depth of ground water – Transpiration – Streamflow
Developed or Mastered skill level		How can evaporation be reduced	How much water is required to produce a given amount of food
Required knowledge		physics mathematics	physics mathematics

(* Idea developed by Peter Fensham, Monash University.)

Frequently, education about water-resources-development can take the form of a unit or project dedicated to a specific theme. Chapter 8 shows some examples.

– a unit on the use of water and its relations with health
– a unit on sewage treatment
– a unit on the lay-out and effects of a water-diversion project for irrigation
– a unit on water pollution and water conservation within a river area.
– a unit on drinking water resources by shallow well pumping.

General conclusions

HANS VAL AALST

Education about water-supply-development cannot be planned adequately on its own.

The relation between water supply, health, food production etc. is complex. The acceptance and proper use of supply systems by the local people varies from place to place and may be a slow process. Available technology is not always adequate. The role of formal general education must not be over-estimated. A more prominent place for vocational education is urgently needed. Perhaps a certain change of science-curricula for primary and lower secondary education to more technological and practical contexts is a possible objective to achieve in the short term. This would also be the most effective in terms of population reached.

The most effective objective for the short term for secondary and tertiary institutions may be to establish co-operation with local water development schemes. This could be borne in mind by water scheme planners. For schools it would mean to offer co-operation with such schemes, specific water-related courses, favourably leading to degrees which are officially rewarded and to offer project work for students as well as information programmes for local people. "Enrichment" of the existing science curricula has limited scope in the short term. In the long term a more radical change of curricula, examination questions and teaching practices is needed. It is possible to specify a general set of aims and content areas, and a scheme for specifying such aims and content areas, for specific age groups as a reference list.

Resources

More information about water

1. First of all ask your local or regional Water Boards for local information, rainfall maps etc.
2. Secondly try to find out which main development projects on water supply have been carried out or are being carried out in your country. These projects often provide excellent Master-Plan documents and progress reports.

3. A general centre for documentation is the IRC International Reference Centre for Community Water Supply, P.O. Box No. 140, 2260 AC Leidschendam in the Netherlands. They also provide all kinds of technical books.
4. A nice study book for teachers might be the Open University unit. *Water Resources*. This is block 5 of the Earth's Physical Resources Course. Address: The Open University, P.O. Box 81, Walton Hall, Milton Keynes, MK7, England.
5. Ohio State University, Columbus, Ohio has an information Reference Centre for Science, Mathematics, and Environmental Education. They provide the water quality Instructional Resources Information System (IRIS). A compilation of Abstracts on water quality and water resources materials.
   Write to: EPA Instrumental Resource Centre
              1200 Chambers Road, Room 310
              Columbus, Ohio 43212
              U.S.A.
6. The Centre for World Development Education, 128 Buckingham Palace Road, London SW1 has a resource centre, from which you might order things, such as the United Nations Water Pack and many others. They provide a catalogue.
7. *Earthscan*, 10 Percy Street, London W1C 0DR, England produce three or four excellent booklets about water resources development including case studies.
8. Probably a University Department may be able to suggest basic textbooks on hydrology, water supply engineering etc.
9. The Committee on Science and Technology in Developing Countries (ICSU/COSTED) produced a volume about exploration techniques for ground water. (COSTED, Indian Institute of Science, Bangalore-560 012, India.)

Some educational materials

1. Probably, your local or national science curriculum centre(s) will have materials on water.
2. There are quite a lot of nice modules on water developed by the: Science Education Centre, University of Philippines, Biliman, Quezan City.
   For primary education:
   – Water and health,
   – Water in your community,
   – Water, water, everywhere.
   For secondary level:
   – Potable water from sea-water,

- Water supply and treatment,
- The drinking water supply of Leyte and Samar,
- Keeping water safe to drink,
- Harmful organisms in water,
- Surface water,
- Ground water.
3. Tatort Rhein – Full reference in Chapter 8 elsewhere in this book.
4. Water for Tanzania full reference in Chapter 8.
5. Water – Australian Science Education Project (ASEP). Includes simple activities and information – uses of water, hydrological cycle, ground water, water in the air, transpiration, pollution etc.

References

Haubrich, H., Tatort Rhein – Braunschweig, 1983.

Van Aalst, Hans, F.; Eijkelhof: A perspective on the implementation of science, technology in society, education at secondary school-level; Proceedings of the second conference on Science, Society and Education, Amsterdam VU, 1983.

8

Some Teaching Examples
On Water Resources

Unit on water and health for primary level

PER LINDSKOG

Linkoping University, Sweden

Aim: The aim of the unit is to create an understanding of the relationship between water supply and health and the importance of sanitation and hygiene.

Water consumption:

Question: How much drinking and cooking water does your family use?

(i) *Drinking:* Count the number of cups of water you and the other members of the family drink in one day. Record the number of cups of water the family drink in 1 day and 1 week. There are about five cups of water in 1 litre.

TABLE 8.1. *Drinking Water*

Family member	Day 1	Day 2	Day 3	Day 4	Day 5	Day 6	Day 7	Total
1								
2								
3								
4								
5								
Total								

(ii) *Cooking:* Measure in cups all the water you use for cooking breakfast, lunch, supper and snack in 1 day. If you have time make a record for 1 week.

153

TABLE 8.2. *Cooking Water*

Day	1	2	3	4	5	6	7	Total
Breakfast								
Lunch								
Supper								
Snack								
Total								

TABLE 8.3. *Total Number of Cups of Water Used*

	Total for 1 week	Divide by 5 to get amount in litres	Divide by 7 to get litres per day	Divide by number of persons in the family to get litres per person per day
Drinking				
Cooking				
Total				

Now you know the total amount of water your family needs in 1 week and per day as well as the amount of water per person each week and day. *The quality of water* used may be as important as the *quantity of the water* as many diseases are *waterborne*.

Your water source and its protection

Question: What water sources are used by the families from which the students come?

Find out the sources of water supply in the community. Do this as a class activity. Your teacher will help you make the necessary arrangements. Select one class from every year level of your school. Ask the students to check their sources of water. You may have to explain the meaning of each water source. Count the number of students in each class who chose a given source of water. Do the same with all the other sources. Summarize your findings in your notebook, in a table like Table 8.4.

TABLE 8.4. *The Sources of Water used by Families in the Community.*

Source	Number of students by Year level				
	First	Second	Third	Fourth	Total
Rain					
Well					
Spring					
River					
Lake					
Public tap					
Private tap					

The safety of these different water sources varies a lot. Taps are usually safest, followed by springs and rain water. If your water source is an unprotected well, it is very easy to give source protection by covering the well and keeping animals away with a fence, Fig. 8.1.

Keep animals away from the well. If this is a problem build a fence with a door that is easily opened and closed.

FIG. 8.1

How to purify your water

Since the harmful micro-organisms in the water come from human waste and garbage, it is important that this waste is disposed of in a way that micro-organisms have no chance of getting into the water. If the sources of water are not protected micro-organisms may be present.

The three main ways of purifying water at home are:

(i) Boiling

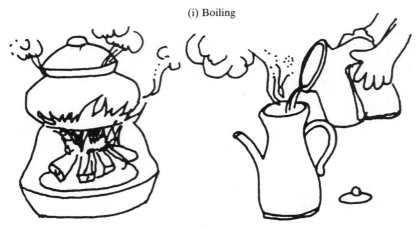

Fig. 8.2

(ii) Filtration

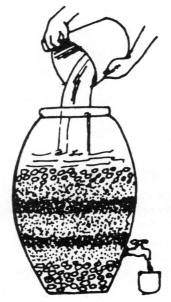

Fig. 8.3

(iii) Addition of chemicals

FIG. 8.4

Boiling water

Pour the water in a cooking pot and put it on the fire place. When the water starts to boil check the time with a watch. Let the water boil for 10 minutes from the time it starts to boil. Then take off the pot and let the water cool.

Filtering water

Materials: Funnel or jar – either plastic or metal
Drinking glass or bottle
Basin
Sand
Small stones
River water

1. Wash the sand and small stones in a basin.
2. Closely pack the funnel or jar with small stones then cover with a layer of sand.
3. Pour a half bottle of river water into the funnel or jar.
4. Compare the water that comes out of the funnel or jar containing a filter of stones and sand with the remaining water in the bottle.

Filtration is the process of separating the particles from the water by allowing the water to pass through filters of sand and gravel.

Water, hygiene and its relation to health

Introduction – routes of transmission of diarrhoeal diseases

Diarrhoeal disease are mainly spread from the excrements to the mouth, although it may also spread with animals (e.g. complyobactu which are spread by chickens). This route of transmission from the excrements to the mouth may be one or more of the following:

1. Waterborne – the infective agents, the pathogens, are in the water when consumed. They may either be in the water at the water source, or they may be introduced into the water during collection or storage.
2. Water-washed – the pathogens are ingested directly or indirectly via fingers, utensils etc.
3. Foodborne – the pathogens have been stored for sometime, the pathogens may multiply.

(i) *Observations of water collection and storage in relation to sanitation and hygiene.*

Ask the pupils to spend 2 hours of continuous observation in the household of a relative or a neighbour (not their own) of:

(a) how water is collected from the water source and how it is stored. For each purpose of using household water (drinking, cooking, washing food, washing utensils, washing clothes, bathing, making bricks etc.) find out:

1. From which water source is the water collected and how is it collected? Is the water-quality good? Is there any risk of pollution from people, from animals?
2. How is the water carried home?
3. Where and how is it stored? Is the storage container carefully cleaned every time it is filled?
4. How often is the water used by whom and for what purpose (see the purposes listed above)?
5. Are there any risks of pollution during storage at home?
   – from hands which touch the water when water is taken out of the storage container?
   – from children who may play with it?
   – from animals drinking out of the water?
   – from anything falling into the water?

(b) the sanitary conditions:
Is there a latrine/toilet? Describe what type.
Is it used by all members of the household?
Is it clean? Are there any flies?

If it is not clean it may be an important route of transmission of disease to the users and may therefore be worse than no latrine.

A clean, well kept latrine is especially important in urban areas or where people live very close to each other.

(c) the hygiene conditions:
  (1) does each of the members of the household wash hands after defecation?
  (2) does the person who cooks food wash his or her hands before starting to work?
  (3) is a cup with a long handle used so that fingers do not touch the water when water is scooped out of the container?
  (4) are the surroundings of the house clean or dirty?
  (5) are animals kept safely?
  (6) how are young children's stools disposed of? A safe disposal of children's stools is crucial, as they may have five or six times as many diarrhoea causing agents as the stools of an adult. When the child has diarrhoea, the stools are even more dangerous. Therefore, discuss with the class the following preventive measures.

(ii) *How to prevent infections*
Discuss with children these effective preventive measures such as:
  – Use water and soap if available to wash soiled cloth, hands and bottoms,
  – if the soiled cloth cannot be washed or leaves have been used for wiping, bury them or throw them in a latrine,
  – sweep up stools dropped on the floor or in the courtyard and bury the sweepings or throw them down a latrine,
  – clean a child's bottom if it is still dirty,
  – an older child can help a younger one to use a latrine,
  – wash spoons, dishes and things that young children have played with,
As each preventive measure is mentioned discuss:
  – how it removes stools from the surroundings and so keeps people from spreading germs,
  – how it removes particles of stools from hands, clothing, spoons, dishes and everything that children play with.
If any measures are mentioned that do not help to prevent germs from spreading, discuss them too. Examples would be:
  – taking a piece of cloth, wiping the child's bottom but leaving the cloth around.
  – simply holding the child out bare-bottomed over the floor or the ground.
Where water is scarce or far away, discuss in the class which of the types of water uses should have highest priority.

(d) Further, precautions: the safe preparation of food and avoidance of storing food for another meal (unless there is a refrigerator); eating a sufficient amount of food to give a good nutritional basis for health especially for children under 5 years.

References

1. Water supply and treatment, 1981; 2. Keep water safe to drink, 1980, Science Education Centre, University of Philippines, Diliman, Quezan City, Philippines.

Sewage treatment

C. J. SANCHORAWAZA

Some information

Human excreta is a major pollutant in water supplied to rural as well as urban areas. Various pathogenic organism are present in excreta.

In rural areas household or community latrines need to be constructed. Several simple designs have been evolved. These latrines should be at least 30 metres away from a water source.

The best latrine has a septic tank attached to it (see Fig. 8.5). After flushing with a small amount of water the excreta and water collect in separate tank. The sewage slowly gets decomposed by bacteria. The septic tank is emptied out with the help of a pump. There are several other types of latrines in use in different parts of the world:

Pit latrine. A pit is dug and used for defecating. The excreta is covered with soil. When the pit gets about ⅔ full it is covered with soil and another pit dug.

Reeds odourless earth closet. This consists of a large pit $1 \times 2 \times 3$ metres deep covered by a concrete slab. The latrine is connected by a sloping shute to the pit which is vented with a pipe.

Pour flush latrine. A water seal is introduced at the lower end of the chute to prevent smells and flies. Flushing is done with about 1 litre of water.

These kinds of latrine are particularly necessary to improve the health of women who may find it difficult to isolate themselves during the day time. If there is a bio-gas plant in the village it may be useful to connect the latrine to it.

Sewage purification in cities. Sewage from the city is brought to the treatment plant by pumping. The sewage purification is done in three stages:

1. Mechanical separation.
2. Biological purification.
3. Chemical purification.

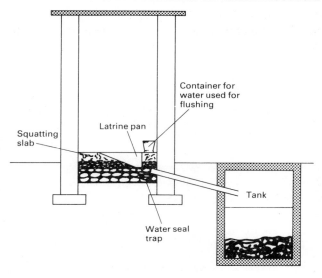

FIG. 8.5

Mechanical separation. The sewage is passed through a grid to remove pieces of stones, plastics and other material. The sewage is next passed through a screen to remove smaller suspended material. The liquid after screening is introduced into large settling tanks and kept for sometime to allow particles to settle down. This settled material is called sludge.

Biological purification. In this process the micro-organisms break the excreta material. In the biological filter method a large round tank is filled with stone, coke or bricks. The sewage is sprayed over them by a sprinkler. A layer of micro-organisms (minute living organisms) form on the stones. These organisms feed on the organic matter of the sewage and purify it.

The sludge is decomposed in a closed container in absence of air to give a gaseous mixture of methane, carbon dioxide and nitrogen. This gas is a good fuel similar to bio-gas. The remaining liquid can be used as a fertilizer as it contains nitrogen, phosphorus and potassium or can be discharged into rivers.

Chemical purification. This is necessarily for industrial pollutants. The chemical treatment is necessary to kill micro-organisms which might be present in sewage after biological purification.

Educational activities

Sewage

1. Find out the number of and types of latrines in your village.

2. Find out the number of cases of diseases caused by sewage contamination e.g.
   (1) Diarrhoea,
   (2) Cholera,
   (3) Hepatitis,
   (4) Worm infestation
(3) Identify water sources from which the sick had taken the water. Try to disinfect water by using chlorine tablets, bleaching powder etc.
(4) What action can be taken to present contamination of water by sewage.
(5) Dehydration is the major problem in diarrhoea and cholera. To prevent dehydration oral rehydration therapy using appropriate amounts of sugar and salt in boiled water is recommended. Boiled rice water can also be used if sugar is not available.
(6) Human and animal waste can be utilized in a bio-gas plant. Visit a bio-gas plant. How useful is this plant?

Periyar–Vaigai project – a case study

EDITH VEDANAYAGAM

Overview of the instructional module

The teaching module, Periyar–Vaigai project presents a case study of a water resource development scheme in South India, which has resulted in raising the agricultural output in the project region. The special feature of this project is the diverting of the waters of a west flowing river eastward to irrigate the parched lands of the Madurai plains. A mini case study of a farmer in a village in the project area is presented to illustrate the benefits derived from this project.

Objectives of the study

To enable the students:

1. To understand the concept of the diversion of river waters of one river to the other, taking advantage of appropriate physical facilities.
2. To comprehend the reasons behind such a diversion.
3. To appreciate the engineering efforts taken and the difficulties surmounted for diverting the waters, during the end of the 19th century, with the limited technology of that time.
4. To study the significance of the climatic conditions and the relative effects on both sides of the water divide (Cardamom Hills).
5. To compare the land utilization and cropping patterns of the pre and post Periyar periods.
6. To see the relationship between the irrigation patterns followed in South India and that of the student's own country.

7. To understand the problems related to land fragmentation in a village such as Jothimanickkam.
8. To comprehend the benefits of Periyar–Vaigai project to farmers in the Madurai plains.

Activities for the students

A map of India (or South India) is essential to the study of this module, preferably a physical map. If a small scale map (1:1,000,000) of South India is available, it will be very helpful in understanding the physical environment of the project area. Further, Fig. 8.8 shows the fragmentation of land in a village – the agricultural land of 164 hectares has 548 fragmented plots owned by 89 people. The students may be encouraged to carry out the following activities after going through the module.

1. Study Figs 8.6 and 8.7 in relation to the map of India or South India and:
   a. Distinguish the main features of the terrain and the rivers.
   b. From a rainfall map indicate the distribution of rainfall in the area.
   c. Outline the factors that contributed to the diversion of the waters of the Periyar river to the Vaigai river.
   d. Indicate the difficulties that were surmounted in the construction of Periyar Dam.

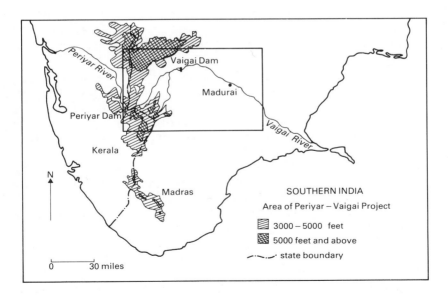

FIG. 8.6

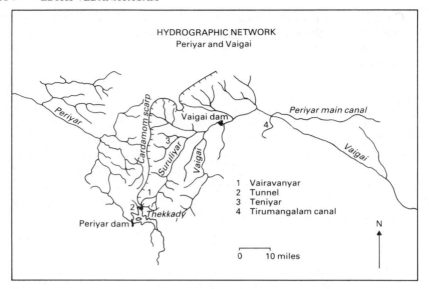

FIG. 8.7

2. (a) What are the major functions of a dam built across a river.
   (b) List the arguments for and against the location chosen for the dam.
       These may be hydrological, societal or geographical.
3. Discuss the drawbacks of the irrigation system during the pre-Periyar
   period. How have they been improved during the post-Periyar–Vaigai
   period? What do you think are some of the disadvantages of an
   irrigation system?
4. Discuss the benefits that have stemmed from the Periyar–Vaigai
   Project, with special reference to Jothimanickkam village of the project
   area?
5. Farmer John has four plots of land scattered over the village land. How
   does he manage to irrigate all these plots? If they were adjacent, what
   would be the advantages?
6. Study Fig. 8.8, the land fragmentation of Jothimanickkam village.
   How does it affect agricultural development of the village? Discuss
   ways of minimizing fragmentation of land.
7. If you were to live in Jothimanickkam village, what would be the
   outcome of the project that you would benefit from most?

Teaching strategies

The teachers may use the unit on Periyar–Vaigai project – a case study, in
the following ways:

1. Considering the unit as an instructional module, the class of students, preferably at the secondary level, can be introduced to the unit by displaying maps of India or South India and the enlarged maps in the unit, especially Figs. 8.6 and 8.7. After a discussion of water resource development in general, the teacher can introduce the Periyar–Vaigai project itself. With a clear idea of the project, the students can be encouraged to read on their own the mini case study of a farmer and then carry out the suggested activities.
2. The whole unit can be considered as a self-instructional module. With the help of the maps, diagrams, transparencies and slides, the students can study the unit, the teacher giving the needed guidance.
3. The unit being a case study in water development schemes in a developing country, the teacher can handle the unit as a case study, moving from the particular to the general.
4. The unit can also be used as a mini course to develop certain learning skills such as skill in the use of maps, skill in enquiry, skill of questioning etc.

Case study of Periyar–Vaigai Project: A water resource development scheme in Tamil Nadu, India

Introduction

The Periyar–Vaigai Project is one of the important water resource developments in South India, designed and constructed in part during the last decade of the 19th century, to accelerate the growth of the economy of Madras state. A noteworthy feature of the project is that the waters of the westward flowing Periyar river have been diverted to flow eastward for use on the east-sloping plains of Madurai. The Periyar dam project which actually diverts the water, was completed in 1896. The Vaigai regulating dam and reservoir were additions, finished in 1959, to provide better control and thus more efficient utilization of the water. The major portion of the water diverted and regulated is utilized for irrigating 122,000 hectares of land in the Madurai district, to benefit an agrarian population of approximately two million persons.

The Periyar project is a major engineering feat of the last century in water diversion because of the tremendous difficulties which were surmounted, especially the problems of remoteness, the intense rainfall, lack of hydrographic data, prevalence of malaria of a virulent type, and the rugged terrain. In addition, it was a significant example of an interstate agreement, since the waters are diverted from Kerala state for use in and for the benefit of the then Madras state. The Periyar–Vaigai project is, thus, a notable example of man's increasing capability for developing resources potentials (Fig. 8.6).

Overview of the physical environment

The Periyar–Vaigai project is situated in an environment which includes the Cardamom Hills the high Cumbum Valley encircled by outlying ranges, and the Madurai plains of the east-sloping plateau of South India. The hills form a rugged mountain complex, whose slopes support dense forests, evergreen broad leafed on higher elevations merging into deciduous forest associations at lower elevations. The plains have been altered by man through agriculture, with the result that only scattered vegetation remains, most of it xerophytes, except along streams and canal courses.

Mountain range. The Cardamom Hills, which constitute the western zone of the project area, are the southward continuation of the Western Ghats. In reality, the Cardamom Hills consist of three main groups: The Annamalai Hills, the Palani Hills, the Cardamom Hills proper, which form the hydrographic divide between the Malabar Coast of Kerala State and the eastern plains.

Madurai Plains. The core of the project area is the Madurai Plains, which lie to the east of the western mountains. These plains are the surface of the igneous block of South India which has been tilted to slope eastward from the mountains to the Bay of Bengal. In the study area, the elevation of the plains ranges downwards from 300 to 90 metres. The soils of the plains have evolved generally to red ferruginous types with some areas of black earth. Nearly all the plains environment has been modified by man's occupance and is or has been cropped.

Climate. The climate of the Periyar–Vaigai project area is greatly influenced by the Cardamom Hills, which form not only the hydrographic divide between the watersheds of Periyar and Vaigai but also constitute a marked climatic and vegetation divide. The west facing slopes of the hills and the narrow coastal plain receive abundant rainfall (4000–5000 mm), associated with the southwest monsoon; but the area east of the Cardamom scarp is a distinct "rain shadow".

The Madurai plains as a whole have a mean annual rainfall of 860 mm. Slightly more than a quarter of it is recorded during the southwest monsoon (early June to end of September) and about half during the northeast monsoon (October to December). January to March is the cool, dry season and April and May comprise the hot season.

During the "cool" dry season, the rainfall is less than 20 mm and the temperature averages between 26°C and 27°C. The season is marked by the rise in temperature to daytime highs of 35–38°C. For a 70-year period in the

Madurai district, the maximum rainfall in any one year was 1290 mm and the minimum was 469 mm. The mean for the period was 940 mm. It is evident that the precipitation in the Madurai district is unreliable in character and the total amount fluctuates greatly from year to year. Moreover, the variations at the beginning of the monsoon period or its end, or its concentration in terms of amount and occurrences may be even more serious than the low total.

Drainage pattern. The Cardamom Hills are the chief watershed of both the Periyar and Vaigai rivers. These two rivers have their source very close to each other but follow entirely different courses, almost in opposite directions. The Periyar river flows westward through Kerala state and empties into the Arabian Sea. The Vaigai runs east and joins Bay of Bengal at Palk strait.

The Periyar river (Fig. 8.7). The Periyar river, the biggest of the Kerala rivers, has its source in the west-facing slopes of the Cardamom Hills at an altitude of approximately 1372 metres. With its several tributaries, the Periyar first flows north and northwest, following structural faults. It then turns westward, flowing through a fault basin at elevation 880 metres. This basin is now utilized for storing the dead waters of the river for the Periyar project and is called Periyar lake. The river then enters a deep canyon and flows almost parallel to the trend of the Cardamom Hills. Turning sharply westward, it breaks out on the western coastal plain, reaching the sea, near Cochin. The catchment area of the headwaters of the river which flows into Periyar lake is 622 square kilometres. The average annual discharge, estimated at the Periyar dam site, over a period of 22 years, is 25,300 million cubic metres, the maximum in any one year being 105,470 million cubic metres.

The Vaigai river (Fig. 8.7). The Vaigai river is formed by the merging of several forest streams, the chief among them being Suruliyar. The river Vaigai rises in the rugged Varashand range at an elevation of approximately 1525 metres. At first, Vaigai flows parallel to Suruliyar, and then turns due north and joins with the combined waters of Suruliyar and Teniyar. The combined headwaters flow northeast and are joined by two other tributaries, both of which have their source in the Palani Hills. The Vaigai, now a deep and rapid river, makes a sharp bend and begins its south-easterly course, which it continues until it reaches the sea (Fig. 8.7).

The Vaigai has a catchment area of 1347 square kilometres of hills and 2253 square kilometres of plains. Before the diversion of Periyar water into the Vaigai system (the river carried from May to September, 0.3 to 4.4. cubic metres a second) the average annual inflow, measured at the Paranai regulator, was 63,977 million cubic metres.

Pre-Periyar resource utilization

The district of Madurai, during the last decade of the 19th century, was far from being prosperous. Subsistence agriculture was the main activity for the majority of the population, industries not having developed to any great extent. The farmers followed the traditional methods of cultivating their fragmented plots with rudimentary implements. The uncertainty of the rainfall and the lack of perennial rivers in the district further handicapped their efforts, and agricultural operations were seldom rewarded by a good crop.

In the Madurai district approximately 87% of the population depended on agricultural pursuits for their existence. They were subsistence farmers whose farm holdings were small, seldom over two hectares.

Moreover, these holdings were commonly sub-divided into several plots, generally scattered within the owner's village boundaries.

Cropping system. During the pre-Periyar days, the most common wet crop was paddy (rice), the area of sugarcane and betel-vine being very small. Of the dry food crops, cholam was the most popular, followed by groundnut, varagu, cumbu, ragi, samai, and horsegram. Cotton and tobacco were industrial cash crops raised on a small scale.

The paddy crop was cultivated from October to January or February, depending on the type of paddy raised. After the harvest of paddy, the farmers grew a dry crop on the same fields. In areas where water was not available for wet crop, only one dry crop was raised per year, normally from September to January.

Irrigation system. The productivity of the fragmented plots mainly depended on the amount and regularity of the monsoon rains, which were noted for their uncertainty. Thus, the need for water storage and regulation was recognized in early times. The farmers of the district, from times immemorial, had used ingenuity in developing various devices for water diversion and distribution to increase the cropping possibilities. These devices for supplementing water were specially used for raising a wet crop like paddy. The three common irrigation sources used at that time, for paddy cultivation were wells, tanks and spring channels.

Thus during the pre-Periyar days, with the help of indigenous devices developed for tapping and collecting water, the farmers commonly cultivated one wet crop per year. But the successful harvesting of this one wet crop, depended to a large extent on the monsoon rains, since only half the water needs could be assured by tanks and wells. Therefore, due to vagaries of the monsoon, crop failure were common.

Analysis of rainfall data. An analysis of the daily rainfall data for a 30 year series, 1931–1960, for Madurai was carried out to indicate the marked variations in the precipitation regime. The variations peculiar to the monsoon rainfall are fourfold. Delay in the commencement, prolonged break during the season, premature cessation, and concentration in one part of the region are the main characteristics of the vagaries of monsoon rains. All these variations are presented in the pattern of the rainfall of Madurai district. However the detailed analysis of monthly and daily rainfall showed that for the 30 year period, there was a macro seasonal variation that seldom followed a regular pattern. Further analysis of daily rainfall indicates that irrigation is essential between June 15 to July 15 for the transplanting of paddy seedlings.

Thus, the physical environment of the locale is that of a "rain shadow" region with notably erratic rainfall. Through centuries the people who have occupied the plains area have been victims of the vagaries of the monsoon rains and have lived precarious agrarian lives.

The Periyar–Vaigai Project

The two rivers, the Periyar and the Vaigai, originally presented a marked contrast in utilization and in the way they affected the land and life of man on the two sides of the Cardamom Hills. The perennial Periyar river flowed uselessly through the forested and well-watered Kerala state to the Arabian Sea, with little use even in the agricultural plains. On the east side of the range the Vaigai was at best a meagre stream, poorly fed by the monsoon rains and in the dry season often dwindled to a trickle, wandering ineffectively through the arid district of Madurai. Nevertheless, Vaigai waters were cherished and intensively used – it has been written that "not a drop" was unused. It is thus easy to understand that the people of the Madurai plains came early to look with envy on the unused water of the west slope.

Conception of the Periyar Project. The idea of diverting the water of the Periyar and utilizing it for irrigating the arid tracts of Madurai district is more than 200 years old. The idea was mooted in 1798 but only in 1884, the then British Government in India approved the scheme for diverting and storing the waters of Periyar and Colonel Pennycuick, chief engineer was given the task of carrying out the whole project.

An interstate agreement was reached, after prolonged negotiations for 2 years, by which the then British Government was to pay annually a sum of Rs. 40,000 ($8,500) for certain specified areas and defined rights, the terms of agreement being 999 years with the option for renewal. Sovereign rights over the site of the dam were reserved by the then Travancore state.

The construction work posed immense difficulties mainly from two sources, the first being the river itself whose water discharge is equal to half the average flow of the Niagara, and sudden and heavy floods were common. The unhealthiness of the locality was the greatest impediment to the progress of work, as the labourers were infected by a virulent type of malaria. Added to this was the damage done to the construction, by wild animals, specially elephants that were bent on destroying a day's construction work by the evening or night. After 8 years of work, in October, 1895, the Periyar dam was completed. It had taken nearly a quarter of a century to complete the scheme and divert the Periyar waters to irrigate the parched Madurai plains.

Periyar Dam and Lake. The Periyar dam which is a masonry dam, 360 metres long and 48 metres high, in the "V" shaped gorge, at an elevation of 1000 metres, stands today as a monument to the engineering skill and enterprise of that period. The Periyar Lake, which has been artificially created by the damming of the Periyar river, has a water surface of 26.5 square kilometres and a useful storage capacity of 445 million cubic metres. The area around the lake has been converted into a wild life sanctuary called Thekkadi and is one of the finest national parks in the whole of India.

From the north arm of the lake, the stored water is led by an open cut and a tunnel to the Vaigai watershed. From the lower end, the water rushes down the face of the hill into the stream Vairavanyar, whence it flows into the Suruliyar and thence into the Vaigai. The quantity of water drawn annually has varied from 570 million m^3 to 700 m^3 up to 1957 and after that increased by 110 million m^3.

Periyar Hydroelectric Project. After prolonged negotiations with the erstwhile Travancore state, the Periyar hydroelectric scheme was the first improvement to be taken up and it was completed in 1954. Under this scheme, the existing irrigation tunnel was widened from 8.55 m^2 to 14.12 m^2 of cross sectional area; a four-bay dam was constructed at the exit of the tunnel; and a power tunnel, 1,278 m long, with a cross section of 14 m^2 was added. Thus, it was possible to draw water from the Periyar river throughout the year for power purposes, instead of during only 9 months for irrigation purposes as was done hitherto.

Vaigai Reservoir Project. In order to impound and store the tail race waters from the hydro-plant during the non-irrigation season, a subsidiary reservoir was necessary. Such a reservoir was completed in 1959 on the Vaigai, 32 kilometres above the Peranai regulator and 9 miles below the confluence of the Suruliyar and the Vaigai. This reservoir also stores some of the surplus that occurs at the Periyar lake during the monsoon season. In addition, it is designed to store to the extent possible, the surpluses of the Vaigai that would otherwise go to waste in the sea. At the same time, there was built a new canal 28 kilometres long, called Tirumangalam canal and the Periyar project was extended in area.

The length of the Vaigai dam is 3,560 metres, its maximum height being 34 metres and gross capacity 193,865 million m^3.

During the construction of the Vaigai reservoir and dam, work was carried out at Thekkadi to lower the existing outlet by another 1.5 metres so as to utilize some of the dead storage of the Periyar lake so that the power developed might be extended throughout the year.

Impact of the project on agricultural land use

The completion of the Periyar–Vaigai water resource project resulted in significant economic changes within the project area. The Suruliyar and Vaigai rivers, formerly reaching flood stage for a week or two and then being nearly dry for almost the rest of the year, have now a nearly constant flow of water most of the year.

Consequently, their waters are able to feed ancient and new channels which branch off from them. As a result, irrigation has been extended to a larger area and there is an assured supply of water for a greatly expanded wet crop land use.

Land benefited by irrigation. In pre-Periyar years the agricultural land use mainly consisted of dry crop cultivation, the wet crops being limited to only small areas having access to water from wells, tanks, and spring channels. It has been estimated that approximately 33% of the land in the study was cultivated during that period. The study area is 8806 km^2. However, the 19th century cropping was notably hazardous and seldom produced adequate crops because of the unreliable rainfall. As a result of the Periyar–Vaigai project, the average area cultivated has increased by 22% but, even more important the water has given essential cropping stability to about a third of the district cropland.

A mini case study of a village and a farmer

(Jothimanickkam Village and Farmer Thevar)

This case study of a representative village is presented in order to show in a quantitive way the pattern of changes and benefits of the Periyar–Vaigai scheme. Jothimanickkam is a sample village, chosen by the writer, the selection being based upon her knowledge of the project area. The entire agricultural land belonging to the village was examined in detail; this included ownership, fragmentation of plots, land tenure, pattern of land use, crop system and changes resulting from the irrigation of land. Some of the salient features of this micro-analysis are presented.

The village. Located on the Madurai plains the village is equi-distant from Madurai and Tirumangalam towns. It receives an annual rainfall between 200 and 230 millimetres. The Vaigai river flows about 15 kilometres north of the village. The chief source of water supply for the agricultural land adjacent to the village is the Jothimanickkam tank which is southwest of the village and the area of the tank bed is 75 hectares and the village itself occupies only 1.31 hectares of land. Water for domestic purposes is secured from two wells in the village and the women carry the water to their house in brass or earthen jugs.

The land. The total land area associated with the village is 255.70 hectares, which includes the area occupied by the village site, roads, ponds and other uncultivable land, totalling 91.25 hectares. Out of the 163.46 hectares of agricultural land, at present 35.31 hectares are used for dry crops such as groundnuts and millets. The remaining area is "wet land" using supplementary irrigation waters mainly for paddy (rice) cultivation.

Land tenure and fragmentation (Fig. 8.8). The agricultural land of the village, 163.46 hectares, is owned by 89 people. Each owner's land is subdivided into a number of plots which are not adjacent to each other. Within the village area of about 2.5 km², there are 548 fragmented plots belonging to the 89 owners. (See Fig. 8.8.) The largest single plot has an area 4.16 hectares and 21 owners have less than 0.4 hectare of land. The chief land owner of the village has 65 plots scattered within the village boundary, the total extent of which is 21.71 hectares. Ten owners hold half the agricultural land of the village and 79 exist on produce of the other half.

This fragmentation of village lands has resulted from the practice of dividing the land among the heirs – children and dependents – who vary in number from 1 to 14. Under the inheritance system each plot is subjected to sub-division so that no heir gets only "good" or "bad" land. The villagers are aware of the uneconomical aspect of the resulting fragmented land units but are reluctant to introduce any other method of sub-division, for fear of receiving less productive land.

A statistical analysis was conducted to examine the relationship among the total area of land owned by each person, number of plots, in each owner's land and the cumulative distance of each owner's plots from the village. The analysis reveals that there is a greater and more significant relationship between hectares and distances and least between the number of plots and distance. The important factor, in terms of problems causing additional work for the farmers and their animals is the size and the distance of the plots and surprisingly not the number of plots.

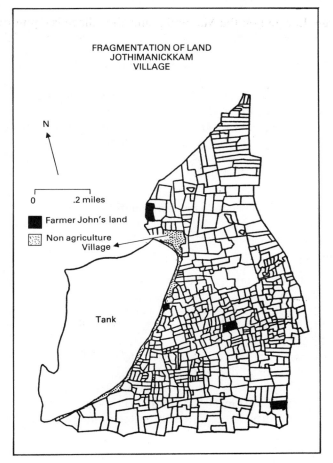

FIG. 8.8

Water supply and irrigation. The irrigation canal, a branch of Tirumangalam Canal, flows northeast and east of the village. It feeds the Jothimanickkam tank and also directly irrigates the land on either side of the canal. The irrigation season is from June to September and the irrigation water is used for raising the first crop of rice. The canal water stored in the tank, as well as the well water, is utilized for raising the second crop.

After the introduction of Vaigai project, the area of wet land increased. A little over 60% of the dry land has been converted into wet land. In addition, the wet land receives a regular supply of water for raising successfully one rice crop per year, whereas in the pre-project days, even the wet crop was precarious. The water stored in the tank also helps in the cultivation of the second crop.

Increased production and profits. Prior to the project when the cultivation depended on the rainfall of the locality, the net produce per hectare ranged from 20 to 30 bags of paddy. After the completion of the project, the yield increased approximately to 55 bags per hectare, due to assured water supply and to increased use of the manure.

The average farmer in the village is now able to produce more than his family needs and the tenant farmer, after paying the landlord's share, is able to feed his family and even make a small profit on his surplus produce. Much of the surplus produce, however, is consumed in the village or sold in adjacent villages. In summary, the water control project has given the village farmers for the first time enough to eat and a small surplus.

Save the Rhine: a teaching unit on water pollution and water conservation

HARTWIG HAUBRICH

Introduction

The current and future water problems all over the world require several teaching units for the different stages of education (e.g. the spiral curriculum "Water" as referred to in Chapter 7). The teaching unit "Save the Rhine" has been used by older secondary school children aged 15–16 years in the Federal Republic of Germany. The unit materials include equipment, articles, slides, overhead transparencies etc. In this teaching unit we have selected some of the student activities to illustrate how a school could deal with water pollution and water conservation within a river system.

The original unit is in German. Information about the original unit may be obtained by contacting the organization listed in the reference on page 185.

Case study: the Rhine

The catchment area of the Rhine belongs to the most densely populated core regions of Europe. Thirty million people use the Rhine water for different purposes. The steadily increasing demand has led to conflicts. The pollution of the Rhine is not an unavoidable feature of a developed industrial country but a result of the absence of laws and international co-operation.

The content-structure of the case study is illustrated in Table 8.5. The scheme shows the different demands of the users on the left and the hydrological potential on the right. The different interest of the users lead to conflicts because the water resources are limited and because national borders limit the protection possible for the whole ecosystem of the Rhine.

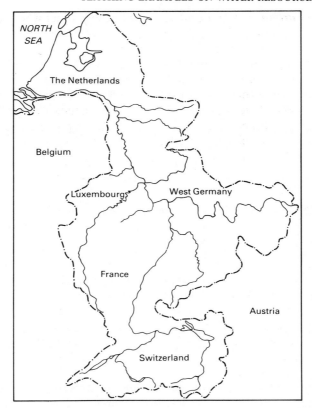

Fig. 8.9. The catchment area of the Rhine.

TABLE 8.5. *Content-structure of the case study "Save the Rhine!"*

Water use	Water resources
Water demand river and ground water for:	*Water supply* *Amount of water*
Industry domestic use navigation fisheries sport recreation hydro-electric power stations	Precipitation runoff transpiration evaporation storage seasonal runoff soil rocks
Sewage from industry, coal and nuclear power stations, households, agriculture	*quality of water* self purification balance of oxygen temperature speed of flow organic and inorganic content

Aims and objectives

The case study has the following aims:

- to make students able and ready to help protect the environment in the private and public sectors of the economy,
- to explain and evaluate the ecological and socio-economic conditions of the water demand and supply in the Rhine catchment area.

The four parts of the whole teaching unit have the following main objectives:

Part	Objectives
Part 1 Planning phase	to divide the topic "water" into sub-topics and to decide upon methods and resources for the whole case study.
Part 2 Pollution	to explain and evaluate causes and effects of Rhine water pollution.
Part 3 Water demand and supply	to describe and explain the relationship between the water demand and supply.
Part 4 Water conservation	to discuss the technical, legal and political measures for water conservation.

Part 1. Planning Phase

Teaching material
Newspaper articles.
Activities: Brainstorming
The students divide the topic into subtopics, collect questions and decide upon methods and resources for studying water problems.

Part 2. Water pollution

Objectives: O_1 – to indicate that lack of oxygen, temperature increases, poison and oil are the main forms of water pollution.
O_2 – to describe the effects of the above kinds of water pollution.
O_3 – to describe how a river dies.

Teaching materials

Pollution by nutritive substances

Newspaper article: No oxygen for thousands of fishes!

"Natural water has the capacity of self purification. But this is endangered if water is too polluted. For example domestic sewage has the same effect as a fertilizer. Algae and other plants but also animals in the food chain grow and increase in number especially in slowly flowing water. When many plants and animals die they need a large amount of oxygen to decay. This process of eutrophication (feeding) can lead to the exhaustion of the oxygen in the water, and the plants and animals in the water die. Further the dead organisms cannot decay and produce a stinking mud and methane gas. At this stage the river or water body is dead.

"The danger of eutrophication is bigger in lakes but also it can happen in slowly running rivers and streams if there is a large production of organic material.

"One of the most important nutritive substances is phosphate which comes from domestic sewage. The farmers also use fertilizers which contain phosphate and which is washed from the fields into the rivers by rain or irrigation. Last but not least the chemical and pharmaceutical industry produces large amounts or organic substances which flow into the Rhine and decrease its power of self purification."

Task: How a healthy river can die?
Please bring the following process into the right sequence!

(a) water plants and animals die
(b) the river is healthy
(c) foul mud is produced
(d) sewage is discharged
(e) the river is dead
(f) water lacks oxygen
(g) rich growth of organisms
(h) big oxygen consumption

Thermal pollution

Newspaper article: Heated rivers kill fishes!

"Temperature plays an important role in the ecosystem of water. Different fishes need different temperatures. Trout like to live in water whose temperature is below 20°C (Celsius) but carp can live in water of 25°C. In different temperature zones of a river there live different fish communities. Changing average temperatures lead to changing fauna.

"Cold water is able to dissolve more oxygen than warm water. Therefore warm water cannot enable as much organic waste to decay as cool water because it contains less oxygen. Many fishes leave warm water derived from industries and power stations and look for cooler regions. If warm domestic and industrial sewage and organic wastes join the warm water, the amount of oxygen in the water becomes less and less and the life of animals and plants is endangered."

Fish	Deadly temperatures
young trout	24.5°C (Celsius)
adult trout	39.5
young salmon	33.8
tench	30
pike	29
perch	31
carp	37.5

Task: Compare table, diagram and maps of the Rhine!

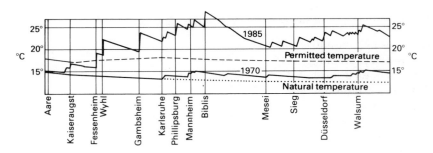

FIG. 8.10(a). Temperature forecasts for the Rhine in autumn if all power stations use freshwater cooling.

Poisoned water

Newspaper article: Yet again fish die in the Rhine – Poison's origin not found yet!

"Sewage which contains poison is one of the biggest dangers for the life in the water and for people who use the water for drinking. Poisoned water is often but not always recognizable by colour, odour and taste. Heavy metals such as lead, cadmium, mercury, copper and nickel which often come from industrial wastes and rubbish heaps are extraordinarily dangerous to the health of man and animal.

"Pesticides, herbicides and insecticides which are used by farmers for protecting their crops often flow with the rain into the ground and river water and endanger the fresh water reservoirs. But they also often kill the plankton and phyton in the water. The decay of these organisms needs oxygen and therefore further lessens the necessary oxygen content of the water. Life is endangered again!"

Task: Bring the following processes in the right sequence:

(a) poison is discharged into water
(b) lack of oxygen leads to the death of fish
(c) there are only few fish and nearly no oxygen in the water

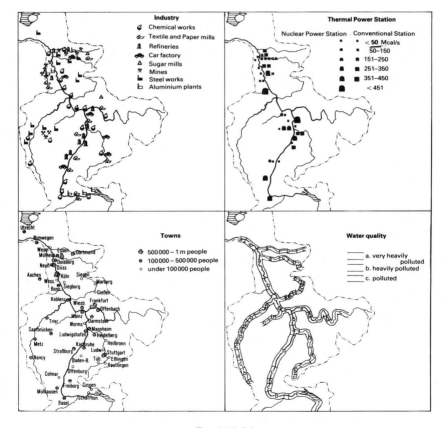

FIG. 8.10 (b)

(d) the river loses oxygen
(e) fish die by poison
(f) there are many fish and enough oxygen in the river.

Oil pollution

Newspaper article: Lorry accident:

"34,000 litres of oil in the Rhine! : One litre of crude oil makes one million litres water unusable. But every year 12,000 tons of oil are discharged into the Rhine. The main source is the Rhine navigation. When ships are cleaned oil residues and other sewage is pumped into the Rhine although this is forbidden. The taste and smell of the water are changed by small quantities of oil. Therefore, it cannot be used as drinking water. But also life in the water is endangered because it is more difficult to decay oil than most other organic substances. Therefore oil can be seen on the surface of the river, many kilometres below the discharge point.

"It also kills micro-organisms which are now unable to clean the polluted water. Water birds are also endangered because oil sticks to their feathers. Oily layers hinder the intake of oxygen from the air."

Task: Compare attributes of oil with the effects of oil pollution!

Summary

The following substances have a negative impact on the quality of water.
1. easily decayable components
2. slowly decayable components
3. salt
4. heavy metals
5. heated water

1. The *easily decayable components* mostly derive from domestic waste. The decaying of these substances decrease the oxygen content of the water – sometimes to zero so that animals die.

2. The *slowly decayable pollutants* do not consume oxygen but they remain in the water and often contaminate it so that it is not potable or is poisonous to people and animals. Such pollutants come from the chemical industry and agriculture such as dangerous chlorides, pesticides and oil residues.

3. *Salt* derives from salt mines and chemical plants as well. The salt in Rhine water, coming from French mines, is one of the biggest problems

for the drinking water supply in The Netherlands because they need the Rhine water.

4. *Heavy metals* such as chromium, copper, iron, manganese, cadmium, nickel, lead and mercury come from metallurgic and chemical industry. They endanger the health of people and animals.

5. *Heated water* is discharged by dwellings, industry and thermal power stations. It minimizes the oxygen content of the water, one of the most important bases for aquatic life.

Part 3. Water demand and water supply

Objectives: O_1 – to show the countries, cities and industry regions in the catchment area of the Rhine in an atlas.

O_2 – to find out that domestic industrial and agricultural sewage causes the most pollution.

O_3 – to explain the self purification of a river.

Task: Compare the maps on industry, cities, thermal power stations and water quality of the Rhine (Fig. 8.10b).

Self-purification

Task: Read the next text and explain why the Rhine water does not become more and more polluted down river. Lower down the river the amount of sewage increases but the pollution intensity of decayable matters isn't increasing in the same way. A healthy river has the ability to purify itself with the help of bacteria and algae. These micro-organisms transform organic substances into inorganic nutritive substances, but they need oxygen for this process. The more organic matter and oxygen there is in water the more micro-organisms develop and decay the organic pollution. But when all the oxygen content is used up then other kinds of bacteria (anaerobic) develop and produce foul smelling gases. Healthy water demands oxygen. Organic matter which is susceptible to biological decomposition is used by aquatic micro-organisms in their metabolic processes. The amount of oxygen removed from the aquatic environment during these processes is termed bio-chemical oxygen demand which is reported as "5-day 20°C BOD." This standard value indicates the amount of oxygen utilized by micro-organisms in 5 days when incubated at a temperature of 20°C.

Main uses of water

Task: Study the diagram (Fig. 8.11) and the tables. Calculate the amount of water used in 1969 and in 2000. Calculate the percentage increase.

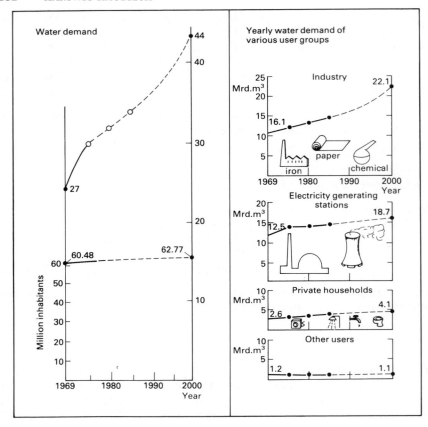

FIG. 8.11

Average daily water demand of one person in the F.R.G.

Drinking and cooking	2–6 litres
Washing machine	20–40 litres
Washing dishes	4–6 litres
Cleaning rooms	3–10 litres
Bathing/showering	30–40 litres

Water demand from some industries

Dairy	per 100 litres of milk	200– 600 litres
Brewery	per 100 litres of beer	800– 1200 litres
Paper plant	per l kg paper	400– 800 litres
Gaswork	per 200 m³ gas	500– 1500 litres
Tannery	per skin	1000– 3000 litres
Slaughter house	per animal	300– 3000 litres
Mine	per ton production	1000– 4000 litres

Laundry	per 100 kg	4000– 8000 litres
Dye-House	per 100 kg	8000–11000 litres
Cellulose	per 200 kg cellulose	20000–50000 litres
Steel works	per ton	30000–50000 litres
Iron works	per ton	50000–85000 litres
Petroleum refinery	per ton	50000–90000 litres

Part 4. Role-playing game: Save the Rhine

Objective: To devise political, legal, national and international measures to protect the Rhine from over pollution.

Role-playing game procedures

1. The class should discuss in groups the nature of the Rhine problem so as to clarify the issues involved.

   The issues should be clearly written up and made available to the whole group.

   Documents in the form of information about the Rhine such as those contained on pages 177–181 should be made available to give a factual background.

2. The class could then be divided into groups representing each state having an interest in the river, i.e. Switzerland (CH), The Federal Republic of Germany (D), France (F), Luxemburg (L), The Netherlands (NL), and a group of "experts" (scientific, legal). Each group would discuss the issues from their point of view, and arrive at a common "natural" position. The "experts" would remain concerned with the scientific and legal issues.

3. The class could then be re-divided so that each group has a representative of each country and one or two "experts". Each group could be simulating an International Commission meeting to devise an environmental charter for the Rhine. This should be in written form and would represent the outcome of the Commission's work.

Example of one outcome

The following charter is an example of the result of such a role-playing game played by 15-year-old students in West Germany.

Environment charter

"The Rhine countries Switzerland, France, West Germany, Luxemburg and Netherlands agree the following environment charter, which could be a basis for environment laws in other countries:

1. *Environment costs*. People and nations who cause environmental problems should pay the costs of their effects and the costs of removing the problem. If it is in the common interest of society, exceptions are possible but they are to be made by the environment ministry. The social market system does not mean that the producer of pollution receives the benefits of this activity and that society pays the environmental costs.

2. *Social restrictions on private and national property*. According to the Charter of the United Nations and to International law, states possess the right to use their natural resources according to their national environmental policy but also have the duty to make sure that activities in their states and under their environment control do not endanger the environment in other countries.

The water of the Rhine is an international navigation route and its use and protection is controlled by International law.

All proprietors of land with ground or surface water have a limited right to construct buildings and to use it for various activities. Water officers have the duty of ensuring a safe public water supply.

3. *Sewage tax*. The producer of water pollution has to pay a sewage tax according to the amount and the toxicity of the sewage. The amount of the tax should be always higher than the purification costs. The state should decide upon transition times for new laws.

4. *Criminal law*. People who pollute water intentionally are to be punished by imprisonment or by fine.

5. *Environment and technology*. It is better to take precautions to prevent environmental problems than to have to solve them later.
   Therefore:

   – only environmentally friendly technology is to be allowed,
   – environmentally friendly technology is to be supported by funds and tax cuts,
   – new sewage works should have a mechanical, biological and chemical purification stage,
   – it is to be decided that the new limits to pollutants should be:

     – less than 200 mg/l chloride-ions at the border with The Netherlands,
     – 2°C maximum warming of the water downstream of a thermal power station,
     – 10 mrem radioactivity per year.

Observation stations are to be established at different points along the Rhine.

According to their danger for the environment certain products are to be grouped under black, grey and beige lists of dangerous products.

6. *International agreements*. The law for storing water pollutants and for discharging sewage and waste should be unified at least in Europe. An independent International Water Project Commission should monitor the Rhine regularly. This commission should research into new methods of analysing and protecting the Rhine water and develop new environmental laws.

7. *Environmental consciousness*. Environment protection needs the active engagement of all citizens in private and public fields. Therefore environmental tasks should remain a matter of a never ending discussion which leads to an environmentally friendly behaviour."

References

Haubrich, Hoch, Keller, Nolzen, Prager, Tatort Rhein – Eine geographische Unterrichtseinheit Zum curriculum "Umweltschutz: Wasser" fur die Klassen 9–10; hg. vom Zentralverband der Deutschen Geographen, Braunschweig 1980.

Water for Tanzania

HANS VAN AALST

A unit for the science curriculum for 14–15-year-old students.

Introduction

Water for Tanzania is a unit for students of 14–15 years. It is one unit of the PLON* physics curriculum in the Netherlands. The central questions of the unit are: Which requirements should a water-pump meet in a rural village in Tanzania? Which pump, out of four should be recommended?

The students have to gather information about a certain village in Tanzania, Kisima from reading texts, films, photographs from the books etc. with the central questions in mind.

After familiarizing themselves with the living conditions the students study in groups the technical and physical details of a pump. They have a choice between four pumps. The four pumps are presented to the students in a leaflet issued by a Dutch firm, and a letter from a Dutch volunteer working in Kenya. In order to study the working of the pump and to determine whether the pump meets any of the six requirements, students could take an

*PLON: Physics Curriculum Development Project, State University Utrecht. Lab. Vaste Stof. Postbus 80.008, 3508 TA Utrecht. The unit is available in English translation.

186 HANS VAN AALST

existing model to pieces or construct a model themselves (this will of course take more time).

As a result of their activities students give a demonstration in front of the class about the pump and their experiences and give their views on each pump. Thereafter a discussion is held about which pump is the best.

Although the unit has been developed for children in the western world – to understand some of the problems involved in designing techniques for specific needs of specific groups, elements can probably be used in developing countries themself.

The pupils materials have five sections:

1. What are you required to do (introduction)
2. What is life like in Tanzania, and what requirements must a village pump meet? (orientation).
3. Instruction for the working groups on the four pumps.
4. How the pumps work.
5. Texts for reference.

A detailed teachers' manual gives additional information for teachers.

In this section, selected parts of the pupil's text have been reproduced to illustrate how the teaching proceeds. Also some questions are added to those given in the teachers' manual.

Evaluation

Evaluation of earlier versions of the unit "Water for Tanzania" resulted in the following:

- A clear introduction and orientation to the central questions and to the things students are expected to do during the unit is crucial. It is not enough to read and hear about it, but doing activities to get the aim clear works better (cf. activities 1–7, selected for this paper).
- Teachers in the Netherlands had difficulty in seeing the relevance of the unit to the physics-curriculum. The use of society-related themes in a science curriculum needs careful discussion and explanation. Also typical assessment-questions have to be given (see the selection in this chapter). The PLON-team decided also to include questions about the unit in the school examinations.
- Pupils appreciate the unit. The final discussion is not easy. First of all students had difficulties in linking technological data to societal demands. Also students tend to defend their "own" pump as the best one, probably because they have been put in that role.

The present version therefore includes the letter from the Government (see below) and list of objectively comparable features, which has to be used (see the "instructions of the working group").

Further information

Additional information may be obtained from the author: Hans F. van Aalst, Camminghalaan 6, 3981 GH Bunnik. He can also provide interested persons with addresses where they can order the English version of the unit.

Introductory activities

1. What are you going to do during this unit?

You and your classmates are on the staff of the (imaginary) Technical Advisory Bureau for Africa (TABA) for the duration of the unit. This firm of consulting engineers has been asked by the Department of Development Co-operation to advise on a pump to be installed in the village of Kisima in Tanzania. Four working groups of TABA are each going to study a separate pump, build a model of it and express their opinion on its suitability. Each group will demonstrate its pump to the other TABA staff members (in other words your classmates) and say what they think about it. The whole "office" will then decide which of the four pumps they will advise the Department to install. You are going to play a role game – the meeting of TABA in which this decision is taken.

2. What is your point of view?

Opinion on Dutch aid to developing countries is very divided. Some people would say

– Send the money to Kisima, then the people can buy the pump that they think best;

Others may hold the view

– We in Holland know all about pumps. It would be better to make a first class pump here and send it to Kisima.

* Have you any arguments against these views?
* Try to give your own opinion.

Your choice of pump will be determined largely by the view you take. If you share the first view, you would not choose a pump at all, but would probably opt for sending a pile of leaflets or do-it-yourself instructions to Kisima. If you agree with the second view, you'll make a special pump here and send that. In this book four pumps are described which represent four different attitudes to development aid.

TABA's Assignment

The imaginary firm of consulting engineers, TABA on whose staff you are, received the following (fictitious) letter from the Department of

Department of Development
Cooperation
The Hague

Technical Advisory Bureau
on Africa
16 Waterstreet
IJsseldam

Dear Sirs

As part of development cooperation between Tanzania and the Netherlands, this
Department has earmarked certain funds for the improvement of the drinking water
supply in the village of Kisima, situated in the Shinyanga region, Tanzania.

A site has been located near the village where ground-water of excellent quality suitable
for drinking is present at an easily accessible depth (5 metres). A pump is to be installed
so that water will be available to the whole village. We have decided together with the
Tanzanian water supply department – Maji, that the pump should meet the following
requirements. (The sequence in which they are given is arbitrary; we have not gone into
the question of which is the most important.)

1. The operation of the pump must not require an expensive source of energy (petrol,
   electricity).
2. The pump must be made of materials obtainable locally as far as possible.
3. The pump must require as little maintenance as possible; it should be possible for the
   villagers to carry out any repairs themselves.
4. The pump must be as cheap as possible.
5. The construction must be such that it will be impossible to pollute the water in or near
   the well.
6. The capacity of the pump must be sufficient to supply the needs of the village.

I invite you to advise the Department on the most suitable type of pump for Kisima. The
pump must conform to at least four of the above six requirements.

You may be interested to know that this is a pilot project. Should the Kisima pump prove
satisfactory and its maintenance raise no particular problems, we plan to install similar
pumps in other villages.

Yours faithfully

J. de Wit
Tanzania Division

Development Cooperation. We cautiously inquired what the Department's
views were on the choice of the pump and whether they had any particular
preference, but apart from the six requirements stated in the letter, they had
no special demands. They said, we have already stated that the order in
which the requirements were given was arbitrary so in other words, you are
free to have your own opinion on the subject:

Activities

1. Tell one another in your own words what TABA's assignment from the
   Department was.

2. If there are words or sentences in the Department's letter which you do not understand, look them up in the dictionary.
3. Think up a reason for each of the requirements laid down by the Department.
4. Are there conflicting requirements? If so, which? why?
5. Write down what you consider to be the two most important requirements and the two least important. Give an explanation.

A Picture of Life in Kisima

The more you know about the village, the better prepared you will be to tackle the problem and the sounder your recommendations about the pump will be. So you must go in search of information about Kisima or about villages in general in Tanzania. You need not all try to find out everything straightaway; share the work. Each one of you can think up a number of questions and try to find the answers to them.

6. Draw up five questions about Kisima that are directly or indirectly connected with the drinking water problem. Examples:

   – What is the rainfall in Kisima?
   – How much water does each villager use daily?
   – Can the villagers read and write?

Instructions for each group

TABA got ideas for four pumps from four different quarters. They are:

1. A displacement pump is made in The Netherlands.
2. A "hose-and-bucket" pump described in a letter from a Dutch Volunteer working in Kenya.
3. A suction pump made in Tanzania. You will find a short report of a talk between a representative of the Tanzanian manufacturer and one of the staff of TABA who happened to be in Tanzania and discovered this small firm in the capital quite by chance.
4. A rope pump described in a South American magazine.

Perhaps one or more of the groups will have their own ideas about a pump for Kisima which they may be able to work out in consultation with the physics teacher.

Each group will examine one pump. In other words each group:

1. Will study how the pump works. How the four groups work is explained below.
2. Will determine which of the Department's six requirements are met by the pump.

3. Will examine on what grounds the pump is recommended and what additional requirements this may entail.
4. Will study a model of the pump or will make one, introducing improvements if possible.
5. Will estimate the cost of the pump.
6. Will advise on the pump giving arguments for and against.

At the end of each of the four short studies of the pumps you will find instructions on how to make the models. The real pumps will be bigger and the materials used will be different but the principle remains the same. We have chosen materials that are easily obtainable in The Netherlands and easy to work with. Quite different materials may be used in Tanzania. When the groups have completed their study of the pumps they will each report their findings at a TABA meeting. The meeting will then discuss which pump is most suitable for Kisima and a decision will be taken.

Working Group 1 – The displacement pump

A leaflet produced by the firm of consulting engineers Verhage BV in Rijndam is reproduced below. The firm, which has carried out a big pump installation project in Tanzania, developed a special Tanzania pump on the displacement pump principle. You will find more information on the displacement pump on page 198.

The Tanzania pump: robust and indestructible

Our firm has developed a hand pump for use in the rural areas of Tanzania. It is based on the Uganda pump used by UNICEF, but has been considerably improved after try-outs in Tanzania itself.

Requirements for a hand pump

A hand pump which can be used for fairly shallow wells (to a depth of 30 metres) in developing countries must meet certain requirements.
Two of the most important are:
1. The pump must be as simple as possible and require practically no maintenance.
2. The cost per pump must be as low as possible.

The parts of the Tanzania pump

Experience has shown that little proper or regular maintenance is carried out on village pumps. The Uganda pump broke down repeatedly. The Tanzania pump is a stronger and improved version of the Uganda pump.

Instead of the expensive brass cylinder which had to be imported, we have used a P.V.C. cylinder. The valves have been replaced by standard parts which are commonly used in hydraulic and pneumatic installations. A diagram of the Tanzania pump showing the different parts is shown in Fig. 8.12.

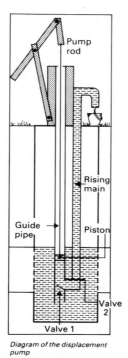

Diagram of the displacement pump

FIG. 8.12

Pumping capacity

Pump cylinders of three different diameters are used: 4, 3, and 2 inches. The pumps have the following capacity at one stroke per second and a 75% effective pumping time:

4″ (inch) cylinder	2,000 litres per hour
3″ (inch) cylinder	1,200 litres per hour
2″ (inch) cylinder	600 litres per hour

The 4 inch cylinder can be used to a depth of about 10 metres, the 3 inch to 20 metres and 2 inch to 30 metres.

Cost of installation and maintenance

One pump costs Fl 1,500, including parts, transport and installation. The price is based on the assumption that 99 other pumps will be installed at the same time in the same region.

Ideally, once a pump is installed, it should always give good quality water without having to be repaired or overhauled. Such a pump does not exist, of course. Every pump needs regular maintenance. Nevertheless, in designing and constructing this pump, our firm has always kept the ideal of a maintenance free pump in mind. That is why it is as cheap as possible to use. Maintenance costs can be reduced further by involving the local population in the pump's maintenance and surveillance. Only two thorough revisions by government mechanics will be needed annually, costing only Fl 100 – a time.

A model of a displacement pump

You can make a model displacement pump from P.V.C. tubes bought at a hardware shop. The piston can be made from two pieces of cork with a rubber disc wedged in between. The disc must fit exactly into the tube. A narrower P.V.C. pipe can be used as the pump rod. The best way to make the valves is to bore a hole in the endpiece of the tube which can be closed with a marble.

Assignments

1. Carry out the assignments given in "instructions for working groups" on page 189. Below you will find additional notes on some of these assignments, which have to be carried out using your model pump.
2. Explain to one another how the model pump works. This is a good way of preparing your demonstration to the class. You can find more information about the working of the displacement pump on page 198.
3. How long does it take to pump up 10 litres of water with your model pump? (Pump steadily and do not hurry) and a real displacement pump? For how long will the pump be used every day if every inhabitant of the village uses 10 litres of water a day?
4. Your model pump is about 1 metre high. You can therefore pump up water from a depth of about 1 metre. How would you have to change your model in order to raise water from a greater depth?
5. Determine the maximum height to which water can be raised by your pump.

Working Group 2 – The hose-and-bucket pump

A product of tradition and development

An interesting letter from Elly van Dam, a volunteer working in a small village in Kenya, Tanzania's northern neighbour, is given below. Together with the villagers she built a hose and bucket pump which was a great success. Her letter explains what the pump looks like, how they built it and what problems they encountered. You can read more about this type of pump on page 199.

Kenya, 23 April

Hallo There

The rainy season has started and all the people from the village have gone to the fields to sow and plant. So I have taken time off to tell you about a pump we built here. It's easy to understand how the pump works. The water in the hose must be at the same level as the water in the bucket. But if you raise the bucket above the discharge outlet, the water will run out. The pump has a lot in common with the traditional "bucket on a rope". The biggest problem when making the pump was to find a length of suitable hose and to fix it to the bucket. Well, I found it in town. And I also found a smith who soldered a short length of metal pipe into the bottom of the bucket.

Best wishes,

Elly

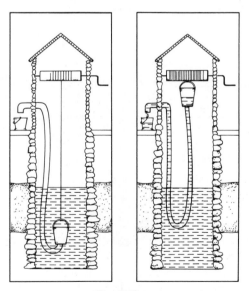

FIG. 8.13

A model of the hose and bucket pump

You can easily make a model of the hose and bucket pump yourselves. Elly has given a few tips in her letter. The material you use depends on what you can find because almost anything is suitable.

Working Group 3 – The suction pump

One of the staff of TABA who is stationed in Dar-es-Salaam, the capital of Tanzania, came across a small pump factory there. He wrote the following article for the TABA house magazine.

The Maji pump, made in Tanzania

You often come across the Maji pump in the villages around Dar-es-Salaam. Maji is the Swahili word for water. The Maji pump is a suction pump and the villagers are very satisfied with it. I made inquiries about it in a number of villages.

A mechanic from the Maji pump factory visits regularly to inspect the pump. The washers are renewed, the valves checked, the bolts tightened, the movable parts greased and the parts that have rusted are red leaded.

If anything breaks down between the regular revisions, the factory is informed and the mechanic arrives within a few days to do the necessary repairs. When the new washers in the piston have been in use for a month, they start leaking through wear and tear. This can be easily fixed by throwing water on the piston, thus creating a water seal, and this is often done in the villages. From the point of view of hygiene this is not to be recommended. The water thrown on the piston is often contaminated and seriously affects the quality of the pump water.

I discussed the problem and the success of the Maji pump with the Managing Director of the factory. He ascribed its success to the service the factory gives. "I'm envious of the high quality of the foreign pumps installed here" he said. He uses mainly cast iron of a rather inferior quality but better quality cast iron is unobtainable in Tanzania. "Yet our pumps are more popular than the foreign ones in the long run. Ours may well break down sooner, but at least we have the spare parts in stock. Spare parts for foreign pumps are simply not to be had."

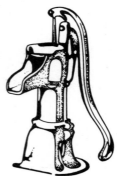

The Maji pump

Fig. 8.14.

He is not unduly worried about the pollution of the water through the water seal: "When I think of the water I used to drink. It is incredible. But I survived. We Tanzanians are tough. The main problem of drinking water supply are not pollution or contamination; they are the distance people have to walk to fetch water and the mud, the pools of water round the wells which are breeding grounds for mosquitoes, the Bilharzia snail and so on. And these problems are solved by installing a Maji pump". He did concede that it was better to have completely clean water. But we have to choose between making a displacement pump and suction pump. In a displacement pump the pistons and valves are under water, so it's difficult to get at them if they need repairing. In a suction pump they are in the top part and easily accessible. So we plumped for a less than ideal suction pump that is easy to repair rather than for a clean displacement pump that is difficult to repair.

The argument that you can't raise water with a suction pump from a depth of more than 6 metres doesn't bother him, as most of the wells aren't deeper than 5 metres anyway. Though the Maji factory currently supplies only villages in the neighbourhood of the capital, the Managing Director has plans for supplying and servicing other parts of Tanzania as well.

A model of a suction pump

You can make a model of a suction pump. The photo shows one made of P.V.C. tubes which you can buy at a hardware shop.

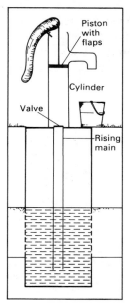

Diagram of the suction pump

Fig. 8.15

The piston can be made from corks, a flexible rubber flap cut from the inner tube of a bicycle tyre and P.V.C. conduit. The suction flap must be fitted into the tube with its edges curled upwards.

Working Group 4 – The rope pump, adaptable to every situation

La "Bomba de Soga" para pozos de agua

Translation from the Spanish. The rope pump: a rope pump in a pipe with water.

With the help of Tom Aarden, the village of Shipibo de San Francisco (Pucalipal) has found a solution to the problem of drinking water supply. A pump has been installed that can provide over 200 people with water.

The pulley can be made from a wagon wheel, bicycle wheel or a wooden wheel.

Note how the discs are cut out of an inner tube. The discs must be slightly bigger than the diameter of the plastic pipe.

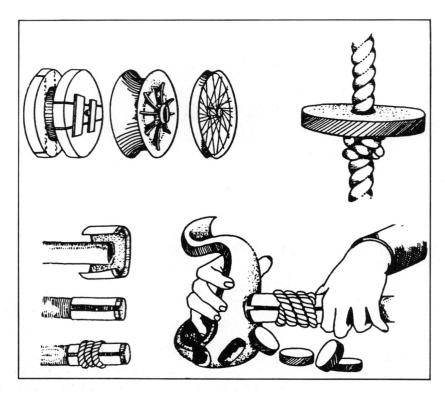

Fɪɢ. 8.16

The water found in the forest is usually contaminated. That is why we wanted some means of providing the people with water that would not endanger their health. A pump with a rope passing through a pipe is the best solution because it is easy to make and not expensive. A big advantage of having a pump is that you no longer need to carry water from a distance.

What do you need. A wheel to act as a pulley, rope (nylon) two plastic pipes one inch in diameter, thick iron pipe, wood, cement and especially ingenuity and the enthusiasm of the whole village.

Heat the plastic pipe at both ends to form a funnel.

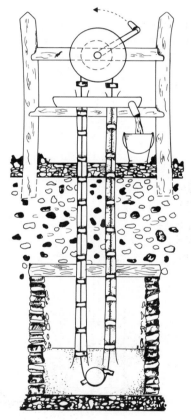

FIG. 8.17

We found this article on a rope pump in a South American magazine on village development. Rope pumps originated in the developing countries where you often come across them in the form of bucket or chain pumps. This rope pump has been improved by a team of engineers in the

Netherlands and is being used in many countries. The article reprinted here describes the situation in a village in Peru where the villagers made the pump themselves. The rope pump is being successfully used in a number of African countries as well. The rubber discs can be replaced by special knots, which simplifies the pump even further.

How the pumps work

How the displacement pump works

The displacement pump works with a submerged piston. When the piston rises, water flows into the cylinder; when the piston is moved downwards, the water from the cylinder is forced upwards. We'll now examine this more closely for each stroke of the pump. The height to which the water can be pumped is determined by the degree to which the valves leak.

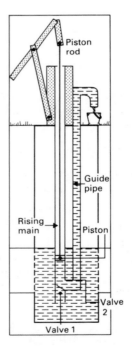

Piston
rod

Guide
pipe

Rising
main

Piston

Valve
2

Valve 1

FIG. 8.18

Questions:

1. Good displacement pumps can pump up water from a depth of 30 metres. The pressure that must be exerted on the water by the piston is quite considerable: 3 atmospheres extra pressure. Explain this.

2. Why is the piston rod in a displacement pump easily damaged.

3. Will there be any difference in the pressure on the valves between wide rising main and a narrow one? Give an explanation.

How the hose-and-bucket pump works

The water in the bucket will always be at the same level as the water in the hose until the bucket is raised above the discharge outlet, when the water will run out.

If you put your finger against the discharge outlet and then lower the bucket, you'll feel it being sucked into the hose. That is because the pressure of the water on your finger is lower than 1 atmosphere (the pressure of the air at sea level).

Questions:
1. One of the disadvantages of the hose-and-bucket pump is that not all of the water in the bucket inside the well can be discharged. There is always water in the hose that cannot be pumped out. Calculate how much water stays in the hose. The hose is 6 metres long with a radius of 1 centimetre (the area of the hose is $\pi r^2 = 3.14$ cm^2).

2. Could the hose-and-bucket be used for deep wells? Give an explanation.

3. If you close the discharge outlet with a cork before lowering the bucket the water in the hose won't run back into the bucket as it is lowered.

   (a) Explain why the water no longer flows back into the bucket.
   (b) Explain why a little of the water does flow back if the bucket is lowered more than 10 metres.
   (c) When the bucket is raised above the discharge outlet, the cork is removed. What is the maximum amount of water that can now flow out of the discharge outlet.

How the suction pump works

The principle of the suction pump has been known for a long time. Dutch village pumps are suction pumps. The piston and valve are above ground. There is therefore air under the piston when the pump is not working. When you start pumping you remove this air which is replaced by water. We will explain this in a number of steps. We will take a few figures to illustrate what we mean.

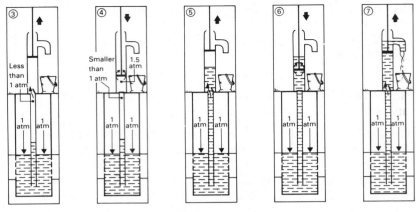

FIG. 8.19

Questions:

1. Why is it not possible in theory to pump up water from a depth of more than 10 metres with a suction pump?

2. Check for yourself what happens if a valve does not shut properly. Would a water seal at the valve help?

3. Name two major disadvantages of a water seal in a suction pump used to supply drinking water.

How the rope pump works

When you start turning the handle of a rope pump, the knots raise the water. Only a small amount of water will leak past each knot because the rope fits tightly into the tube. This creates a water seal. The water between the knots lower down must therefore be lifted as the knots rise. If it were not, there would be a vacuum between two knots because no air can get in, there being a water seal above. But it is impossible to have a vacuum between two knots, which is why more and more knots will bring up water until it comes out at the top. The greater the depth from which you raise water, the greater the pressure on the lowest knots, and the more water will be lost through leakage. Only at a great depth will the leakage downwards be equal to the amount of water to be raised, which means that the pump can no longer work.

Questions

1. Someone is trying out a home-made rope pump. The pump can raise water from a depth of 6 metres. He fixes a rubber disc cut from an inner tube on the top of each knot. The discs fit into the tubes. He sees that the pump

can now raise water from a depth (or to a height) of 12 metres. Explain why the pump now works better.

2. If the knots in the rope fit exactly into the pipe the pump doesn't work. Explain.

3. Will the pump still work if one knot is too small?

4. How is the height to which water can be raised affected if the knots are slightly worn?

5. Why would it be wrong to lower and raise the rope through tubes of the same diameter?

Some test questions

1. In an African village a displacement pump has been installed. Unfortunately, the valves are missing.

  (a) Draw how the valves should be mounted in the pump. For each valve there are two possibilities:

  (b) Is water coming out the pump when you pull the lever up or when you push it down? Explain your answer and use in your explanation whether the valves are open or closed.

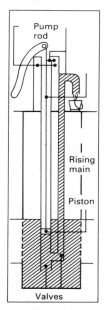

FIG. 8.21

    (c)   Because valves can only be constructed by local available materials, the valves leak a little bit. Find out what the consequences of this could be for the functioning of the pump.

2.   In a village in Tanzania a suction pump is being installed. The pump is made of cast iron (Fig. 8.22).

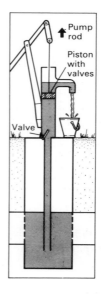

FIG. 8.22

The piston and the valve are made of leather. The village-people fetched their water until now out of an open well.

(a)   Describe how the water comes in the cylinder as the piston rises.

(b)   Give one reason why this pump can only be used for wells which are not too deep.

(c)   Give two advantages for the villagers of the use of this pump, compared with the use of an open well.

(d)   Give two possible disadvantages of installation of this type of pump in the village.

Ground water, sample activities for secondary education

ROY PALLETT

Ground water, in many cases, is found deep in the ground. It has to be brought to the surface to be useful. How can we obtain water from the ground. This activity shows the main ideas in well construction.

Activity

You will need:

Transparent jar or beaker, plastic vial with its bottom cut out, flat stick or wooden spatula, coarse sand (the kind used for aquarium water).

Fill ⅔ of the jar with sand. Pour water into the jar to fill the pores between sand particles until the water level reaches halfway up the jar.

With a stick, make a hole in the sand nearest the side of the jar so that you may observe what happens in the hole. Remove the sand from the hole to let water flow in and fill it.

Push the plastic vial into the water hole. Remove the sand from inside the vial.

1. Which water level is higher – that in the vial or in the sand?
2. What does the top surface of water in the sand and in the vial represent?

You have constructed a miniature well.

3. Is it a good well? Why or why not?

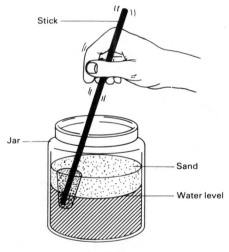

Stick

Jar

Sand

Water level

Fɪɢ. 8.23

In actual construction, wells are lined with stones, bricks, or tile pipes to strengthen the wall and prevent collapse (Fig. 8.24). If water intended for home use is obtained from a water table well, the well should be sealed from seepage at the soil zone to prevent contamination. A water table well for household use should never be constructed at the downslope from a refuse or sewage disposal area. Pumped wells are best constructed with a screen at the aquifer level to protect the pump from grains of sand which could be sucked in.

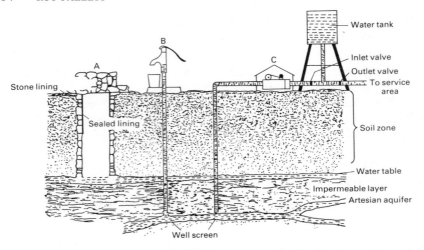

FIG. 8.24. A shallow dug well with a sealed lining at upper walls. B. a hand-pumped artesian well. C. a machine-pumped artesian well.

Most people in villages get their water supply from wells. The well may be a hand-dug open hole or a drilled hole reaching the water table zone. This is a shallow well. Deep wells are bored or drilled by machine to several hundred metres into either a water table zone or an artesian aquifer. (Selected from: Ground water: Philippine Environment series: Water Resources. Science Education Centre, University of the Philippines, Dilimun, Quezon City.)

Look at your ground water

The following pages show a format for presenting ground water exercises. The topic selected is "soil water movement". Many related topics can be presented in this way such as: the study of aquifers, the local water budget etc.

The unit selected here is in use in some Australian schools. Further details or information about other examples can be obtained by writing to Roy Pallett, Math/Science Reserve Centre, 229 Campbell Street, Hobart, Tasmania, 7000, Australia.

Pupils' text

Question:
How does water move into the earth?

Introduction

Have you ever seen water seeping or flowing from a hillside? How fast does ground water move through the pore spaces in earth materials? Can water move upward through soil? In this investigation you will find evidence to answer some of these questions and others by examining properties of earth materials that affect the flow of water through soil materials.

Objectives

When you have finished this investigation, you should be able to:
1. describe the effects of a change in soil particle size on each of the following:
   a. porosity   c. water retention
   b. permeability   d. capillarity.
2. Relate these concepts to actual ground water movement in rocks and soils in your area:

Method

1. Set up the column as shown in the diagram. You will be provided with quantities of different sized particles, place 100 ml of one of the sized particles in the column, making sure that the wire screen is in place to prevent the particles from running out.

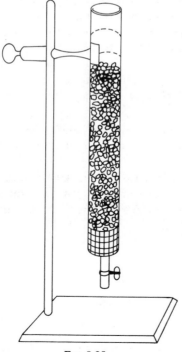

Fig. 8.25

2. Measure and record the amount of water needed to just cover the upper surface of the particles and the time necessary for the wetting front to reach the bottom of the tube. This will provide a relative measure of the infiltration rate.

3. Open the clamp and allow the water to drain into a clean dry beaker. Remove the beaker when the flow is reduced to dripping, and measure the volume. Calculate the amount of water that was retained by the particles.

4. Repeat the procedure, using as many different sized particles as you are directed to do.

5. Make observations and measurements of the demonstrations that your teacher has prepared for:
   (a) the amount of water necessary to just cover the upper surface of 100 ml of a loose soil consisting of a mixture of particle sizes,
   (b) the rates of capillary action in three soils consisting of different but uniform particle sizes.

6. Prepare graphs of each variable observed (i.e. amount of water needed to fill the pore spaces, time necessary for infiltration, amount of water retained in the soil and capillary movement) vs time. Examine your graphs and draw inferences from them.

Questions:

1. What soil conditions are necessary for infiltration to occur?
2. Describe the relationship between the permeability of soil material and its particular size.
3. How far downward will water molecules move after they have infiltrated loose soil?
4. What factors influence the porosity of soil materials?
5. Which soil particle size retains the greatest amount of water?
6. What is the relationship between the capillarity and soil particle size?
7. How can you relate, what you have learned to actual ground water movement in rocks and soils in your area?

Teachers' text

Materials

Ring stand and column clamp; plastic or glass column, at least 30 cm long; column outlet with clamp fitting; wire screen in bottom of column 100 ml graduated cylinder; two 400 ml beakers (larger, if available); sorted earth materials (sieved, sand, gravel, etc.).

Suggested approach

1. Keep prelab discussion brief. Review the hydrologic cycle, in general, and infiltration of water into soil, specifically.

The following questions can be raised:

   a. What factors control the amount of water that a soil can hold?
   b. What factors control the rate at which water can keep infiltrating into soil?
   c. What factors control the amount of water retained in a soil after it is drained?
   d. How does water move through soil?
   e. What direction does water move through soil?
   f. How could any or all of these factors be measured?

2. Have the students set up the apparatus, measure, and record data concerning each variable.

3. Conduct class demonstration as follows:

   a. Place 100 ml of loose soil consisting of a mixture of particle sizes in a plastic tube, and measure the amount of water necessary to just cover the upper surface of the particles.
   b. Set up three plastic tubes each about ¾ filled with different-sized particles (i.e. fine sand, coarse sand, and gravel). Submerge the bases of the tubes equidistant into beakers of water leaving the clamp open so that the water is in contact with the base of the soil column. Mark the level to which the water has risen with a grease pencil, using 2 minute time intervals. Allow students to measure and record these measurements during the class period. The apparatus can be left on display for days with a new mark being made on a once or twice per day basis. The rate of rise will decrease rapidly after the first half hour.

4. Have the students graph their results and draw inferences from the graphs.

Precautions

1. Wet particles should be removed and tubes cleaned and dried before re-running the investigation (push a paper towel through the tube with a long stick). If this is not done allowances must be made for the water that is retained.

2. The larger the particles, the harder it is to estimate when the surface is just covered with water. Some approximating may be necessary.

3. No particle larger than ⅙ of the column diameter will work effectively because of poor packing.

Typical results

Students results will be quite varied, but you should expect the following:

1. There should be enough *class* data to convince the students that porosity is relatively independent of grain size.
2. The smaller the particles, the slower the rate of infiltration (low permeability).
3. The smaller the particles, the higher the rate (and amount) of capillarity.
4. The smaller the particles, the greater the amount of water retained.

Modifications

1. Whenever possible use earth materials; when available, use beads, shot, etc.
2. Three or four tubes with different grain size soils can be set up with bases of the tubes submerged in water and left for a couple of days to show how high the capillary water will rise if given time.
3. Water retention in soils is related to the surface tension of water. To demonstrate this phenomenon, the following demonstration can be done. Fill two *new* test tubes (make certain lips of the tubes are not scratched) to level full, one with water and the other with ethyl alcohol. The tubes must be *level* full. Drop small ball bearings (BB) from a height of 1 cm into each tube, and count the number dropped before the liquid begins to overflow the test tube.

   The higher surface tension in water should allow a considerably larger number of BB's to be dropped into the tube before overflow occurs.

PART IV

Mineral Resources

Team Leader: EILEEN BARRETT

9

Mineral Resources

NORMAN J. GRAVES

University of London Institute of Education, U.K.

General introduction

As already indicated in Chapter 2, mineral resources are important to the economic life of all countries. It is perhaps not appreciated that we are surrounded by minerals in various forms during our everyday life. Buildings, motor vehicles, energy providing fuels such as petroleum and coal all have mineral origins. This means, in effect, that they have been obtained from the ground, or we say that they have a geological origin. The technical and socio-economic changes which have occurred in the past such as the British Industrial Revolution or the more recent development of electronics have all depended to a greater or lesser extent on minerals, whether this has been coal to raise steam in the 19th century, or the silicon chip for computers in the second half of the 20th century.

Problems of mineral exploitation

To some extent the desire to obtain certain minerals depends on finding a use for them. This may depend on technological progress. For example bauxite, the ore from which aluminium is derived, was not used until it became known that a light metal could be derived from it which was malleable and could be used to make objects whose weight was not heavy. Thus minerals may exist but not be perceived as a resource by the local population.

If a use is known for a particular mineral, then the next problem is that of finding it. Minerals may be easy to find particularly if they are on or very close to the surface of the earth, as is the case of gneiss in the area around Bangalore in India, which is used for road building, for facing buildings and many other purposes. But many minerals are not so obviously present. Thus the exploration for minerals is an important activity. We are probably aware of the exploration for petroleum or mineral oil because this activity is often in the news. However, the search for coal, copper, lead and zinc, for gold and silver, for rare minerals like titanium ore also goes on. The techniques

211

used for finding minerals vary, but most involve some drilling into the earth (or the sea bed) and therefore tend to disturb local activities. In some cases the search is easy, in others the search is a long and an expensive one. More and more the search for minerals involves the use of elaborate technology, but there is still scope for finding locally useful minerals by people using relatively simple means. Some of these will be described.

Once a useful mineral has been located, it needs to be mined or quarried. We use the term quarry to indicate the means of excavating a mineral which is not too far below the surface. Thus one speaks of a clay quarry, or of a slate quarry or of a granite quarry. The term mining indicates that the mineral to be obtained is some distance below the earth's surface and can only be reached by digging out a vertical or oblique shaft linked to galleries that run underground to the mineral to be obtained. Much coal, gold, copper and lead are mined. Again, although it is still possible to undertake small scale operations, the greater proportion of most minerals is obtained by large scale methods of mining and quarrying. Thus this involves an enormous investment of capital; it effectively sterilizes many hectares of land which then cannot be used for other purposes and it may require the use of large quantities of labour. Once a mineral has been won from the earth, it is seldom in such a state that it may be used immediately in manufacturing industry or as a fuel. It usually requires some processing. The simplest case is probably coal, which usually only requires sorting into various sized lumps and washing. But copper ore, for example, needs separating from the rock from which it is obtained, and requires to be converted from a compound (e.g. copper pyrites, $CuFeS_2$) into copper and refined. This may often be done near the mine and therefore also requires the extensive use of land and capital. Sometimes the processing is done at some distance from the source of production and near to the markets. This is often the case for petroleum which may be exported as crude oil and refined in the importing country. The very fact that minerals are finite, that is, they do not, like water, renew themselves naturally, means that their exploitation will some day end. Thus a great deal of attention must be paid to conserving mineral resources, that is to limiting the rate at which they are being exploited. One mechanism for ensuring this is to raise the price of the mineral so as to limit the demand for it and/or its wasteful use. Thus the raising of the price of petroleum by the Oil Producing and Exporting Countries (OPEC) was partly to conserve the oil resources of the member states of OPEC. Thus the conservation of mineral resources is an important issue in the modern world. Another is that of environmental protection.

Inevitably the excavation of a large quarry or the drilling of a shaft for a mine will create a great deal of environmental disturbance. Part of this may be the temporary disturbance of noise and trucks carrying away rocks and rubble. Also the landscape may be so changed that the mine or quarry becomes an "eyesore", that is what was once a pleasant landscape is no longer so. Further processing plants may release into the atmosphere dust and fumes which may be harmful to people and animals.

It is therefore important that those responsible for the development of mineral resources bear these environmental issues in mind and take precautions to minimize the damage done to the surroundings of a mine, quarry or mineral works.

Ethical considerations

To some extent the protection of the environment is an ethical issue. To exploit a mineral without taking into account the harmful effect this may have on people in the surrounding area is to act in an un-ethical or immoral way. Ethics are concerned with the "rightness" or "wrongness" of certain actions and behaviours. One is normally concerned with the ethics of inter-personal relationships between members of a family or between friends and acquaintances. But organizations may also take actions which may benefit the "firm" but harm other people or other firms. Many important issues arise out of the actions of individuals and firms in the course of exploring for and exploiting mineral resources. For example in exploration, companies need to negotiate the right to drill in particular areas. What kind of compensation should be paid to the owner of the land which is disturbed and possibly damaged in the process? Should a firm take advantage of the ignorance of certain owners as to the true value of their land when it contains mineral resources? When an organization requires a lot of labour to work in mines as in South Africa, is it right to bring male miners only and isolate them from their families? When a company makes huge profits from mining operation, how should these be used? When two processes may be used in refining a mineral, one is safer but more expensive than the other, which should be used? Clearly all these questions have an economic aspect, but they also have an important ethical aspect. What is economic in the sense of making the best use of scarce resource is not also automatically ethically right. There are often conflicts of values which need to be resolved. In the past they have probably been ignored and the economic aspect has dominated the decision-making process.

10

The Educational Aspects of Mineral Resources

NORMAN J. GRAVES
University of London Institute of Education, U.K.

Introduction

This brief chapter is essentially concerned to discuss the aims of educational activities in relation to the exploration, exploitation and processing of mineral resources. It is not concerned with detailed suggestions for educational work, these come in the chapters that follow. It is here argued that teaching about mineral resource development is a relatively neglected activity, given the importance that minerals have in our daily life. Consequently it is hoped that the suggestions which follow may help teachers to undertake activities which will help students to appreciate the part that minerals play in industry and commerce and how these help to raise the standard of living.

Implications for primary education

In primary schools children are usually taught the primary skills of communication: oral and written or printed communication and to some extent graphical communication, that is the understanding of pictorial signs. They are also taught elementary number work, hence the usually quoted 3 R's, reading, writing and reckoning (or arithmetic) as being the essential curriculum of primary schools. But if education involves learning to live as well as learning to earn a living, then opening the mind of young children to other aspects of human endeavour is important. Thus today Environmental Studies and/or Environmental Science are usually part of the curriculum. It is in this area that the study of mineral resources may be introduced. It is suggested here that the aims should be limited to examining local rocks for their appearance, hardness, feel and for their use. This can be undertaken both within and outside the classroom. Visits to local quarries may be possible. The school itself may be made of many minerals and these should be observed and possibly classified. Thus gradually there is built up in the mind of the primary school pupil an idea of what minerals are, where they come from and what some of them are used for.

Implications for secondary education

In secondary education, science or even physics, chemistry and biology may appear on the timetable. Similarly geography as a separate subject or as part of social studies will be part of the curriculum. Therefore the teaching of aspects of mineral resources exploration, exploitation and processing may take place within those curriculum areas. Here the aim becomes that of using the mineral resources areas as a means of teaching some elementary science, earth science technology and economic geography. Thus during the secondary years of schooling, students will gradually become aware of (1) the methods used in mineral exploration and the technology involved, for example in seismic prospecting; (2) the nature of the physical and chemical properties of certain minerals; (3) the physical and chemical principles used in the technology of mineral ore processing and refining; (4) the economic, social, political and ethical issues arising from mineral resource exploitation. Inevitably the teacher will need to be selective in choosing the activities since the range of possibilities is enormous.

Implications for higher education

In higher education, the student is usually much more specialized in what he studies. Consequently probably some of the aspects will be treated in depth and others on which the student is not specializing will be covered more superficially. A student specializing in physics may be less knowledgeable on the chemical properties of minerals than on their structure. A student in a school of mines will specialize in geology and mining technology and may be less familiar with the economic and social issues involved. Nevertheless, it is argued here that all students in higher education whose concern is in some way linked to mineral resources, should be given some awareness of the totality of the issues involved over and above their own specialization.

Mineral resources, education and development

It needs to be borne in mind that this book is written in the context of a conference on "Science and Technology Education and Future Human Needs". Future human needs may be very different in the 21st century from those of the 20th century, but it will still be true that many areas of the world will need to raise their average income per head of the population, if each person is to have a reasonable standard of living. Thus within the developing world there is a need to use education to enable an acceleration of mineral resource development within the countries concerned for the benefit of the inhabitants. This means the use of both small scale mineral development and large scale mineral exploitation. Schools and colleges should therefore seize the opportunity of demonstrating to pupils and students how they can play a part in the search for and exploitation of mineral resources on a local basis. It may be borne in mind that the smaller the scale of development, the less is the amount of capital required and the smaller is the disturbance to the environment. All educational institutions can in some small way play their part in helping the development process.

Clearly the underlying values which inform decisions about development will necessarily arise. Consequently teaching about mineral resource development affords the teacher with an opportunity to use value clarification and value analysis techniques which form part of the modern curriculum. The chapters which follow will consist of some straightforward statements about minerals, their exploration, exploitation and processing and some suggested educational activities for teachers.

11
The Nature of Minerals

What are minerals

MICHAEL KATZ

University of New South Wales, Australia

If you examine rocks using a magnifying glass, you will find that most of them consist of a variety of different sorts of particles called minerals. All rocks are naturally occurring crystalline substances with specific physical properties and chemical composition, for example, *salt* (sodium chloride) has 39% sodium, 61% chlorine. Although not strictly mineral, coal, oil, natural gas are usually included in this group.

Due to their special physical properties and/or chemical compositions some minerals may be of great economic importance e.g. iron, gold. Minerals are considered as a resource for human beings. If a mineral is rich in one or more metals it is known as ore.

Uses

Minerals have many and varied uses and are an essential part of our everyday life. Minerals and mineral products are all around us. In the classroom the piece of chalk, the slate board, the graphite in a pencil, walls, ceiling and roof are all made from minerals. You may have on you mineral products such as the metal in your watch, keys, ring, spectacles, cosmetics, etc. More specific examples include gem stones (rubies, emeralds), steel from iron ore, clay in pottery and china and of course the coal, oil or gas you burn and the petrol used in car engines.

Distribution

Minerals are widely distributed all over the earth and virtually all countries have some economic minerals deposits. For example some countries like Zambia are very rich in copper ore, while others have smaller deposits of minerals like graphite (e.g. Sri Lanka). Minerals may be distributed locally, regionally, nationally or multinationally. Sand and gravel are widely available as a mineral but other mineral deposits occur in a very limited number of localities, e.g. cryolite which only occurs in Greenland.

Origins

Minerals are formed by processes in the earth's crust that are weathering, sedimentation, burial, metamorphosis (changes brought by heat and pressure, e.g. clay being changed to slate) and melting. These processes form respectively soils, alluvium, sedimentary rocks, metamorphic rocks and igneous rocks. These processes, known as the geological cycle, have been active, probably since the birth of the planet some 4000 million years ago (see Fig. 11.1).

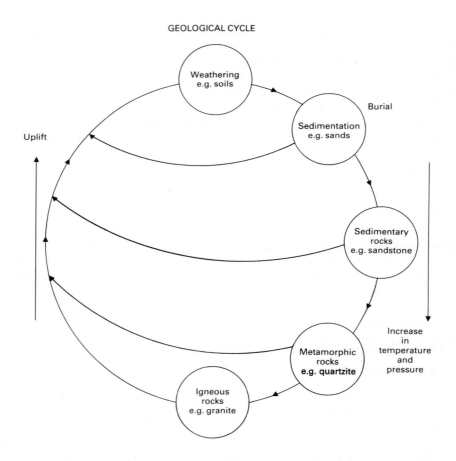

FIG. 11.1

Mineral resources

Igneous deposits

Igneous rocks are very rich in mineral deposits. Minerals of great commercial importance such as iron, copper, nickel, chromite and platinum appeared with the cooling and consolidation of molten formed rocks. With the intrusion of igneous rocks into the earth's crust, the cracks and fissures in the crust were filled by gases and liquids forming lodes and veins. In these lodes and veins, minerals are found in association, such as copper with nickel, silver with lead, and zinc and iron with manganese.

Sedimentary deposits

These are the minerals which are found in the layers or strata of the sedimentary rocks such as coal, iron ore, bauxite, rock salt, gypsum, potash, manganese etc. A few sedimentary rocks such as limestone, clay and chalk are important as building materials.

Alluvial deposits

Sometimes minerals are removed from parent rocks and deposited at the bases of hills and valley bottoms, as a result of erosion and transport. These are known as placer deposits. Tin of Malaysia, gold of Yukon in Canada, and diamond of South-West Africa are examples of this type.

Oceanic minerals

The ocean water has great potential for different types of minerals, but physical difficulties and resultant cost discourage the exploitation. Yet about 30% of world's supply of common salt, 60% of magnesium and 70% of bromine are obtained from this source. Some minerals are found on the deep ocean floors, and may become important sources of manganese and nickel.

Types of Minerals

Metallic minerals

These include iron ore, precious metals such as gold, silver and platinum, and non-ferrous metals like copper, zinc, lead, tin and bauxite. The metallic minerals are found in the ancient Baltic and Canadian Shields and the Plateaux of India, Brazil, Africa and Australia which are either igneous formations or have been transformed into metamorphic rocks. The young folded mountains of the Rockies and Andes are also rich in metallic minerals.

Of all the minerals iron ore is most widely distributed and is found in about 5% of the earth's crust. It is indispensable for an industrial society. Precious metals are high density minerals used for industrial as well as domestic purposes. Among the non-ferrous metals, copper is used for electrical goods, zinc for galvanizing (protecting) sheet steel from rust, lead for pipes and roofing and aluminum for the aircraft and electrical industries.

Non-metallic minerals

These minerals are used in (i) industry and (ii) agriculture. Some industrial minerals are graphite, mica, asbestos, sulphur and rock salt. Sulphur and rock salt are used in the chemical industry, graphite for carbon brushes in electric motors, atomic moderators and special crucibles as needed in gold extraction. Mica and asbestos are resistant to heat and, therefore, used for roofing. Asbestos is not favoured at present because its fibres harm human lungs. In the agricultural category are nitrates, phosphates and potash. All of these are rich bases for chemical fertilizers. Potash is also used in the manufacture of explosives, glass, paper, soap and medicines. Diamonds, emeralds, rubies, sapphires and opals, etc. represent yet another category of minerals which are important for jewellery and ornamental work. Diamonds are used for industrial purposes as well.

Pupil activity

Mineral identification

There are some very simple tests used to identify minerals. One is to examine the way the mineral reflects light, i.e. its lustre. Another is to describe the colour of the mineral; metallic minerals can be brass, silver or copper coloured. Non-metallic minerals are of many colours – pink, red, yellow, brown, green and blue. The colour of the mineral in powdered form, known as its streak, is also a useful indicator; this may be black, brown, green or yellow.

Important minerals are characterized in terms of lustre, colour and/or streak. Other properties include density/weight, hardness, taste, smell, feel and the general appearance (texture, structure). The density may be light to heavy, and the hardness soft or hard. Sometimes minerals have a distinctive taste and smell. However, these properties may be unpleasant, if not dangerous to test. The general appearance of the mineral or rock such as glossy, foamy, spotted, veined or fibrous, may be useful in identifying the mineral.

Exercise

Get students to observe a number of minerals, rock or metal in terms of the following properties:

1. Lustre – metallic or non-metallic.
2. Colour – of mineral.
3. Streak – of mineral powder.
4. Density – heavy or light.
5. Hardness – soft: mineral can be scratched by finger nail.
   hard: the mineral scratches glass.
6. Appearance.
7. Optional tests – feel, smell, taste

It is advisable to start with fairly obviously contrasting rocks or minerals and then go on to more subtly contrasting rocks.

The importance and extent of mineral resources

EILEEN BARRETT, IAN FOSTER, CHRISTOPHER COGGINS

Introduction

The teacher should begin this topic by giving the student concrete relevant experiences concerning the student's own relationship to mineral resources. This should give an awareness of the impact that these materials have on society and of the effect of their presence or absence in the future.

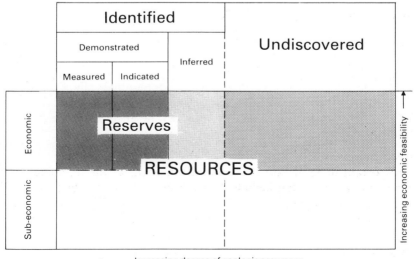

FIG. 11.2

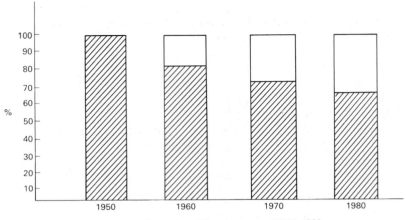

Proportion of Bauxite exported 1950–1980
from Developing Countries – The shaded
area represents the proportion exported.

Fig. 11.3

Our dependence on minerals

The teacher should ask the student to list all those materials on his or her person which are or have been derived from mineral resources. Often the student may be unsure about particular items. In this case they should be encouraged to consult a reference source. This may be a book or the teacher though student research should be encouraged.

At this stage the list may be incomplete or incorrect. In this case the teacher should consider directing students to retain it for editing at the conclusion of the topic. The same exercise should now be carried out within the student's immediate environment, for instance the classroom or home kitchen, and then finally on a wider regional or national scale. Do not forget mineral-derived energy sources.

These latter two lists will almost certainly be incomplete and may be retained for later editing.

Our mineral resources

Taking the list of mineral-derived materials in the local environment these should now be classified into four groups based on the source of supply.

(a) local
(b) regional
(c) national
(d) foreign

Some materials may appear in two or more groups. The class would investigate the reason for this. This section will later link with the section on the distribution of minerals in the world.

Taking the list used in (p. 224) above, they should now be classified into new groupings. These are:

(a) metals, e.g. gold, copper
(b) metals derived from minerals, e.g. iron
(c) gemstones, e.g. diamonds
(d) ceramics, bricks, pottery, tiles etc.
(e) compounds derived from minerals, e.g. nitrates
(f) compounds and elements derived from petrochemical sources, e.g. kerosene.

The distribution of mineral resources

Ores containing useful minerals are only extracted in certain areas despite the fact that the derived element or compound may be found widely distributed in the earth's crust. An appreciation of this fact and the background to it may be developed in students from the following exercise.

Use a pie-chart to graph the relative abundance by % mass of elements in the earth's crust (approx. 40 km thick). This does not include oceans or the atmosphere.

Oxygen	46.6%	
Silicon	27.7	
Metals		
Aluminium	8.2	
Iron	5.1	
Calcium	3.6	
Sodium	2.8	
Potassium	2.6	Metals 25.3%
Magnesium	2.1	
Titanium	0.4	
Manganese	0.1	
Others	0.1	
Non-Metals		
Hydrogen	0.1	
Phosphorus	0.1	Non-Metals 0.4%
Carbon	0.03	
Others	0.1	

Drawing pie-graph means drawing a diagram like Fig. 11.4. In order to draw the sectors to the circle, it is necessary to convert the percentages into degrees. Since there are 360° in a circle, each percentage equals 3.6'. Draw a further pie-chart of the metals' abundance relative to the total proportion of metals.

e.g. Aluminium $\dfrac{8.2}{25.3} \times \dfrac{100}{1} = 32.4\%$ of all metals.

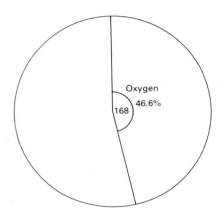

FIG. 11.4

The minerals containing the various elements are distributed very unevenly in the earth's crust. The decision to exploit a particular deposit depends on many factors such as concentration, market value, transportation, environmental factors and many others. For one country, Australia, in 1983, the minimum metal content of ores making exploitation worthwhile is shown in the table below.

TABLE 11.1

Metal	% Mass average in crust	Minimum % of metal in ores for mining to be worthwhile
iron	5.3	50
aluminium	8.2	40
zinc	0.013	8
nickel	0.008	2
lead	0.002	2
copper	0.007	1
tin	0.004	1
uranium	0.0004	0.3
silver	0.00001	0.01
gold	0.0000005	0.001

Students should investigate and discuss what factors can lead to deposits of lower than economic levels being mined. What is the impact of such decisions locally, nationally and globally?

National resources

To focus the student's mind on the resources of the country in which he or she lives the following exercise is suggested.

The table below shows the major mineral resources of India. It would be helpful to have available a map on which location of these resources are shown.

India's Major Mineral Resources (source: *Mining Annual Review*) (Data for 1983)

Metallic minerals and metals	Production	Notes
Iron ore	39×10^6 t	5th in world production. 60% of ore exported.
Bauxite	2×10^6 t	6th in world production.
Manganese ore	1.4×10^6 t	5th in world. 40% of ore exported (more could be exported – there is a conservation policy).
Chromite	363,000 t	8th in world production.
Copper (as cathodes)	36,000 t	
Zinc (metal)	70,000	
Lead (metal)	15,400 t	
Gold	2100 kg	
Silver	18300 kg	
Steel	10×10^6 t	Orissa direct reduction plant.
Aluminium	210,000 t	Quantity limited because of power problems.
Fuel minerals		
Coal	131×10^6 t	5th in world. Coal is India's largest resource.
Lignite*	6.5×10^6 t	Reserves $3,500 \times 10^6$, of which $3,300 \times 10^6$ t are in and around Neyveli in Tamil Nadu. The Neyveli Lignite Corporation operates an integrated project consisting of open-cast lignite mine producing 6.5×10^6 t/year, a 600 MW thermal power station, a fertilizer plant with capacity of 152,000 t/y of urea, a briqueting and carbonization plant producing 327,000 t/y of carbonized briquettes and a clay washing plant producing 6000 t/y of washed clay. 0.9% of world output – developing towards self-sufficiency.

* This figure has been estimated for the purpose of the student exercise

t = tonne = 1000 kg

Pupils are instructed to produce a bar chart of the above data.

It will soon be apparent that a single bar is inadequate, to cover the whole range (from 2100 Kg to 131×10^6t).

The next step is to remove part of the data and construct a further chart for those commodities which hardly show up on the original chart:

chromite

copper

zinc

lead

aluminium

Gold and silver are still problematic and their small contribution by *mass* to productivity is obvious.

TABLE 11.2. *Monetary Value of the Products July 1985*

Metal	Price per tonne UK£
aluminium	1100
copper	1090
gold	14,000,000 (approx.)
lead	304
silver	153,000 (approx.)
zinc	617

NB   Gold and silver prices are usually quoted in troy oz.
where 1 troy oz = 31.1 g

Students might calculate the potential income of the metals produced in one year by their country using the latest prices available (usually published in a national newspaper).

This exercise also brings out the price variation for different metals. To some extent this can be related to the grade of ore mined. It also relates to the cost of processing the ore. For instance, the minimum % of aluminium in ores mined is approximately 50% whereas that for copper is 1% (Table 11.1) and the metal prices are very similar.

Pupils might consider how the two metals are *produced* and which parts of the process would be expected to be costly.

For example, production of both metals involves *electrolysis*, and electricity is expensive. However, in the case of copper electro-refining, the income from precious metals recovered during the process is often sufficient to pay for the electricity required.

Data Handling

This exercise is designed to:

(1) illustrate the distribution of mineral reserves, mineral output between developed and developing countries, and the resulting trade which occurs between countries;

(2) show how minerals resources are subdivided into resources which need to be discovered, and evaluated on the basis of economic factors.

Questions

1. Using Table 11.3, examine the figures for copper, chromite, nickel, bauxite and phosphate reserves. Compare the percentage figures for 1973 and 1979 for the three groups of countries and suggest reasons for any changes between 1973 and 1979.

2. Using Table 11.3 examine the reserve tonnages for each mineral for 1973 and 1979. Now look at Fig. 11.2 and see if you can explain why reserve tonnages for some minerals have increased.

3. Using Table 11.4 draw bar graphs for each mineral to show the proportion of net exports. Comment on the different proportions for each mineral. Comment on the changes between 1950 and 1980.

An example for bauxite is given in Fig. 11.3.

TABLE 11.3. *World's Mining Reserves of some Mineral Raw Materials and their Distribution (in %) between Industrialized Countries (I), Developing Market Economies (D) and State Economy Nations (S)*

	1973				1979			
	World total (10^6 tonnes)	I	D	S	World total (10^6 tonnes)	I	D	S
Copper	375.5	41	45	14	550.8	29	58	13
Lead	103.6	70	13	17	156.7	67	15	18
Zinc	185.3	69	15	16	241.0	73	12	15
Tin	4.3	4	79	17	9.7	8	66	26
Iron	87,700.0	35	29	36	93,600.0	35	31	34
Manganese Ore	1,920.0	52	19	29	1,835.0	53	9	38
Chromite	1,690.0	96	3	1	3,541.0	65	29	6
Nickel	68.0	44	41	15	82.0	22	48	30
Bauxite	11,871.9	38	56	6	23,400.0	25	72	3
Fluorite	135.3	52	39	9	303.0	58	32	10
Phosphate	4,649.3	39	43	18	70,920.0	17	70	13

Source: Mining and Infrastructure in Developing Countries Natural Resources and Development Institute for Scientific Cooperation, Tubingen, 1982, vol. 16, p. 28.

Explanation	Industrialized countries	e.g. U.S.A., Canada, United Kingdom, France, etc.
	Developing market economies	e.g. Chile, Zambia, India, etc.
	State economy nations	e.g. U.S.S.R., Poland

TABLE 11.4. *Developing Market Economies: Mineral Production and Consumption*

		1950 %	1960 %	1970 %	1980 %
Bauxite	Production	54.0	66.4	61.0	52.3
	Consumption	—	9.5	13.0	
	Net exports	100.0	85.1	77.8	50.1
Copper	Production	40.4	43.8	36.8	38.8
	Consumption	4.7	4.5	3.6	
	Net exports	89.0	90.4	89.9	63.4
Iron ore	Production	8.3	19.7	23.7	25.6
	Consumption	3.8	4.5	3.9	
	Net exports	54.0	77.4	83.4	69.6
Lead	Production	29.2	27.5	18.5	17.9
	Consumption	4.9	3.5	7.2	
	Net exports	81.2	86.0	56.8	53.8
Manganese	Production	39.2	36.0	34.8	26.4
	Consumption	1.1	4.8	1.4	
	Net exports	97.4	86.9	95.8	61.3
Nickel	Production	—	4.5	11.0	35.8
	Consumption	—	0.5	1.4	
	Net exports	75.0	89.0	89.1	
Phosphate	Production	40.4	39.6	31.1	26.4
	Consumption	1.7	7.4	6.0	
	Net exports	96.0	81.0	62.8	73.1
Tin	Production	89.7	69.4	72.9	77.0
	Consumption	7.5	7.2	7.9	
	Net exports	91.9	88.6	88.7	57.5
Zinc	Production	21.9	24.7	14.2	18.2
	Consumption	3.3	6.5	7.5	
	Net exports	85.0	74.4	64.6	95.6

(i) 1950–70 figures from Bosson and Varon (1977) based on estimated minehead value of ore and concentrate.

(ii) 1980 figures from British Geological Survey World Mineral Statistics, based on minehead tonnages of ore and concentrate.

China clay

Where is it exploited?

An alternative exercise on a particular commodity is illustrated here.

China clay is found in many parts of the world but only exploited in some countries.

TABLE 11.5. *World Annual Production in the mid 1980s*

Europe	Tonnes	The Americas	Tonnes
Austria	77,000	Argentina	84,000
Belgium	130,000	Brazil	418,000
Bulgaria	248,000	Chile	60,000
Czechoslovakia	550,000	Mexico	205,000
France	364,000	Paraguay	61,000
German Democratic Republic		United States	6,362,000
	220,000	Venezuela	72,000
German Federal Republic	370,000		
Greece	47,000	SE Asia, Far East, Australia	
Hungary	55,000		Tonnes
Poland	52,000		
Portugal	63,000	Australia	254,000
Romania	90,000	India	132,000
Spain	100,000	Indonesia	89,000
U.K.	2,421,000	Japan	218,000
		Korea	175,000
Africa, Middle East, U.S.S.R.		Malaysia	441,000
	Tonnes	New Zealand	55,000
		Pakistan	44,000
Algeria	17,000	Taiwan	96,000
Egypt	32,000	Thailand	20,000
Ethiopia	22,000		
Iran	89,000		
South Africa	128,000		
Turkey	38,000		
U.S.S.R.	2,900,000		

By each figure write the letters A, B, C or D to indicate the following ranges.

A – up to 100,000 tonnes
B – 101,000 to 250,000 tonnes
C – 251,000 to 500,000 tonnes
D – for any countries producing more than 500,000 tonnes

Note your total numbers in each category below.

Range   No. of countries in range

  A

  B

  C

  D

Which three countries are the major producers?

1.

2.

3.

Copy the map of the World (Fig. 11.5) and colour it by country, using the following colour code:

BLUE	for category A
GREEN	for category B
YELLOW	for category C
RED	for category D

Fig. 11.5

Remember to put a key on the map.

Constructing a pie-chart

Add up the totals of all the world china clay production in 1982

Part of the world	*Total production (tonnes)*
Europe	
The Americas	
Africa, Middle East, U.S.S.R.	
SE Asia, Far East, Australia	
World Total	

Now calculate the proportion of 360° that each of your four sectors will occupy.

To calculate the no. of degrees use the formula:

$$\text{No. of degrees} = \frac{\text{Total production for part of world}}{\text{World total production}} \times \frac{360}{1}$$

Production (tonnes)	No. of degrees	Part of the world
1.		
2.		
3.		
4.		
TOTAL	360°	

Draw a circle (using compasses) and measure out in degrees the four sectors (using a protractor).

Where does it go?

What are world export figures like?

Look at the Table 11.6 which shows "Exports of china clay". Make a new "League Table" by the side of that table, in order of quantity of exports – largest first, as shown in tonnes.

TABLE 11.6(a). *Exports of China Clay (a Typical Year in the 1980s)*

TABLE 11.6(b). *League Table*

Country	Tonnes	Position	Country
Austria	29,075	1	
Belgium–Luxemburg	12,605	2	
Czechoslovakia	133,984	3	
Denmark	990	4	
France	181,617	5	
Hong Kong	10,250	6	
Hungary	6,496	7	
Indonesia	5,313	8	
Italy	30,008	9	
Japan	4,522	10	
Korea, Republic of	76,920	11	
Netherlands	79,203	12	
Singapore	1,941	13	
South Africa	1,798	14	
Soviet Union	32,800	15	
Sweden	886	16	
United Kingdom	2,468,058	17	
U.S.A.	1,263,341	18	
West Germany	102,005	19	
Yugoslavia	6,587	20	

Refer to p. 231 where you considered the three major PRODUCERS in the world.

Copy and complete Table 11.7 to show both producers and exporters.

TABLE 11.7

Position	World producers	Position	World exporters
1st 2nd 3rd		1st 2nd 3rd	

What does this tell you about the United Kingdom?

Conclusion

This chapter has been concerned with giving a brief account of the nature of minerals and their occurrence in the earth's surface. Various exercises have been suggested that students in schools might undertake. It should be clear that these are merely samples of what teachers could do. Thus the exercise on China clay for younger children could be done for a different mineral, depending on the opportunities available in the locality.

The next chapter will examine the way in which geologists explore for minerals.

12
Mineral Exploration

History

A. W. L. DUDENEY
University of London, U.K.

The practice of mining and processing stretches back to remote antiquity. By 3000 BC techniques were well established for, about this time, the Mediterranean island of Cyprus was noted for its mines and had given us the name Cyprian metal, later called copper. These mines and others contributed to the dominance of Ionians, Phoenicians, Greeks, and Romans over their Stone Age enemies; they had about them that aura of prosperity and progress which has remained typical of successful mines the world over. In AD 1556 the first major treatise had been written, Georgius Agricola's "De Re Metallica", which pictures for us an already sophisticated industry.

Nonetheless, the last 40 years have seen more materials discovered or made available for mining by technical progress than all that had been mined since our remote ancestors found the first metallic pellets in the campfire hearths made of greenish rocks. Our main preoccupation must therefore be with modern mining and processing, or, more precisely, with today's mineral industry.

Traditional prospecting

MICHAEL KATZ

An example of an activity suitable for developing countries

Villagers, farmers, herdsmen and nomadic tribes can be potential prospectors and miners. As the most important resources of developing countries are the human resources the contribution of these individuals to mineral resource development can be important particularly if they have some training and are exposed to the fundamentals of the geosciences. Strategies for geoscience education in developing countries place most emphasis on tertiary level institution building and on strengthening both the graduate and post-graduate sectors. The role of geoscience education at the secondary and even primary levels is also receiving some attention. However a practical, direct and grass roots approach to this problem of geoscience education would be prospector courses in the rural-village areas.

For example, villagers could play a very important role as "barefoot" geologists or prospectors in locating a wide range of potential resources, as the legendary, and still active, prospectors/miners have done in Canada, U.S.A., Australia, Finland and elsewhere. This group can be encouraged, supported and trained at a very low cost and with potentially very high returns. In contrast, untrained prospectors and miners who are lured to "gold rushes" in many developing countries, have difficulty in interpreting geological maps and reports and in their continual search for precious, get-rich-quick, deposits crisscross areas containing other valuable resources which they are not trained to recognize and evaluate. If they had some geological knowledge they would be in a better position to identify a wide range of mineral resources in many inaccessible areas that would be an invaluable contribution to the country's resource assessment.

The villager-herdsmen have an intimate, instinctive knowledge of their environment and they are aware of the topography, water holes, and rock types. These rural people often set up cottage industries in quarrying, ornamental and gem stones, rock crafts and building stones, and they are keenly aware of rocks of unusual colour, lustre, density, and breakage and shaping properties. Thus they can, with little training, be converted into village geologists trained in prospecting for mineral resources. In certain situations they also can be trained to take routine measurements on, and possibly maintain various geological, geophysical and geochemical equipment.

TABLE 12.1. *Draft Syllabus*

Content
  Elements of mineralogy and lithology
  Weathering and soils
  Geological maps
  Ore deposits and industrial minerals
  Construction and building material
  Prospecting techniques – geological, geochemical, geophysical, geobotanical-zoological

Equipment
  Topographic maps
  Geological maps
  Airphotos
  Stereoscopes
  Traversing equipment – pace, chain and compass
  Handlens
  Simple geochemical, geophysical and engineering equipment

Skills
  Simple tests to recognize common minerals and rocks
  Properties of economic and industrial minerals
  Drawing and interpretation of simple geological maps
  Use of compass, chain or pace for traversing
  Operation and maintenance of simple geochemical, geophysical and engineering equipment
  Sampling techniques.

Although there is still a need for prospecting for valuable commodities in developing countries, the present day metal glut and low prices places commodity-dependent developing countries (e.g. Zambia – copper) in an economic crisis. The developing countries resource needs have changed in the last few years and a more broad mineral resource based background is required on all levels of national development and conservation. This changing role of geosciences in development must be taken into account in the training of the village geologist. This includes the search for industrial minerals, building materials and fertilizers.

The tasks are enormous, but a start in this direction, which could have some immediate and tangible results, would be a village geologist training programme for an appropriate, small scale, community-based cottage industry level of involvement (see Table 12.1). This could, in the first instance, concentrate on local industrial minerals (e.g. phosphate for fertilizer and building materials e.g. sand and gravel).

Techniques for mineral exploration

EILEEN BARRETT

In common with most geological formations, orebodies are mixtures or deposits of minerals which formed long before the development of mankind. Orebodies are, however, characterized by their economic value and are to be distinguished from mineral deposits in general which have little or no economic value and cannot be worked profitably. Although they can occur almost anywhere geographically, orebodies are rare and their distribution is irregular. The prosperity of many individuals and nations has long been associated with the ability to find and exploit them.

Originally many metal deposits and other orebodies were easily found despite their rarity, because they outcropped or protruded like currants on the surface of a cake. With a little know-how it was possible to "get rich quick". Nowadays, with few undiscovered outcrops remaining, the search has become more sophisticated. Its appeal has changed from the romantic to the applied scientific; its responsibility from the lone prospector to the large mining concern.

Orebodies are peculiarities in the larger matrix of host rocks and they tend to have different and striking properties which can give clues to their existence, even if buried. In the first place, they tend to occur in particular geological situations so a search may start with available geological maps and records. Many parts of the world remain unmapped in sufficient detail, however.

Secondly, orebodies tend to intermix slightly with the surrounding rocks, soil, and water courses by dissolution and dissemination of minerals. They may therefore be located by a geochemical search.

Some of the content of the orebody "smears" into surrounding rock and to a greater extent into any nearby soil which has a looser structure. Particles may be transported by water to form enriched sediments downstream or the minerals may dissolve to give an enriched solution. The overall effect is to widen the area over which the orebody can be detected and, in particular, to make it evident at the surface. Some industrially valuable materials, such as those of copper, are toxic to many plants and those few plants that are resistant tend to predominate in the area of an orebody. If searching for copper in an arid region, therefore, one might look for the California poppy which thrives in copper-rich soil.

Geochemical prospecting involves taking a large number of samples variously from soil, rock, sediment, water, and vegetation and subjecting them to chemical analyses in the hope of finding anomalously high concentrations of elements of value. Deduction may then lead to the orebody itself, if it exists.

Thirdly, orebodies tend to interfere with the gravitational, magnetic, and electrical fields around them and may therefore be located by a geophysical search.

Variations in gravitational field strength with local density changes are only of the order of a millionth of the magnitude of the field strength itself. Very careful work is therefore required, particularly when a few metres error in estimates of height above sea level can make a nonsense of any results. In corresponding geochemical searches we might be involved with concentrations of valuable elements as little as 0.5 p.p.m.* above their background concentrations. Applied scientific searches are thus by no means as simple in practice as the basic theory would appear to suggest but they have resulted in some notable discoveries of ore. In all cases useful information and data are available from government geological surveys and from mining companies. The three main methods of exploring for minerals are summarized in Table 12.2.

TABLE 12.2. *Mineral Exploration*

Method	Means	Evidence	Equipment	Typical mineral
Geological	Direct observation	Mineral outcrop, oil	Simple	Gold
Geochemical	Chemical analysis of water, soil, rock, sediment vegetation	Geochemical anomaly	More complicated field kits and laboratory instruments	Copper
Geophysical	Physical measurements of density-gravity magnetic properties of rocks	A geophysical anomaly	Sophisticated magnetometers gravity meters seismic equipment	Oil

* p.p.m. = parts per million

Simple student activities

(1) Mix light sand and some heavy particles in a pan. Add water and tilt the pan to separate the heavy particles. This method is still used in looking for gold.

(2) Bury a piece of discarded steel in a sand pit. Using a strong magnet, pass over the sand pit in a series of random or systematic paths to locate the piece of iron.

(3) With a selection of rocks in the classroom use vinegar to identify the limestone.

A student activity based on mineral exploration

EILEEN BARRETT AND MICHAEL KATZ

Introduction

This activity, as described, is more suitable for older students. It could, however, be simplified for younger students.

The geological (Fig. 12.1) map has been produced by geologists of The Geological Survey Department of Sri Lanka (Publication No. RG/010/69). Rock outcrops (i.e. rocks visible on the surface) are identified in conjunction with aerial photographs (satellite images may also be used) and topographical maps. The geologist uses simple tools such as a hammer to break the rock, and a handlens to identify the minerals within the rock and thus name the rock. In addition a compass is used to measure the direction of the rocks and a clinometer to measure their inclination or dip.

All rocks and minerals may have economic use and thus their location and distribution is important in local national and international development of mineral resources.

Description of the map

(1) Scale is 1 cm = 1 km.

(2) Most of the topographic and other land information is absent except that:
   (a) Rivers and roads are shown. A colour map (which is usual for many geological maps) would be easier to use.
   (b) Coastline is shown as a solid line in the extreme southwest with a coral reef off shore.
   (c) A forest reserve is marked in the extreme north-east.

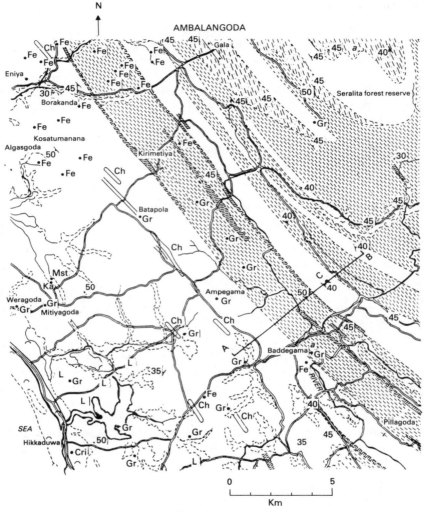

FIG. 12.1

(3) Geology – the rock formations.

gneiss (one type of metamorphic rock) layered

marble

another gneiss – layered

another gneiss – rather massive and less layered

is alluvium (clay) found in the river valleys, together with sand and gravel

↘ is the symbol which shows the direction and dip of the rock

↘⁴⁰ indicates that the rock ridges run N–W to S–E and that the dip is 40° from the horizontal in the NE direction

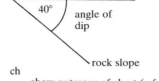

40°   angle of
       dip

       ↘ rock slope

ch   ch
⟲ or ══ show outcrops of chert (a form of silica)

● Gr   is a location of a graphite outcrop

● Fe   indicates iron outcrop

● Ka   indicates kaolin (china clay outcrop)

● Mst   indicates moonstone (a gemstone outcrop)

(some of the map is filled in by inference as it is impossible to actually traverse the whole area. · indicates a *known* outcrop location but deposits could be more continuous than indicated)

Student exercises

Two exercises are suggested:
(1) The student is asked to consider the village of Baddegama and to consult the map in order to locate potential mineral resources, both for local use and for wider usage.

Questions which might be asked
Locate Baddegama on the map.
(a) Does it have good road or river connections?
(b) How far is it to the nearest coastal town? (Hikkaduwa)
  (1) in a straight line
  (2) travelling by road
The villagers are mainly involved in agriculture. They obtain their materials for building and for day to day living *locally*. Their soil is rather acidic.

(2) List any mineral and other resources which might contribute to their life and occupation.
Construct a table listing these resources and give the approximate distances BY ROAD from Baddegama.

Answers might include:
  (a) Marble for use as a building material or for conversion to lime as a fertilizer for acid soils (complementary science teaching on soil pH measurement).
  (b) The local gneisses can be used for building. The layered ones in particular are easier to cleave into slabs of required dimensions, although massive unlayered rocks generally have more strength and resistance to weathering.
  (c) A river flows within 1 km of the village and therefore indicates irrigation possibilities.
  (d) Clay supplies for pottery, bricks and tiles are found in the river valleys – The nearest *marked* supplies are about 3 km away from the village.
  (e) Fuel is needed for the *lime and brick* kilns (*charcoal is the most likely local fuel to be used*). It is intended to develop a large town on the coast. Some of the buildings will be constructed in concrete.
  (3) Can you locate the raw materials needed for the production of concrete? (knowledge of what concrete is made of is required).

Answers
Marble and clay might provide the main constituents of cement. Gypsum is normally added to cement to control the setting time and no gypsum deposits are shown – but quantities needed are relatively small. Much fuel is needed and would need to be imported. Aggregate (sand and gravel) for concrete is available in the river valley.

  (4) Are there any resources which might be mined on a small scale and used to develop a local village industry?

Answers
Graphite and iron ore are the only *really* local deposits. Iron ore can sometimes be used in powder form as a dye. With good road access the products might be sold as exports or for further refinement and manufacture within the country.

  (5) What other resources are located at greater distances from the village? Could any lend themselves to large-scale mining?

Answers
There appears to be an abundance of iron ore which might be mined on a large scale. Kaolin occurs in one location and might be used in pottery. Graphite outcrops are numerous which might indicate more extensive deposits underground – hence large-scale mining. Chert can be used for constructions, ornamental uses. Moonstone is used for jewellery.

Three-dimensional exercises (for students with a greater geological background)

(a) Draw a section from A–B to a given scale –
 (1) Draw a line A–B (indicate your horizontal scale).
 (2) From the map mark on line A–B, points where different rock formations intersect line A–B.
 (3) From structural information ·40 draw a line 40° from the horizontal inclined towards B.
 (4) Fill in the section by using symbols for the different rock formations.

(b) If you draw a vertical hole at C how many metres would it take to reach the marble (zebra stripes)?

Answer 80 metres.

Student activity on exploration for younger pupils

Where does China clay come from?

Making the map. When China clay is discovered, the mining company's geologists carry out a detailed survey of the area in order to determine the extent of the deposit. The geologist carefully examines old quarries and crags and any other rocks seen (exposed) at the surface. Rivery valleys are especially valuable because river erosion often exposes bedrock in the river bed and valley sides. All the information discovered is recorded on a map such as Fig. 12.2 and when this has been done the geologist then draws in the boundaries between the different types of rock which are then coloured in.

Exercise . . . You are the geologist.

Study the map very carefully and check all the symbols used. The boundary between the slate and granite has been drawn through the road cutting on the northern edge of map.

Using the evidence on the northern edge of map

(a) complete the boundary between granite and slate
(b) outline the areas where China clay occurs
(c) colour in the slate area grey; granite area red; China clay area yellow.

This finished map is an important reference document . . . but having found the China clay deposit what would you do next?

(d) Using the scale on the map, estimate the area covered by the largest deposit (roughly between A and B on the map). You could draw a rectangle to cover as nearly as possible the area of the China clay.

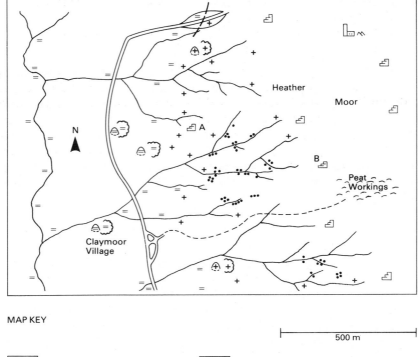

MAP KEY

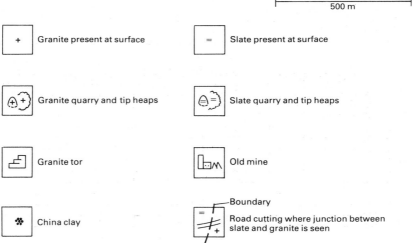

FIG. 12.2. China clay exploration – making (the geological) a map of the deposit.

(e) Measure its length and width using the scale given.

Length = _____m
Width = _____m
Area = _____m^2

(f) Join tor A to tor B. The next stage of exploration will be along this line
Measure the line AB = mm
What distance does this represent? (Use the scale given)

Exploring underground. Before going ahead with excavation, the mining
company must find out if the clay deposit is big enough to make working it
worthwhile. To do this, boreholes are drilled into the china clay and the drill
cores measured and the details recorded (logged). Ten boreholes were
drilled at regular intervals along the line A–B, see map. The results of this
work are recorded on diagram (Fig. 12.3). The information (data) from
borehole 1 has been drawn on the section. Plot in the data from the other
borehole logs and then draw in the boundary between the granite and china
clay.

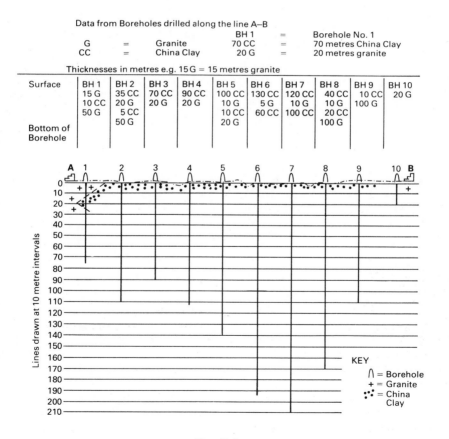

Data from Boreholes drilled along the line A–B

			BH 1	=	Borehole No. 1
G	=	Granite	70 CC	=	70 metres China Clay
CC	=	China Clay	20 G	=	20 metres granite

Thicknesses in metres e.g. 15 G = 15 metres granite

Surface	BH 1	BH 2	BH 3	BH 4	BH 5	BH 6	BH 7	BH 8	BH 9	BH 10
	15 G	35 CC	70 CC	90 CC	100 CC	130 CC	120 CC	40 CC	10 CC	20 G
	10 CC	20 G	20 G	20 G	10 G	5 G	10 G	10 G	100 G	
	50 G	5 CC			10 CC	60 CC	100 CC	20 CC		
Bottom of		50 G			20 G			100 G		
Borehole										

Lines drawn at 10 metre intervals

KEY

∩ = Borehole
+ = Granite
∴ = China Clay

FIG. 12.3

Conclusion

As you can see much mineral exploration involves mapping, since the mining engineers need to know in what area minerals are and how near or how far from the surface they are situated. The depth of a mineral may make a difference as to whether it is worth mining or not. If you are looking for local mineral resources to develop, then you are most likely to look for easily accessible deposits which can be exploited on a small scale. This means usually surface or near surface deposits like clay, granite or even iron ore. Thus you need to know what to look for and whether it can be easily transported to a village or to the nearest small town. Some of the exercises in the early part of this chapter may help you to find certain minerals in your home area.

13

Mining and Processing

Large-scale and small-scale mining

CHRISTOPHER COGGINS

Luton College of Higher Education U.K.

The numerous activities which come under the general heading of mining can be subdivided in a number of ways. This section proposes to make a distinction in terms of scale of operation and in terms of specific activities associated with mineral resource development. Although small-scale mining may be appropriate in many developing countries either using limited technology or producing smaller quantities with modern technology, the emphasis here will be on the first category often called artisanal mining.

Large-scale mining on the other hand implies the application of energy and technology to produce substantial quantities, possibly several million tonnes per year. Given the first nature of mineral resources, such large-scale mining is often conducted by large national or multi-national companies and the mineral produced is sold in world markets.

Between these two extremes there is a considerable variety of scale. This is influenced by mineral type, resource size, geographical location, supply and demand together with political considerations. With reference to small-scale mining throughout the world, Table 13.1 illustrates its contribution in value terms for a wide range of minerals. The absence of certain minerals (especially oil) indicates the complementary role of large-scale mining, which is also evident from Table 13.1 for some minerals.

As an activity mining is concerned with locating the mineral deposit, planning and construction of the mine, mineral extraction, and initial processing whereby the mineral is separated from (some of) the waste material. All of these operations have to take place where a mineral is actually found. Further sophisticated mineral processing and refining operations may more appropriately be termed manufacturing. The life cycle of a particular mining operation may be shown diagrammatically with initial output building up to a maximum output and then eventual decline as the mineral deposit is economically or geologically exhausted. If economic, technical or political factors change, a particular mineral deposit may be re-evaluated and mining may result. Such renewed mining activity may be

TABLE 13.1. *Estimate Value of the Small-Scale Mining Sector (1982 Data)*

Mineral	Gross value of output ($ million)	Share of small scale mining (%)	Gross value of small scale mining ($ millions)
Antimony	126	45	57
Asbestos	1,444	10	144
Barite	300	60	180
Beryllium	38	100	38
Chromite	633	50	316
Clays	2,592	75	1,944
Cobalt	675	10	68
Copper	12,812	8	1,025
Feldspar	124	80	99
Fluorspar	745	90	670
Gold	16,060	10	1,606
Graphite	221	90	199
Gypsum	682	70	477
Iron ore	32,638	12	3,917
Lead	1,977	11	217
Manganese	1,634	18	294
Mercury	77	90	69
Phosphate rock	3,788	10	379
Pumice	114	90	103
Salt	2,703	20	541
Sand and gravel	10,103	30	3,031
Silver	2,962	10	296
Stone	14,957	30	4,487
Talc	182	90	164
Tin	3,118	15	468
Tungsten	272	80	218
Vermiculite	51	90	46
Zinc	5,064	11	557
Others	21,473	—	—
TOTALS	$137,565		$21,610

repeated several times, and may involve a change in scale as well as the recognition of associated minerals within the deposit. Many old lead mines in the United Kingdom have been reopened in order to extract fluorspar and barytes.

This life cycle of a commercial mine is illustrated in the diagram, while Table 13.2 compares small-scale (artisanal) mining and large-scale mining operations.

TABLE 13.2. *The Life Cycle of Mining*

	Small-scale artisanal) mining	Large-scale mining
Exploration	Local knowledge (often incomplete), stimulus of local markets, emphasis on surface deposits.	Geochemical and geophysical methods locate buried deposits. Company centred.
	Not all discoveries become mines	
Planning and Construction	Often piecemeal, but rapid informal negotiations short-term commitments	Formal negotiation of lease and market contracts often over several years. Long-term commitment.
	Very little mineral will be mined at this stage	
Mineral extraction	Labour intensive (often part-time). Limited technology, and dangerous conditions, small output from shallow pits, quarries or *adits* (horizontal tunnels into a hill side) selective mining with little waste ore.	Advanced mining technology and heavy capital commitment. Continuous operations. Large output of mineral plus waste ore from deep shafts or large open pits. Safety legislation and accident prevention.
	Minerals are removed from the mineral deposit	
Mineral processing	Hand breaking and hand sorting. Simple concentration using gravity.	Frequently involves complex physical and chemical processes to separate mineral from ore, requiring capital equipment and much energy.
	The mineral is rarely usable in its crude state	
Mineral use	Mainly local markets	Large distance transport more common, national and global markets.
	Minerals form major inputs into industrial processes	
Cessation of mining	A regular occurrence ephemeral nature	May be determined by geological, political or economic sectors.
	Economic and social disruption	
Renewed mining activity	Intermittent small-scale mining *or* large scale commercial evolution	Small-scale scavenging *or* large-scale reinvestment.
	Ultimately the mineral deposit will be depleted/exhausted	
Reclamation	Unlikely by mine operations	Now usually forms part of original contract
	Heaps and holes may be put to other uses	

The mining industry – studies of the mining of four minerals

G. A. COX, H. HAWES, D. G. W. NORRIS AND T. C. SWINFEN

The world contains a bewildering number and variety of useful minerals which are mined by a large number of different methods. Here we study only: copper ore, mineral beach sands, coal, uranium ore. These four illustrate the wide range of issues involved in mining.

Copper

Sources and importance

Copper, lead, and zinc are some of the common "base metals" (in contrast to the "noble" or "precious" metals). After iron and aluminium they are by far the most important industrial metals, widely used in the pure form and as constituents of alloys such as brass (copper and zinc). Bronze (copper and tin) has been used for thousands of years, but the world consumption of copper expanded greatly in the second half of the 19th century with the development of the use of electricity. Copper wires carry electric current in heavy cables, in the wiring in a building, in the circuits in machines and television sets, and in the fine windings found in the smallest electric motors. Copper has replaced lead and other metals in water pipes, both for the hot and cold supplies to household taps and the small-diameter piping used in central heating systems. A typical motor car contains about 20 kg of copper.

TABLE 13.3. *Estimated World Production of Copper*

Year	Output (tonnes)
1880	157,000
1968	6,000,000
1975	7,140,000

World resources are very large so there should be no shortage of the metal in the foreseeable future. Identified copper resources throughout the world in 1975 totalled 440 million tonnes, enough to last for 60 years at the 1975 rate of production. New discoveries increase this figure from year to year.

An additional 290 million tonnes were assumed to exist in unprospected deposits which would be economically recoverable, and at least 700 million tonnes in deposits which at present are not economic to mine (about half of this occurring in deep-sea nodules).

The main world suppliers of copper now are the U.S.A., Chile, Canada, U.S.S.R., Zambia, and Zaire. The U.K. imports copper mainly from Canada (20%), Zambia (26%), and Chile (18%).

Copper ore

The main source of copper is newly-mined ore. An ore deposit can be defined as "a mineral concentration which can be exploited commercially" and this implies that international metal markets determine whether or not a mineral deposit is an ore.

Copper ore deposits are widely distributed, both geographically and geologically. The most common copper mineral is a sulphide, such as "copper pyrites" (chalcopyrite, iron copper sulphide). The mineral may be dispersed through different *types of rock and later may have suffered* chemical changes of some kind.

Mining the ore

The size and shape of the mineral deposit determine the method of mining to be used. The waste material covering the ore body is called the

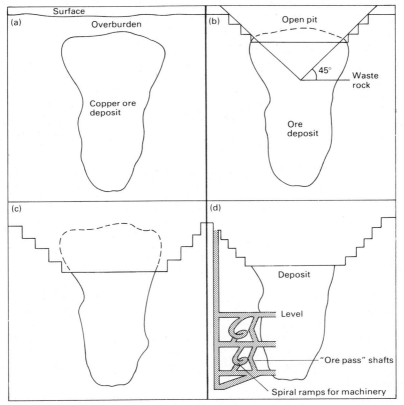

FIG. 13.1. Mining a copper ore deposit. Underground mining is more costly than open-pit mining and so the percentage of copper in the ore (the *grade*) must be higher if the mine is to be economic. Most of the copper mining operations which are now being started use open-pit methods.

overburden. If this is fairly easy to remove, and if the ore body is big enough, open-pit mining methods are used. Fig. 13.1(a) shows an ore body and Figs. 13.1(b) and (c) successive stages in the open-pit mining of it. As the pit deepens the proportion of waste rock increases and eventually the mine becomes uneconomic. It might be possible to mine the rest of the deposit by underground methods, as shown in Fig. 13.1(d).

Concentrating the ore

Due to the low percentage of copper in the (low-grade) ores mined nowadays, the mineral content must first be concentrated as described below.

The ore is crushed and ground in water to a slurry so fine that the particles of the valuable minerals become separated from those of waste rock. One method of concentration is to add suitable chemicals to the slurry so that when air is bubbled through it (Fig. 13.2) only the copper-bearing minerals stick to the bubbles. These rise to the top as a froth which can be skimmed off, filtered, and dried to yield copper concentrates. This process is known as froth flotation and is much used in base metal mining operations. Flotation has also been used to rework tailings from old mines.

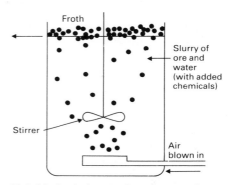

Froth

Slurry of ore and water (with added chemicals)

Stirrer

Air blown in

FIG. 13.2. Mechanical separation of copper slurry.

Smelting

Smelting is the process by which a metal compound or mineral concentrate is made to yield the metal itself. The smelting of copper is a complex series of chemical reactions, involving molten substances at high temperatures.

Copper concentrate and coke are heated with sand in a controlled air blast (Fig. 13.3). The coke burns to provide heat and the iron is converted to a slag of iron silicate which floats on a layer of "matte" (copper (I) sulphide, Cu_2S). These liquids do not mix and can be drawn off separately from the bottom of the furnace (like the iron and slag from a blast furnace). In a second stage the matte is heated again in a controlled supply of air. The reactions are complicated. The end products are copper metal and sulphur dioxide (SO_2) (and, of course, slag).

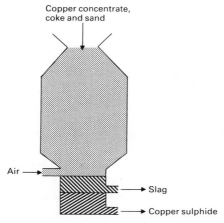

Fig. 13.3. Mechanical separation of copper slurry.

The resultant metal is not pure enough for electrical uses, so copper of at least 99.9% purity is produced by electrolysis (Fig. 13.4).

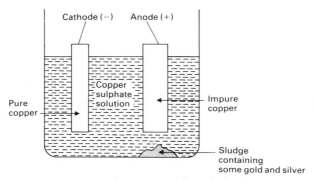

Fig. 13.4. Refining copper electrolytically.

Pure copper is deposited on the cathode and the impure copper anode dissolves. A sludge of impurities "anode mud" builds up under the anode. The valuable metals which can be extracted from the anode sludge help to pay for the cost of purification.

Gold, silver, and molybdenum are the main by-products of the extraction of copper from low-grade copper sulphide ores. When millions of tonnes of ore are mined each year these elements, although present only in very low concentrations, have an important effect on the economics of the process.

For example, Paguna is a low-grade copper deposit on the island of Bougainville in the South-West Pacific. It makes a substantial proportion of its profit from gold production and is one of the world's largest gold producers. Certain of the rare metals such as rhenium, palladium, selenium, and tellurium are also often obtained from the copper and molybdenum concentrates.

Economic issues

The average grade which is mined at present by open-pit methods ranges from 0.5% copper in Western Canada to 1.0% copper in Chile. As mining and metallurgical techniques improve, lower and lower grade ores can be mined. Not all the metal contained in the ore can be economically extracted, so improvements in the efficiency of extraction are constantly being sought.

Commercial exploitation of low-grade ores is made possible by open-pit mining because, by such methods, the ore can be mined at the rate of tens of thousands of tonnes per day at a very low cost per tonne. Open-pit mining uses huge excavators and giant lorries (with capacities of up to 200 tonnes) or railway systems. Large amounts of ore can be removed each day using relatively few workers. Despite the vast amounts of material to be shifted, much more copper per worker is produced from open-pit than from underground operations.

Copper is an important world commodity. Its price is particularly sensitive to fluctuations in demand: over the past 15 years world prices have varied between £230 and £1400 per tonne. Due to the world industrial recession during the 1970s there is a glut of copper and prices have fallen. Consequently some mines are producing copper at a financial loss. This has disastrous effects on the economy of a country like Chile or Zaire which is highly dependent on copper production. In such countries production must nevertheless be continued to provide employment and to earn foreign exchange.

Throughout the world, capital costs for major new mining projects have risen even more rapidly in the past 7 or 8 years than the general inflation rate. The capital cost of developing a new copper mining complex, from mine to metal, has risen to at least £4500 per tonne of annual copper production. This means that a new operation based on mining 20,000 tonnes per day of copper ore containing 0.75% copper (that is about 55,000 tonnes of copper per year) requires a capital investment of about £250 million. The costs of exploration, development, production, processing, and transport have all risen steeply, through inflation.

However much the price of copper fluctuates we must expect the average figure to rise considerably in the future because of the rise in the capital cost of a new mine. The consequences of this increase in price do not, surprisingly, benefit the Third World producers. Before an ore deposit can be exploited transport systems must be made available, and so on. This means that it is much more attractive either to expand existing mines or to open new mines in developed countries where roads, railways, or power stations already exist.

Environmental issues

Mining copper deposits by the open-pit method presents a number of environmental problems. The hole in the ground produced by mining 190 million tonnes of ore and waste (to obtain 360,000 tonnes of copper) would be about one kilometre in diameter and 100 metres deep. Far bigger pits than this already exist, for example in Arizona.

The cost of filling the hole with waste material after the ore has been extracted would be so enormous that it has never been done. All the waste from the pit will be in the form of a slurry of about equal volumes of fine powder and water. This slurry creates a big disposal problem, partly because of its sheer volume and partly because it can produce toxic solutions which contaminate streams and rivers. The mine described above would need a leak-proof "tailings pond", perhaps of area of 4 km^2 and 20 metres deep, into which the slurry could be discharged.

The smelting operation produces large quantities of sulphur dioxide gas which is an unpleasant atmospheric pollutant. It might possibly be dispersed from high chimneys but the strict pollution-control laws in developed countries would probably require its separation from the other waste gases. This is an expensive process, and may increase the cost of the copper by 10–15%. Many countries may not be able to afford to enforce anti-pollution laws.

Mineral beach sands

Nature and importance

Ordinary sand is a familiar material, often consisting mainly of small grains of quartz coloured by iron oxide impurities. Pure quartz is white, and sand can be white or various shades of yellow to dark brown. It may contain other minerals which could be profitably extracted.

Many of the world's beaches consist of various kinds of rock fragments, of different shapes and sizes, together with smaller grains of sand. These particles are the product of the mechanical and chemical breakdown of solid rock formations, and have been carried to the seashore by rivers or possibly by glaciers. Some of the minerals in the rock become too finely powdered to settle out on the beach, and so the composition of the beach sand is not the same as that of the original rock. The commonest mineral present is generally quartz. Most of the sand used in the construction industry comes from other sources such as beds of rivers and glacial deposits.

Beach sands may contain magnetite, ilmenite, rutile, zircon, quartz cassiterite (tin ore), monazite (cerium and thorium ore), diamonds, gold, metals of the platinum group, and a variety of gemstones.

TABLE 13.4. *Uses of Some Beach Sand Minerals*

Mineral	Uses
Magnetite	Iron ore (though too often contaminated by titanium compounds).
Ilmenite	Titanium ore (titanium metal is used in aircraft bodies and engines).
Rutile	Titanium ore. Rutile is also a high quality white pigment used in paints, enamels, and paper-making.
Zircon	For ceramics, furnace linings, and the sand moulds used in metal casting.
Quartz	Glass-making, ceramics, sand used in the construction industry (but not much of this is beach sand because of the salt content)

Australia is the leading producer of rutile, zircon, and ilmenite from beach sand deposits. Many other countries have important coastal deposits, including Brazil, South Africa, India, Sri Lanka, the Philippines, U.S.A., Malaysia, New Zealand, and Canada. The world demand for beach sand minerals is increasing and output is increasing accordingly.

Not all beaches contain these valuable minerals in economically recoverable amounts. These minerals are much denser than quartz. Waves and along-shore currents carry them, separate them from other minerals, and deposit them in particular areas along the shore (Fig. 13.5). The action of the wind may concentrate the minerals further, since lighter particles are blown away to make dunes.

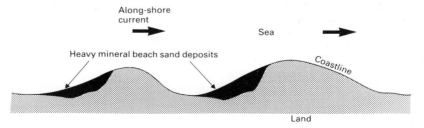

Deposition of valuable minerals along a shore

FIG. 13.5. Plan view.

Mining beach sands

Before decisions can be made about investment the mining company must know how valuable the deposits are. By suitable exploration methods, including drilling, the prospecting team obtains samples of the sands for laboratory analysis. The dimensions of the deposit and the amounts of the valuable minerals present are determined and a suitable method of purification and extraction devised. The total amount of heavy minerals recoverable from the deposit must be enough to pay back the investment required for the mining and concentrating plants, and also to provide a satisfactory return on that investment for at least 5 years and preferably for 10 or more. The company must be sure that there will be enough labour to work the plant and that a market exists for the products. Usually the beach sand deposits are mined by suction dredges floating in small ponds.

A rotary cutter head loosens the sand and a large suction pump lifts it and transports it to the wet concentrating plant. The first stage of concentration consists of separating the heavy minerals from the unwanted low-density quartz. The wet concentrates are usually dried and then go through various magnetic and electrostatic separators, of a type depending on the characteristics of the minerals to be recovered or rejected. For instance, rutile is non-magnetic whereas ilmenite is weakly magnetic and magnetite highly so. Rutile and ilmenite are conductors whereas zircon is not. These processes are chosen and modified to treat the mixture found in a particular beach sand deposit.

Economic issues

Beach sand mining must be highly mechanized to be economical and it is therefore a capital-intensive industry (that is, it needs a large capital investment to set it up but has comparatively low labour and running costs). The capital cost of starting such an operation would be about £14,000 for each tonne per hour of the planned extraction rate. For example, if the rate of extraction is 1000 tonnes per hour the capital cost will be

$$£14,000 \times 1000 \text{ or } £14 \text{ million}$$

Approximate values of three important minerals obtained from beach sands are given in Table 13.5.

TABLE 13.5

Mineral	Price per tonne (June 1979)
Ilmenite	£ 11
Rutile	£107
Zircon	£ 46

Obviously the amount of rutile present is economically more important than the amount of ilmenite.

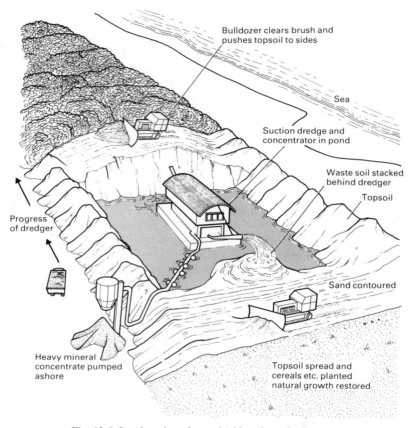

Fig. 13.6. Landscaping of a worked beach sand mine.

At present magnetite from beach sand is not usually sufficiently pure to be useful, but it can be stockpiled for further processing in the hope that in the future it may be economic. New Zealand, however, exports magnetite on a large scale to Japan where it is used as one raw material for certain titanium alloy steels. Beaches are regarded at times as being fragile and important eco-systems and as important recreation resources. However, the land on which the mineral beach sands is found often appears to have little direct economic value before the mining operations. Figure 13.6 shows how the land surface may be revegetated after the mining operations. This process may minimize the long-term impact of mining and may also be profitable if it is used for agricultural purposes or residential developments.

Coal

Nature and importance

Coal is the fuel which made the Industrial Revolution possible. Because it is abundant it will be an important source of energy for many years to come, and it will last much longer than oil.

Coal is a "fossil" fuel, originating from plants. In the Carboniferous and Permian Era of the Earth's history (about 300 million years ago), plants grew in profusion and their partially decayed vegetable remains provided the starting point for coal formation. Buried under layers of sediment, squeezed by enormous pressures, and slightly heated, the peaty mass changed progressively into the various forms of coal. The main content of coal is carbon, with some hydrogen and varying amounts of nitrogen, oxygen, and sulphur. Inorganic impurities do not burn and are left as "ash" after combustion.

The products of the various stages in coal formation, from dark brown, porous peat to black, dense anthracite, are shown in Fig. 13.7.

Coal has two main uses; as a fuel and as a source of useful chemicals. It is used as a fuel for heating buildings, for supplying heat to industrial processes, and for boiling water to make steam. The steam may be used in power stations to generate electricity or it may be used in factories as a source of energy or as a chemical raw material.

When coal is heated in the absence of air a solid fuel called "coke" is produced and a mixture of volatile substances driven off. This process is

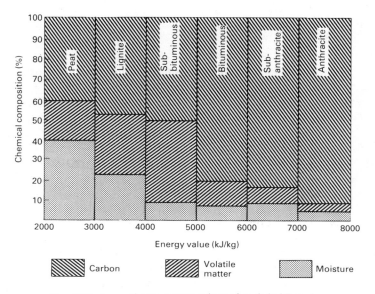

FIG. 13.7. Approximate energy values of coals in kJ per kg.

called destructive distillation. The main products besides coke are "coal-gas", "ammoniacal liquor" (a watery liquid containing ammonia) and "coal tar". All these can be processed to yield useful products. Before the 1930s the chemical industry was based on coal tar in the way that it is now based on oil.

Processes are now being developed to obtain a synthetic crude oil and synthetic "natural gas" from coal. Liquid fuels are so convenient (in road transport, for example) that the production of syncrude will probably become very important in the future. Because of oil embargoes, South Africa is building coal conversion plants designed to satisfy 74% of her liquid fuel requirements.

Production figures

World production of coal in 1975 amounted to 3200 million tonnes. Estimates of the amount of coal in beds at least 30 cm thick and within 1200 metres of the surface have been made. We cannot predict now how much of this coal will be economically mineable in the future so the estimates are not precise. The world's coal deposits should be adequate for the next 500 to 5000 years.

Coal mining

Coal is mined either by open-pit methods (called open cast in some countries) or by underground mining. If the soil and rock layers above the coal bed (the overburden) are comparatively thin they can be scraped aside and the coal dug out. Open cast mining of this type is much cheaper than underground mining because far fewer men are required to produce a given amount of coal. The mechanical diggers used are very large – for example the largest walking drag-line in use at present can dig up 150 m^3 of overburden and dump it 90 metres away in about a minute and a quarter. The coal may be carried out of the mining area in lorries with capacities of 60 tonnes or more.

For underground mining vertical shafts and tunnels must be driven through rock and machinery is required for ventilation, pumping, underground transport, and vertical hoisting, all of which is expensive. Several tonnes of coal can be produced per man-shift though this can vary according to local conditions and methods.

Coal processing

However coal is mined, it usually contains useless rock from the strata above and below the coal or from pockets of rock within the coal seam itself.

Before delivery to the consumer the coal must be cleaned and dried. This may be quite easy or it may involve elaborate equipment.

The waste products, after being dried, might be used as fill material for nearby road construction. Alternatively they are dumped in some kind of waste tip which might later be landscaped or planted over.

Economic issues

Some coal is used in plants or power stations near the mine. More frequently, however, the coal must be shipped to its destination by road, rail, river barge, or deep-water cargo ship. Transport costs may be a sizeable proportion of the final price of the coal.

There are so many factors involved that it is almost impossible to quote a "world price" for coal. Political considerations arise too: a government subsidy may be given to encourage internal production of fuel and imports discouraged or forbidden.

Environmental issues

Underground mining is hazardous. Roof falls, explosions, or machinery accidents may cause physical injuries. Coal deposits are particularly liable to produce poisonous or flammable gases so good ventilation is essential. Great care must be taken to avoid naked flames and every kind of spark.

Dust must be controlled by adequate ventilation. Continued exposure to dust can lead to disease in the long term: pneumoconiosis used to be an all too frequent illness among coal miners.

Old underground workings may cave in, resulting in subsidence of the surface land. To refill the mines with waste material to prevent collapse is expensive, and waste tips ("slag-heaps") are often created instead.

Subsidence can affect roads, buildings, and service pipelines. In populated areas, compensation has to be paid for damage to property caused by subsidence. Waste-tips may be eyesores and they can also be very dangerous if they have not been carefully sited. If they contain too much water sudden and disastrous landslides may occur.

Open cast mining alienates and causes massive changes to vast areas of the land surface. Rehabilitation, if effective, minimizes the long-term effect though the land may not return to its original state.

Uranium

Sources and importance

Until World War II uranium was of little importance and uranium ore was mined for the minute quantities of radium it contained (used medically to treat cancers).

The successful explosion of the first atomic bombs dramatically demonstrated that a use for uranium had been discovered. The nuclear fission process, when controlled, is used in reactors to provide heat and hence to generate electricity. As more nuclear power stations are built the world demand for uranium rises. In 1975 over 660 nuclear power stations were operating, being built, or firmly planned, and many more have since been confirmed.

The major world producers of uranium are the U.S.A., Canada, and South Africa, although Australian production will become important during the next 10 years. In 1975 world production of uranium was 25,000 tonnes: by 1985 it had reached 45,000 tonnes. Published reserves contain about 650,000 tonnes of the metal with estimated additional resources of 620,000 tonnes.

The most common uranium minerals are pitchblende and uraninite: both contain uranium oxide. These minerals have been found in various types of deposit. Twenty years ago the majority of, and the highest grade of, deposits then known were of the vein type. However, the two basic types which now account for over 80% of present low-cost reserves are the ancient placer-type deposits (such as Elliot Lake in Canada and the Witwatersrand in South Africa) and the "plateau" or sandstone type deposits (such as the Colorado plateau in the U.S.A., and plateaus in Niger and Argentina).

A geologically unusual but economically important source of uranium occurs in the bedded deposits of the Witwatersrand in South Africa. These are worked mainly for their gold content and the uranium may be recovered as a by-product. A typical South African ore body on the Witwatersrand is 2500 million years old, shaped like a river delta several hundred square kilometres in area and up to 1 metre thick. This vast sheet may be so riddled with faults and variations in thickness that very careful sampling and testing are required to evaluate the deposit correctly. One tonne of Witwatersrand ore may contain 30 kg pyrites, 0.2 kg uranium oxide, and less than 10 g gold, but the value of the gold recovered far exceeds the value of the uranium content.

Processing the ore

Uranium ore is ground to a fine powder and is then leached with hot acid for about 18 hours. The slurry is filtered. The solid contains silica and other waste minerals. The liquid contains the uranium in a form which dissolves readily in a kerosene-based solvent. The solvent is passed in one direction through a series of connected vessels and the uranium solution passes in the other. Counter-current solvent extraction of this kind can be very efficient. The solvent is made to give up its burden of uranium and is re-used. Further processing yields the product, uranium oxide, U_3O_8, for fuelling power stations.

Economic issues

A 1000 MW power station needs 500–550 tonnes of uranium oxide when it is built and then 150 tonnes per year for refuelling. It is very expensive to build but comparatively cheap to run; technological improvements are likely. Fusion reactors, using no uranium, could replace fission reactors but the basic reaction – the hydrogen bomb – has not yet been controlled and fusion power is still a dream.

Environmental issues

In a typical South African gold or uranium mine the deposits are thin and the miners have about 1 metre of height to work in. The atmosphere is hot and dusty, requiring refrigerated ventilation. Radon, a radioactive gas, is given off from the rock and methane gas is also present giving the risk of fire. There is a constant risk of rock falls but on average uranium mining is less hazardous than coal-mining. Above ground, there is a large volume of waste slurry which has to be contained in a tailings pond, and the tailings are slightly radioactive so that leakages from the pond are undesirable.

The environmental problems and general issues involved in the transport of fuel and the operation of nuclear power stations have generated considerable controversy. This may have an effect on the future economics of the industry.

Case Study of the Panguna Copper Mine in Bougainville Island

CHRISTOPHER BUNKER

Introduction

The Bougainville copper mine at Panguna in the North Solomons, is the fourth largest copper mine in the world.

The Bougainville copper mine produces copper concentrate, that is copper containing mineral grains ready for smelting. The copper concentrate contains a significant amount of gold, and so the mine is a copper/gold mine. The mine is such a large one that it puts Papua New Guinea up into the list of the top 17 copper producing areas of the world, and up into the top 10 gold producing countries of the world.

The latest Western world copper production figures for 1983 (taken from Boulay 1984) are shown in Table 13.6. It will be seen from the table that world production has actually been falling over the past few years.

This has been caused by the general recession in world trade, as copper is mostly used in electrical devices, and world demand for them has been low.

The recent upturn in the world economy has not yet affected either prices or production, as stockpiles are being used up.

Copper is recycled in times of economic depression, and in 1983 mine

TABLE 13.6. *Mine Production (000 t)*

	1981	1982	1983
Yugoslavia	111	119	110
Other Europe	184	186	197
South Africa	211	207	211
Zaire	505	503	503
Zambia	587	581	570
Other Africa	95	113	116
Philippines	302	292	275
Other Asia	210	262	294
Canada	691	612	615
U.S.	1,538	1,140	1,046
Chile	1,081	1,240	1,257
Mexico	230	239	193
Peru	328	256	317
Other America	18	27	42
Australia	231	245	265
Papua New Guinea	165	170	183
Western World	6,487	6,292	6,194

production was 6,194,000 tonnes, but refining output was 7,249,000 tonnes Stocks as metal unsold amount to 1,500,000 tonnes, or several months supply.

In these circumstances mines tend to close, and in 1983 over 35 mines were closed, taking over 970,000 tonne/year capacity out of service, and the world capacity "waiting in the wings" is about 1,145,000 tonnes/year.

There is thus great over-capacity in the world for copper production. Because of this, prices have been falling, and the *real terms* price of copper was the lowest since 1945 during 1982–83.

This then is the background against which copper mining has been operating in the past few years. But Panguna does not only produce copper – in 1983 there were produced, besides the 183,000 tonnes of copper, 18 tonnes of gold and 47 tonnes of silver.

The gold price has been moderately high, but falling from the high of a few years ago, until it is now only about $400 per ounce – (gold ounces are 31.1 g, somewhat larger than ordinary ounces, which are 28.3 g) – that is about $US 13 per gramme.

Panguna mine has been able to operate at a profit over the past few years because it is already well established, is efficiently run, produced copper on long-term contracts, and has gold and silver as by-products of considerable value.

The Panguna open pit is currently roughly circular, about 1 kilometre in diameter, and about half a kilometre deep.

Panguna is described geologically as a porphyry copper/gold deposit, and it was discovered and mined in the 1930s, as a gold mine, a part of the Kieta goldfield proclaimed in 1924. It was not however until 1964 that the economic value of the already known copper mineralization was recognized, the gold mines having long been abandoned.

Following the expenditure of K400,000,000, production from the mine began in 1972.

The map in Fig. 13.8, shows for comparison, the distribution of porphyry copper mines and major prospects in the S.W. Pacific area.

Location of the major porphyry copper deposits in the southwestern Pacific and Australia. Deposits indicated on this map are: (1) Taysan, Luzon; (2) Mamut, Sabah (Borneo); (3) Tombuililato District, Sulawesi; (4) Koloula, Guadalcanal; (5) Panguna, Bougainville; (6) Esis, New Britain; (7) Plesyumi, New Britain; (8) Star Mountain District, Papua New Guinea; (9) OK Tedi, Papua New Guinea; (10) Yandera, Papua New Guinea; (11) Moonmera, Queensland; (12) Coalstoun, Queensland; (13) Copper Hill, New South Wales.

Porphyry copper deposits are late events associated with volcanism magmatic area.

Fig. 13.8

The exploitation of the deposit

The mining of the ore is a matter of setting up a spiral system of horizontal and vertical surfaces, not unlike giant steps, which are called "benches". The spiral nature of the benches allows machinery to move around the pit from place to place, and the mining proceeds by destroying the benches with explosives so that the broken rock falls to the bench below (which gets wider) before the bench below is similarly mined.

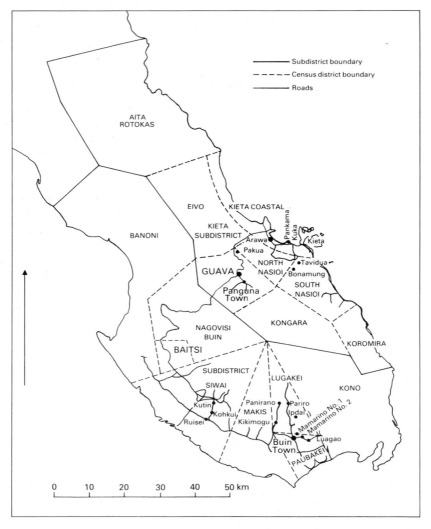

FIG. 13.9. Map of Southern Bougainville.

The biggest single feature of the mine is the "haul road", a very wide highway upon which the huge trucks roll, carrying ore to the first stage of processing and waste to the dumps.

The waste, which contains a fraction of 1% of copper mineral is taken away from the pit, and dumped when it forms giant scree slopes on the adjacent mountain side.

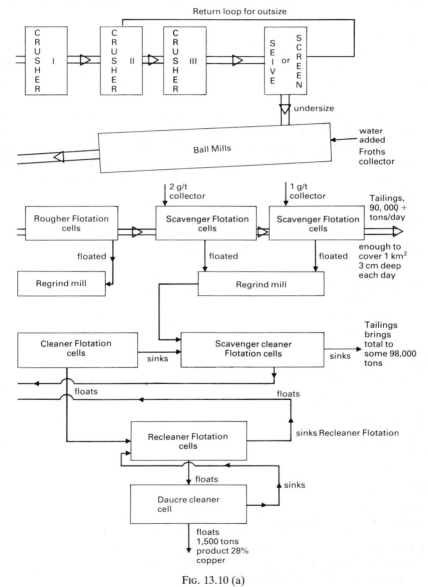

FIG. 13.10 (a)

It is important to appreciate that there is no real alternative to this dumping, but the fracturing of the rock into lumps exposes huge volumes of rock to the effect of rain and atmosphere, which poses problems for the future.

The mine acts as a huge rain trap, and it has to be pumped dry (providing water for the concentrator plant). A horizontal tunnel (adit) is being dug through the mountain to allow easy drainage as the mine becomes very deep.

The map of southern Bougainville (Fig. 13.9), shows the situation of Panguna, in the high mountain of the island. To develop the mine, the township of Arawa had to be built – incidentally dissolving a very fine plantation – and the large highway built to the mine site and town of Panguna. The special mining lease covers not only the mine itself, but also the river which runs from the mine area down to the sea on the west coast of the island.

The rock is blasted out of the hillside, hauled out of the pit and then crushed and treated as shown in Fig. 13.10(a). The process is designed to re-treat the tails at every stage to keep the losses to a minimum. Even so, several tons of copper go with the tailings every day.

The concentrate from the mine travels to the coast in a pipeline, and after thickening by removal of water, is taken by ship to Japan for refining and recovery of the gold and silver from the anode slimes left after purification by electrolysis.

Fig. 13.10 (b) shows a complete copper production process.

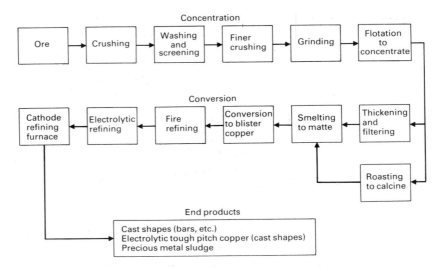

FIG. 13.10 (b). Generalized flow chart showing the process of copper refining.

The negotiation process in developing countries

It is now generally recognized that inequitable agreements must be re-negotiated – and it is unfortunately also understood that once a mine is started, it is a hostage to fortune in its host country. This generally results in mining companies trying to get the best possible terms to begin with, and to host country "putting the screws on" at a later stage.

Tax "holidays" are a frequent device used to assure a mining company that it will be able to recover its investment in the early years of a mine, and often these tax "holiday" years are used by the mining company to full advantage of the company.

Taxation law is complex, and "costs" can generally be set against income to arrive at a profit, which can then be taxed. These costs need to be examined very carefully by a host country, as it is not merely enough to ascertain that the costs have actually been incurred, it is essential also to be sure that cost figures have not been inflated (by for example buying at inflated prices from overseas subsidiary companies) or profits artificially reduced (by selling at a low price to subsidiary companies). There is distinction here somewhere between legitimate accounting practice and fraud, and modern practice is to allow the host country access to the documentation and the decision-making process as it occurs. There is no doubt that Third World countries have in the past been "taken for a ride" by the multinational mining companies – see for example *Africa Undermined*.

The setting up of the Bougainville copper mine in the late 1960s and early 1970s was complicated by the fact that the early negotiations were made with

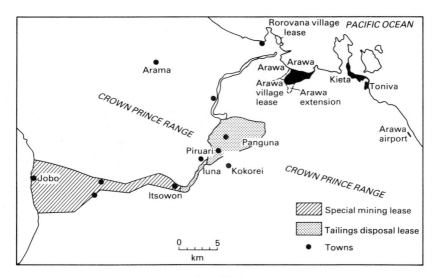

FIG. 13.11

Australian Government departments, but later ones with Papua New Guinea department during the run-up to independence in 1975.

Land tenure in P.N.G. is complex, and special leases were required for a number of purposes, as shown in the map (Fig. 13.11). The problems experienced by the mine management in negotiation with local land owners were very considerable, and partly at least due to non-recognition by the mining company of the legitimacy of many of what seemed at first sight to be outrageous compensation claims.

When the mine got going, copper prices were very high throughout the world, and B.C.L. was able to repay half of its loans and *still* declare a huge profit at the end of the first year of operations.

In the outcry following this, the agreement was re-negotiated.

Costs/Benefits

The benefit to the P.N.G. economy of Bougainville Copper mine is immense – and after the re-distribution of income to give a fairer share to the North Solomons took place, the effect shows not only in the general economy but also in Bougainville itself.

The cost, when placed in the context of P.N.G. as a whole, is small but real. At the end of the day, there will be a huge hole in the ground, some huge heaps of waste rock and a river valley full of sediment.

Ecology, waste and tailings disposal

The waste rock containing sulphides is heaped up in great scree slopes, subject to the effect of rain, sunlight, and oxygen. Under these conditions sulphides become oxidized to sulphates, and an acid solution containing heavy metal ions is released. At present the buffering action of the tailings is such that heavy metal ions are precipitated in the tailings, and so the waste heaps do not pose a present hazard. In the future however, the waste heaps leachate will be a problem, and the Joba river may become poisoned along its length unless precautions are taken.

The tailings disposal from Panguna goes into the headwaters of the Joba river, which just cannot carry it, and the valley is filling up with sand, a delta being built up at the coast itself. The valley is filling up so fast . . . about 2 m per year in places near to the mine, that there is some doubt as to whether the drainage adit will ever work satisfactorily. Even if, for some reason, heavy metal ions do reach the sea, then the buffering action of the sea-water will ensure that no heavy metals remain in solution.

The valley being filled with sand constitutes a real ecological disaster for that valley – but it is only one of many on the island.

The damage to the island as a whole is very limited – and well within which the total ecology can withstand. In future years, provided that precautions are taken to deal with acid waste leachate from the waste heaps, the jungle will re-colonize the waste areas (the leguminous tree *Lucina glauca* being an effective plant in this respect) and eventually the present moonscape will vanish. The 1930s moonscape left after the gold mining at Bulolo has now begun to revert to bush, and it is only the occasional relic of the mining boom that tells one that the bush on the river flats near Bulolo is not a natural landscape. The Joba river may be the same.

Some thoughts about education

How much of all this needs to be taught? Bunker (1984) gives some answers – and these are partly to do with the geology and mineral processing themselves, and partly to do with the impact and perception of the mining industry by the population at large.

A democracy will be in danger of having an inappropriate mining policy unless the population has an attitude of mind which asks, in effect, "let's look at the deal – what are the benefits and what are the costs of mining this resource?". If a democracy does not have this kind of attitude, then there is a danger that worthwhile projects will be cancelled or that impossible ecological demands will be made or that resources will be exploited ruthlessly for immediate profit.

The caveats above apply to a democracy. A totalitarian state can do whatever the leaders decide, and it has to be admitted that in some totalitarian states with centralized economies and an abhorrence of capitalism a more responsible attitude is shown to resources then in some capitalist countries. In a capitalist economy, the profit motive defines what is ore and what is not ore, and a mine may eventually close with large amounts of metal unmined because it was not economic, though the technology for its extraction exists. The manager of a mine in a capitalist country may regret leaving the metal in the ground where it may never be used, but he cannot afford the luxury of getting it all out and go bankrupt. No such market forces influence the manager of a mine in a non-capitalist country, and he can make the decision, if he likes, to get it all out thus conserving a non-renewable resource for future generations.

Mining can certainly despoil an area, but, unless it is "strip mining" to obtain a sedimentary deposit, it is limited in extent, and the shared wealth can be huge.

Mining and processing – a summary

EILEEN BARRETT

The chart in Fig. 13.12 summarizes common processes involved in the treatment of mineral resources found in the solid form and shows some typical products.

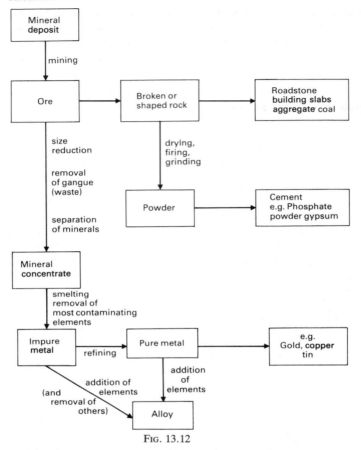

Fig. 13.12

Stone quarry operation (e.g. Bangalore, India)

MICHAEL KATZ

In areas where rocks outcrop they are often quarried for building stone, for road stone and aggregate (smallish pieces of rock used in making concrete). Large slabs of rock are removed from the quarry face either by manual splitting using wedges or by using explosives. These large slabs are then shaped and dressed to the sizes necessary for various applications. If the rock is attractive and long-lasting it can be made into gravestones, for building, and building stones. Less attractive stone can be used for street paving, fences and posts. The waste stone can also be used for road construction and aggregate for concrete, as well as for terrazzo (an attractive cement and stone mixture). Thus all the rock is used and there is little or no waste.

The quarrying operations often result in unpleasant environmental results. These include bare rock faces and large holes. This land could be reclaimed by filling in the holes and the bare rock surfaces covered in vegetation. The quarry pits and holes can also be used as construction sites (e.g. in Bangalore, India, a stadium-amphitheatre will be constructed on one quarry site and a shopping centre on another), for water storage or for waste disposal.

Processing to form concentrates

EILEEN BARRETT

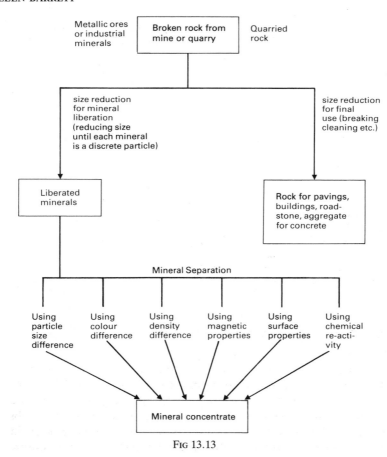

FIG 13.13

Mineral separation

This may simply involve breaking and sizing by sieving (or "screening") as for some of the building materials. The product from a gravel pit consists of gravel of a few centimetres diameter down to fine sand. The product is normally separated by sieving into several size ranges. These are then remixed as required for different uses.

The *Separation* methods needed rely on:

(a) the properties of the minerals to be separated,
(b) the size to which they have been reduced to achieve liberation

For example, the material Bauxite consists mainly of hydrated aluminium oxide and hydrated iron oxide with some silica. The aluminium oxide is white and the iron oxide red. However a colour separation is impossible as the mineral particles are so small.

In this case the only effective separation is a chemical method where the aluminium oxide is selectively dissolved in alkali then reprecipitated.

Table 13.7 below gives some examples of mineral separation techniques based on the two factors of size and properties.

TABLE 13.7

Separation method	Mineral properly used	Size of "particles"	Mineral(s) separated
Hand or radiation sorting	Colour	50–100 mm	rock with visible diamond
Jigging	Density	5 mm	galena/quartz
Heavy media	Density	50 mm	coal/shale
Magnetic	Magnetic	Variable	Magnetite quartz
Settling tanks	Particle size	2 μm–50 μm	Small kaolinite particles from larger ones
Froth flotation	Surface properties -hydrophobicity	200 μm	copper sulphides or other sulphides/ silicate minerals
"Heap" leading	Reactivity to sulphuric acid	variables	copper "oxides"/ silicate minerals

Some minerals may need to be dried for sale or further processing after the separation stage. Some method of solid–liquid separation is used followed by heating if the product needs to be absolutely water-free.

Treatment of concentrates to produce a final product

Further treatments usually involve chemical reactions to convert the mineral to a metal or other useful product.

Some examples are quoted below:

(1) Production of lime fertilizer by heating limestone.
(2) Production of superphosphate fertilizer by treating phosphate rock with sulphuric acid and potash.
(3) Roasting metal sulphides (e.g. those of lead, zinc, copper) to form oxides.
(4) Reduction of metal oxides to metals.
(5) Refining or extraction from solution by electrolysis (e.g. electrorefining of copper, electrowinning of zinc).

Many of these processes may be performed at considerable distances from the mine, in close conjunction with manufacturing industry.

Exercises on processing minerals

EILEEN BARRETT

Hand sorting – by colour

(a) Provide a jar of different minerals or maize and pebbles or other items of approx. 5 mm diameter for the pupils to separate.
Ask them to note the time it takes to achieve a complete separation.
(b) Provide a jar (equal volume of (a)) of coloured items such as rice or wheat and sand of approximately 1 mm diameter (or less) and repeat the exercise. Again they should note the time it takes to achieve a separation (or they should find how much they can separate in the same time as in (a)) – it will take a long time! This could also be done by a "*thought experiment*".

Question
What limits the value of achieving a separation using colour?
(The long time needed for small particles.)

Density separation

The suggested exercise can fit into a science course after density measurements have been introduced. The density of a piece of rock can first be measured followed by a session on separation by density differences.

One way of separating sulphide minerals from waste rock is to exploit density differences.

Densities are as follows:

ZnS	3900–4200 kg m^{-3}
PbS	7400–7600 kg m^{-3}
Waste (some form of silicate rock probably)	2600–1700 kg m^{-3}

If the minerals can be liberated at a fairly coarse size (a few mm) it is possible to separate them using a JIG.

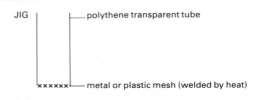

JIG   polythene transparent tube

xxxxx — metal or plastic mesh (welded by heat)

Fig. 13.14

The Jig is shaken up and down in the water (JIGGED). Pulses of water travelling upwards through the mesh as the jig moves downwards lift the minerals. The denser ones settle to the bottom and the less dense ones to the top.

Instead of the minerals quoted, you can use others which are available.

The use of heavy "media"

Coal and shale are the two main mineral/rock types dug out in coal mining.

	Density (kg m^{-3})
Coal	1400
Shale	2200

Coal separation may use jigs or "heavy media". A suspension of fine magnetite in water is produced so that its apparent fluid density is intermediate between those of coal and shale. Coal floats and shale sinks. Fine sand can also provide the medium in place of magnetite. (In industry, magnetite is used as it can be recovered magnetically by passing the wash water with magnetite under a rotating magnetic drum.)

The basic idea could be demonstrated by using wood and "stone" in a container of water.

Magnetic separation

This is easily demonstrated by mixing iron or steel objects with other items and using a bar magnet.

If iron filings and another fine powder are available this shows separation at a smaller particle size range.

Separation based on particle size

The traditional experiment of shaking soil in a jar of water then allowing it to settle into layers could be used here (see Fig. 13.15).

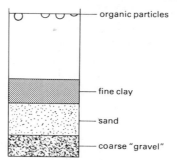

jar +
water +
soil after
shaking and
settling

— organic particles

— fine clay

— sand

— coarse "gravel"

FIG. 13.15

The rate of settling can be used to estimate particle "size" as indicated in this example of kaolinite (or China clay as it is known in the U.K.).

An extension of this, if apparatus and chemicals are available relates to FLOCCULATION. This is used not only in processing but is very important in disposal of *fine waste* which is usually suspended in water. It is also used in water treatment to clarify the water. The usual additive in this case is "ALUM" or aluminium sulphate.

The example given below could be adapted for different clays and different circumstances.

Removing some of the water

The slurry contains more water than the processing plant can cope with. Some of the water is removed by allowing the china clay to settle in large tanks (see the Resource Sheet).

It is important to make the clay particles settle out as quickly as possible so that the clay can carry on to the next part of the process. Chemicals are added to make small particles cling together or FLOCCULATE. The simplest way to make them flocculate is to change the pH (acidity/alkalinity) of the suspension.

Experiment –
to find the pH which helps particles settle most rapidly.

Set up fire test tubes each with 1 cm depth of dry powdered china clay. Add distilled water until the test tubes are three quarters full. In addition, to four, of them add 5 drops of the solution indicated in the diagram.

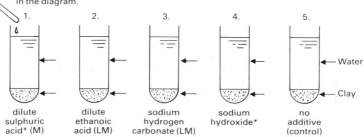

1.	2.	3.	4.	5.
dilute sulphuric acid* (M)	dilute ethanoic acid (LM)	sodium hydrogen carbonate (LM)	sodium hydroxide*	no additive (control)

← Water

← Clay

(** BEWARE **: these substances are dangerous if spilled. Clear up any spills immediately – ask teacher for advice).

Stopper the tubes and shake well. Note the order in which the settling occurs – most rapid first.

FIG. 13.16

In the U.K. process, it is necessary to *flocculate* the clay to increase the rate of settling to remove some of the water. At a later stage, it is *deflocculated* to decrease the rate of settling in order to give as slow a settling rate as possible. This enables a better separation of particles of different sizes to be achieved. Alteration of the pH and/or addition of other chemicals bring about flocculation or deflocculation.

Froth flotation

This technique relies on altering the surface of selected mineral particles so that they become HYDROPHOBIC (water "hating").

The particles are suspended in water by agitation (or stirring) and air is blown through. The hydrophobic particles are attracted to the air bubbles and rise, with the bubbles, to the surface, where they can be skimmed off.

Chemical leaching

Copper carbonate and an insoluble substance such as charcoal powder is treated with dilute sulphuric acid. The resulting mixture is filtered to reveal blue copper sulphate solution. This demonstrates the principle of acid leaching.

Some sulphide deposits generate their own sulphuric acid (with the assistance of bacteria). The mined material is crushed and piled into a "heap" then the acidic water pumped from the mine is sprayed over the heap to dissolve out copper ions. The copper can be retrieved from solution by using scrap iron to displace it (an iron mail would suffice).

Treatment of concentrates

Two fairly simple examples are given:
(1) Heating limestone to form quicklime is a part of many chemistry courses.

The marble is heated very strongly for 10 minutes then allowed to cool. The cooled product is placed in a dish and water is added slowly. Much heat is generated and the pH of the solution around the solid indicates alkalinity.

The heated product is QUICKLIME

The product after water addition is SLAKED LIME
(2) Reduction of metal oxides to metals.

An oxide such as lead oxide can be reduced to the metal by heating with carbon. This can be done in a test tube (when carbon dioxide can be detected as a product) or on a charcoal block (Fig. 13.17).

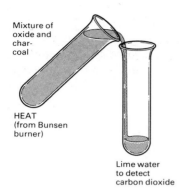

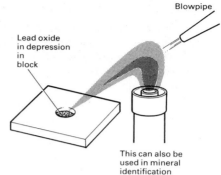

FIG. 13.17

Investigating a local mine – a student activity

PETER SPARGO, THOMAS VARGHESE AND EILEEN BARRETT

Have you ever thought of getting your pupils to visit a mine near where they live – even if it is a small one? They can learn a very great deal from such a visit, as well as having a lot of fun! First contact the manager or owner of the mine (or quarry, or clay pit) to confirm how many students may visit the mine and at what time. If possible visit the mine yourself before taking your students there, as this will help you to answer any questions. To make the visit worthwhile it is important that the students not only *look*, but also *think*, and to encourage this a pupil worksheet is a good idea. Here is an example; it should be completed by pupils as they tour the mine. The visit should be followed by a class discussion as soon as possible afterwards.

1. What is the name of the mine? _____
2. Before you visited the mine, what did you think was mined there? _____
3. How far is the mine from your school? _____ km.
4. What is the name of the material which is mined at this mine? (There may be more than one). _____
    _____
5. Is this material sold just as it is mined, or is it purified or treated in some way before leaving the mine? _____
6. If this material *is* treated in some way before leaving, describe briefly what is done to it on the mine (for example the material may be separated by size, heated, or crushed). _____
7. Where is the product of the mine sent for further processing, and how is it transported there? (For example it may be railed to a factory 500 km away) _____
8. In what final form does society use the product of this mine? _____
9. What mining method is used? For example does mining take place in a hole or trench in the ground, or does it take place out of sight underground? _____

10. List the major pieces of equipment you saw on the mine. _____
11. How many people are employed on the mine? _____
12. Does the mine only operate during the day, or both day and night? _____
13. Did you see anything on the mine that reminded you of some science that you have learned at school? (For example, a filter, an electric motor, or a magnet) _____
14. Did the people working on the mine wear any special protective clothing? If so, describe the role this clothing played? _____
15. Did you notice any other safety measures being used? _____

Waste production and waste disposal

A large mine produces an enormous amount of waste rock. New operations can be designed to minimize hazards and facilitate procedures of backfilling with low costs. Example is provided by the German lignite industry in which huge open pit mines progress across the countryside and the waste is put back and spread to form new ground for farms and villages. On the other hand, it can be very expensive to dump waste material underground.

Processing of ores usually results in two types of large tonnage waste – sands and slimes, slimes are allowed to settle in defined *tailings ponds* in order to recover water for re-use and to avoid releasing effluent to rivers. The sands are deposited in mounds or used to fill pits where mining has ceased.

The tailings and sand are sometimes concentrated again for extracting low grade ore – e.g. tailings plant of copper production in Zambia, gold from waste dumps in South Africa. Tailings are often mixed with cement and pumped underground to fill in the space from which material has been extracted. This sets and provides support so that the supportive pillars of ore can now be removed and extraction is more efficient. Water soluble materials have a tendency to escape into the drainage system. The outflow of industrial process water may cause local pollution by acid, and heavy metals such as lead, cadmium and mercury. This could be prevented by redirecting the effluent strains back to the plant for recycling and removing the soluble contaminants by precipitation. Sometimes the tailings are neutralized by using lime.

The other waste products from the mining operations are waste gases and smoke. Examples are sulphur dioxide, carbon monoxide etc. . . . sulphur dioxide is removed by converting it into sulphuric acid and by absorbing it on slaked lime. Smoke and dust particles emitted are removed using electrostatic precipitators.

What other examples of waste production can you mention?

Can you suggest a reasonable method of disposal?

Down in the dumps – China clay waste

What happens to the waste?

Find out what percentage of waste material remains after the China clay has been removed.

Most of this waste is sand and rocks. You may remember from the introduction that this is deposited from the end of a CONVEYOR to produce a SPOIL TIP.

Try to produce a "spoil tip" by tipping some wet sand out of a beaker or bucket on to a tray. Pour it out so that it forms a "hill".

Now measure the ANGLE OF REPOSE, that is the angle the tip makes with the horizontal: (Fig. 13.18)

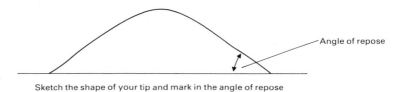

Angle of repose

Sketch the shape of your tip and mark in the angle of repose

Fig. 13.18

Does this shape of tip conform with local regulations? Draw a diagram to show how tips are now shaped compared with the old conical tips.

Conclusion

The mining and processing of mineral resources are complicated both in a technical sense and in an economic sense. Clearly scientific knowledge has been used extensively in developing ways of converting a mass of rock into a useful metal or fuel. Alas, technical knowledge on its own does not solve all the problems. There are economic questions to be asked about prices and costs to discover whether the ore is worth mining. Should the mining be on a small scale by artisans or on a large scale by companies? It may depend on whether the mineral is for local use in small quantities or for the world market. Even if these problems are solved, there remains the environmental impact that mining will have on the landscape and on the vegetation and animals. Finally, how should the wealth created by the large-scale exploitation of a mineral resource be shared between the company and the nationals of the host country?

It is to the impact of mineral resource development that we now turn.

14

The Impact of Mineral Resource Development

Introduction

CHRISTOPHER COGGINS

Luton College of Higher Education, U.K.

Mineral resource development will have many ramifications: on the physical environment, on economic activity and income generation, and the lives of individual people and society. Such impacts will vary according to mineral type, the nature and scale of mining methods and the geographical scale of study. The following paragraphs illustrate such impacts with reference to developing countries.

To the individual, mining may represent a source of employment, perhaps on a part-time basis in conjunction with seasonal agricultural activity. He may operate on a self-employed or employee basis, and his family may provide moral help. The mine may provide basic household materials, utensils and possibly agricultural inputs. In addition there may be an opportunity to sell some of his agricultural surplus. It is unlikely that such an individual will be concerned with environmental issues, although safety and survival will be important considerations.

At the regional level mining may represent a distinctive element within both the landscape and the local economy. Exploitation of a mineral deposit will result in changes in surface topography, vegetation removal and the deposition of waste material. Environmental impact will be most significant at this scale. Mining operations on such a scale will increasingly be dominated by commercial operations, with capital investment complementing labour inputs.

The need to expand, or even construct a new township and supporting infrastructure (transport, power supply, water supply) will create a new focus of economic development within the region. Such a focus may rely on external investment and the mineral may be exported from the region. The result is an island of commercial economic development within an agricultural region, perhaps remote from other urban centres. Such a dual economy will create economic contrasts between the mine-based economy and the pre-existing economy, together with labour migration.

Nationally, mineral resource development will be considered important in raising income through export earnings. National governments may accept external sources of technology and capital, supported by skilled labour, in order to exploit material mineral resources. Such international transfer to technology and skills has been very important in stimulating economic development. Without adequate safeguards, however, there is the likelihood that mineral exports will be crude ore, and that there will be little mineral processing and mineral transformation – both of which add considerable value to the product. Reliance on world markets and prices may also cause problems. Consequently, national governments may take action in order to mitigate or remove some of these economic problems. Participation directly in mineral resource development and restrictions on foreign-based operations will reduce the reliance on global markets and decision-making, especially where indigenous industry is stimulated to use the mineral resource. Social and environmental issues will be responded to at national level, often as a result of pressure group activities. Legislation on working practices, health and safety and environmental protection are common responses.

Superimposed on all of these scales is the global perspective. During the last hundred years mineral resource development has increasingly become dominated by large companies, many of them multi-national. The finite nature of mineral resources, and a long history of exploitation in developed countries led to a pattern of interdependence at the global scale, with minerals being transported over increasingly greater distances. Issues of national development and national economic independence have compounded the shortage of mineral resources, with resulting discussions about limits to growth or sustainable growth, resource substitution, recycling and conservation. In environmental terms the impact of mineral resource development is a component of global concern for resources in general and for a deteriorating global environment.

Mining in Buenafortuna – a simulation of decision-making

G. A. COX, W. HAWES, D. G. NORRIS AND T. C. SWINFEN

Background information

The independent republic of Buenafortuna lies on the north-eastern coast of the South American continent. To the N it has a coast line on the Atlantic, it is bounded on the W and S by Campogrande and on the E and S by Colonopatria. It has an area of 150,000 km^2, with an estimated population of 2 million.

Buenafortuna is situated between latitudes 4° and 9°N and longitude 42° and 48°W. The country is divided structurally into two clearly marked regions, the Coastal Plain and the hilly Buenafortuna Plateau.

The country is drained by four principal river systems, the Blanco, Amarillo, Verde and Tinto all of which flow NE into the Atlantic Ocean. The Verde is by far the largest and is navigable by small coastal vessels upstream for about 50 kilometres.

The climate of Buenafortuna is typically equatorial in character. The North-East Trade wind blows in the coastal areas all year round being strongest and steadiest in winter but interrupted in summer by calms and variable periods. There is a variation in climate between the coastal areas and the Plateau of the interior. The Coastal area is wet (2500 mm rain per annum) with no real dry season but December–January and May–July are periods of heavier rainfall. The Plateau tends to be even wetter especially those areas open to the North-East Trades (3000 mm per annum) although sheltered valleys may be significantly drier.

As is usual in equatorial areas temperatures are remarkably uniform, with the annual range always less than 2°C. The coastal areas are hot (around 30°C) while in the mountains the average temperature is 21°C at 1500 metres, and still as high as 16°C at 2500 metres.

The greater proportion of the inhabitants live in the coastal plain with an estimated 600,000 living in or near the capital and main port Puerto Valiente, situated near the mouth of the R. Verde. The country's second city of Terrano Tacito, with about 200,000 inhabitants, also lies on the coast in a bay between the R. Blanco and the R. Amarillo. The only other sizeable towns are Puerto Pascado (30,000 inhabitants) in the N near the border with Campogrande and Wakiroja (70,000 inhabitants) at the mouth of the R. Tinto on the border with Colonopatria. The remainder of the country is sparsely populated, mainly by the few remaining Amerindians, and large areas are uninhabited.

The people

The original inhabitants of the area were the Waki Amerindians. They were conquered and subjugated by the Spaniards who settled in the coastal region in the 16th century. The Spanish colonial era ended in 1830 when after little bloodshed Buenafortuna gained its independence from Spain under Rodrigo Valiente who soon afterwards became the first President. Since that time Buenafortuna has enjoyed a peaceful and until recently isolated existence. The inhabitants, now mostly of mixed race with some pure Waki, a few of African descent and even fewer Europeans, are singularly cheerful and peace-loving. They have cordial relations with the people of neighbouring countries, are democratic in outlook and pro-American. The official language is Spanish and 90% of the people are Roman Catholic. There have been few political upheavals. The present Head of State is President Rodriguez and there is a 36-member Parliament elected through universal suffrage every 4 years.

The coastal plain with its extensive sandy beaches occupies about a sixth of the land area and is backed by broad rolling savannahs. These in turn give way to the foothills and mountains of the interior which is in the S and E are covered by dense high tropical forest interrrupted with patches of low bush and small farms. Here average elevations increase gently from sea level at the coast to 500–600 m in the foothills and to 3500 m in the highest parts of the mountain range.

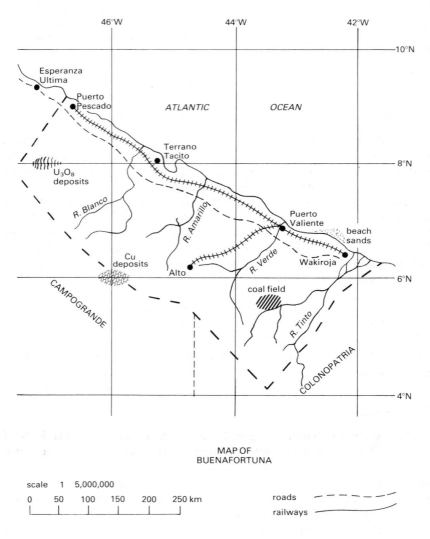

MAP OF
BUENAFORTUNA

scale   1   5,000,000

0   50   100   150   200   250 km

roads
railways

FIG. 14.1

Transport

Except in the coastal region there are few roads. A dirt all-weather road runs parallel to the coast connecting all four principal towns. A single track narrow gauge railway also runs along the coast with a branch line from Puerto Valiente running SW for 150 km to Alto in the interior for transportation of timber to the port. There is an excellent international airport (constructed by the Americans during World War II) 25 km outside the capital. The other three major towns have airfields capable of handling medium twin-engined aircraft and there are some 15 airstrips dotted about the country which can be used by light aircraft. In the interior travel is by boat or canoe on the larger rivers and creeks and by foot trail between villages. By sea Puerto Valiente to the Panama Canal is 4000 km; to New York 5400 km; and to Rotterdam 8300 km.

Mineral resources

Buenafortuna is fortunate in having an active and far-sighted Minister of Lands and Mines. Because of his efforts the mineral potential of the country, until recently overlooked, is being brought to the attention of foreign oil companies and international mining houses.

Apart from the now acknowledged off-shore oil possibilities a wide range of non-ferrous, precious metal and fossil fuel minerals of economic importance is believed to exist in the favourable pre-Cambrian rocks of the interior and the late Palaeozoic formations of the coastal region. Following regional geological mapping, airborne geophysical surveys and side scanning radar imagery sponsored by the United Nations Development Programme (U.N.D.P.) and the United States Geological Survey (U.S.G.S.) the Buenafortuna Geological Survey (B.G.S.) has recently reported the discovery of significant deposits of iron, manganese, copper, asbestos, uranium, coal, bauxite and lateritic nickel, precious metals both of hard rock and placer type, and also extensive heavy mineral beach sands on the coast.

The economy

The economy is based on agriculture which accounts for over 70% of exports. These consist of bananas, cocoa, coffee, coconut and palm oil, rubber and tobacco. All these products are produced on a small scale from numerous isolated farms and plantations. The timber and fishing industries have become increasingly important over the past 10 years and there are now a dozen foreign logging companies operating saw-mills in the interior on the plateau and there are several small fish and shrimp canning factories in Puerto Pescado, the principal fishing port, and in Terrano Tacito. Apart from these there are virtually no mechanized industries. The government is actively promoting rice and sugar cane cultivation in the coastal region with a view to cutting imports of these foodstuffs and thus reducing the foreign trade deficit.

Unemployment is very high and currently estimated at 35% of those able to work. This problem will become more acute with the rapid increase of population and the increasing proportion of young people attending schools, technical colleges and the small but expanding national university.

The coal project

Deposits of good grade coal were discovered 15 years ago in the eastern hinterland of Buenafortuna. The deposits lie near the main tributary of the River Tinto, 200 km SW of the port of Wakiroja, 1200 m above sea level. They are situated in hilly country thickly covered with vegetation.

The coal formations have been thoroughly investigated and extensive drilling has revealed the presence of 15 coal seams. However only three seams in one particular area are considered to be commercially exploitable at present.

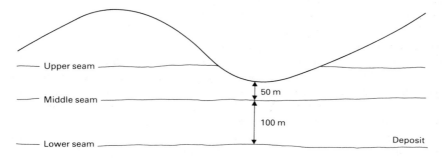

FIG. 14.2. Section through coal deposit.

TABLE 14.1

Dimensions	Area		Average thickness
	Hectares	Million m²	
Upper seam	536	5.36	0.70 m
Middle seam	293	2.93	0.80 m
Lower seam	469	4.69	1.20 m

(1 Hectare = 10,000 m²)

There may be a demand for coal at a projected power plant which would be constructed either near the port of Puerto Valiente on the Atlantic coast or near the site of the mine. The neighbouring countries of Campogrande and Colonopatria have also expressed their interest in importing coal from Buenafortuna. However, before a decision can be reached to develop the coal deposit in the Tinto valley, an economic study has to be carried out to ensure that the coal can be mined profitably.

All the necessary preliminary investigations have been completed in Buenafortuna. Thus the cost of settling up the mining operation, the cost of transport and the income from sales have all been estimated.

The copper project

Many years ago geologists who were mapping the mountainous region of the frontier of Buenafortuna and the neighbouring country of Campogrande, near the headwaters of the Rio Amarillo, came across an extensive area of copper mineralization. All the visible (i.e. surface) evidence indicated a large copper deposit, which a systematic drilling programme has since confirmed.

In addition to copper, the deposit also contains some molybdenum, gold and silver. Investigation showed there were three principal blocks of ore, A, B, C, as shown below on the section through the orebody.

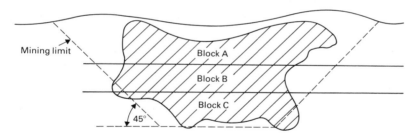

FIG. 14.3

TABLE 14.2. *Section through Copper*

	Volume of ore (million m³)	Volume of waste rock (million m³)
Block A	36	19
Block B	23	20
Block C	23	23
Overall total	82	62

The beach sand project

The beaches and inland dunes which occur along the Atlantic coast of Buenafortuna contain concentrations of minerals. All have been prospected, but at present only the deposits of Playa Wakiroja which lie along the coast, 100 km east of the capital Puerto Valiente, appear to contain sufficient minerals for commercial exploitation to be feasible.

Before mining operation to exploit the heavy minerals in beach sands is set up the economic feasibility of the project must be carefully examined. There must be sufficient valuable material in each tonne of beach sand to cover all the costs of extraction and processing, including capital investment, interest on loans, royalties and taxes.

All the necessary preliminary work, including surveys, drilling of bore holes, examination and analysis of samples, laboratory tests and pilot plant testing has been carried out in Buenafortuna. Other important information has been collected regarding costs of operating, transport, market prices and the extent of involvement by the Government of Buenafortuna.

The rectangular sector shown below has the highest mineral content and is the only area likely to warrant further investigation at present.

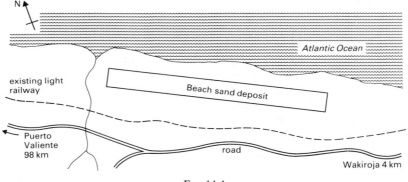

Fig. 14.4

Table 14.3. *Dimensions of Deposit*

Average length	10 000 m
Average width	550 m
Average depth	10 m

For section refer to Map of Buenafortuna

The uranium project

A large low grade deposit of uranium has been discovered in the north-west of Buenafortuna. Extensive investigations have been carried out to establish the extent, type and grade of the deposit.

TABLE 14.4. *Dimensions of Deposit*

Average width	40 m
Maximum depth	510 m
Total volume	6.4 million m^3

This deposit outcrops at the surface, is approximately lens shaped and has a downward dip of 65° to the south-east. At the surface the deposit has an apparent width of about 6 m and extends for over 550 m. The uraninite (uranium oxide) in the deposit is of most interest, but there is also about 3% of iron pyrites, which could be used to produce sulphuric acid for the uranium extraction process and other industrial purposes.

The uranium content of the ore has been carefully analysed and found to be subject to wide variation. An average recoverable content of 0.6 kg of uranium oxide per tonne of ore is necessary for it to be economically worthwhile to exploit the deposit.

The deposit has one major fault and many minor ones. Very careful, accurate mining is important to avoid mining too much waste rock.

The method of processing has been established from physical and chemical analyses of the ore and tested in a pilot plant. Information about the capital cost, operating cost, bank loan conditions and the prices obtainable have all been collected in Buenafortuna.

Handling the simulation with a class

Introduction

In this exercise students are asked to assess the desirability of developing four different mineral deposits in the imaginary country of Buenafortuna, and then to present their findings to the Minister for Mining and Industry so that it can be decided which deposit should be exploited to the greatest advantage of Buenafortuna.

The four mineral deposits which might be developed are (1) Coal, (2) Copper, (3) Beach Sands, (4) Uranium.

Educational aims and objectives

1. To give some understanding of the technical, economic, political and social factors affecting a new mining project in a developing country.
2. To provide the students with an opportunity to gain confidence in handling data, working with numbers, analysing information and making decisions, as well as debating and communicating with other people.

Organization and timing

It is assumed that the students will have available background information on the mining industry, and that they are ready to apply their knowledge to problems which, though in one sense imaginary, are nevertheless a realistic simplification of those which a developing country might face.

The following is a suggested procedure, based on the experience of those who derived the exercise and those who tried it with their students. Teachers can of course modify it to meet their own requirements.

1. Distribute the information in advance so that they are read before the exercise begins.
2. In class discuss the Republic of Buenafortuna to make sure that the background information has been read and understood. Discussion should turn to the economic state of the country and the need to develop the mining deposits. Divide the students into four groups, assigning one of the minerals to each group. Make sure that each group understands the mining methods appropriate to its mineral product.

   Each group is to regard itself as an independent commission set up by the Minister for Mining and Industry to report on the feasibility of developing a particular deposit. In a later lesson it will report its findings verbally to the other groups and to the Minister (i.e. the teacher).

   Each group should consider the social factors which would be affected by the development of its mineral. This is the important part of the exercise and specific questions can be asked by the teacher: such questions are given below.

Questions which might be put to the groups

1. How much land would be affected?
   This can be determined from background information.
2. What would be the consequence in terms of pollution, noise and the disruption of the local community?
   In a densely populated country like Britain or Bangladesh these would be important questions. In Buenafortuna the areas to be exploited are almost uninhabited. The only problem of any importance is the pollution of local rivers and streams by leakage from the waste tailings of the copper mine.
3. Are there any health hazards for workers or local people?
   Workers in underground mines risk physical injury, explosions and long-term health problems caused by dust, but modern techniques have reduced these hazards very substantially. Slippage of waste-tips could be a problem if the mine is anywhere near a village. Industry always involves some risk of physical injury, but apart from that these

projects carry few health hazards for workers or local people. Sulphur dioxide could be a problem if the copper concentrates were smelted in Buenafortuna.

4. Could the land be restored for any useful purpose after the operation?

The coal mine will affect relatively little land. The sand dunes are of limited agricultural use before mining development but afterwards the land could be made suitable for a number of purposes. The copper development will leave a large hole in the ground and tailings dumps which could be planted with grass and trees. There will also be smaller quantities of mine waste from the uranium and coal mines.

5. Where would the mineral be processed and used?

Initial processing to obtain concentrates from the uranium, copper and beach sands deposits would be carried out at the mine sites in Buenafortuna, but the mineral concentrates would then be exported for further treatment and use. The Government might well press for the further processing to be carried out locally, so that new industries using the final products might be developed. The coal would be cleaned at the mine site. It could be the chosen fuel for a proposed power station and the neighbouring countries are showing an interest in the possibility of purchasing it, as well as excess electric power from the power station.

6. Could other industries be developed as a result?

Except in the case of coal this is unlikely at present. The Government may press for a copper smelter and metal fabrication (see 5 above): this is frequently a part of the negotiations between mining companies and governments.

7. How long would the projects last?

Coal	22 years
Copper	25 years
Beach sands	14 years
Uranium	20 years

Pupils would need to be told this

8. What would happen to the workers after the project finished?

This is a thorny question that has to be faced in the development of any finite deposit. The decline of the mining industry in Cornwall, U.K. is an example; Cornish miners have emigrated to use their skills all over the world because of the lack of work in Cornwall. Nevertheless the workers would probably have been unemployed anyway if the mining had never started. Mining operations often encourage further local exploration which results in the development of new mines.

9. Would existing agriculture or forestry be affected by the project?

Not in the case of beach sands. Mining coal may slightly affect forestry in the area. The main problem caused by mining copper would be leakage of acid waters from the mine tailings. The uranium mining project would take place in a desert area anyway.

10. What roads, railways, housing and community services would be provided?

Students should be encouraged to make suggestions about the organization of transport bearing in mind existing roads and railways, natural physical features like rivers and mountainous terrain and the total mass of material that must be taken away from the site each year. Housing and community services would have to be provided at the site for workers and their families.

11. What total labour force would be required and what proportion of it could be local people?

Reasonable estimates for the Buenafortuna projects are:

Beach sands:	100 + 10 expatriates
Copper:	400 + 20 expatriates
Coal:	1200 + 45 expatriates
Uranium:	800 + 90 expatriates

12. What demand and what markets exist for the product?

Coal would be used in Buenafortuna or neighbouring countries, possibly to fuel power stations. The copper concentrate would be exported and there could be sales problems because world demand is low at present and world production capacity is too great. The demand for beach sand minerals is rapidly expanding. The demand for uranium may be expected to increase as fossil fuels are depleted.

13. Would it be better to retain the deposit for exploitation in the future?

With increasing world demand and possibly decreasing supplies profits could well be higher in the future, especially for copper. However the discovery of large new deposits elsewhere or new technology could reduce the value of the Buenafortuna deposits.

14. Might agricultural developments be more important than mining?

Unlike some undeveloped areas Buenafortuna can feed its people adequately so the answer depends on whether or not there might be a large export market for agricultural and forestry products.

15. Are there any useful by-products of the mining operations?

When copper is exploited, molybdenum, gold and silver are sometimes recovered as byproducts; they are all useful and there is a ready market for them. Whether the copper is refined in Buenafortuna or elsewhere the value of these metals is credited to the mining company. The tailings are useless. The shale mined with the coal might be used as a "fill material" for road-making, etc. but it is of poor quality.

The local construction industry might find the beach sand tailings useful. The magnetite could become saleable some time in the future.

The iron pyrites from the uranium deposit could be used to make sulphuric acid.

16. Does the deposit have any strategic importance?

   Uranium, copper and titanium would be of great importance in time of war but deposits are found world-wide so those in Buenafortuna would probably not be particularly important, and the coal deposits would be even less so.

17. Are there any international political implications?

   In the negotiations between the Government and the mining company the latter will be based in some other country and may seek markets in many others. Other governments may be interested in the strategic minerals.

   The copper deposit is on the border between Buenafortuna and Campogrande. This could cause boundary disputes. Immigrant workers from Campogrande might be employed in the mine.

Extracurricular activities: the Science Club

THOMAS VARGHESE

An example from Zambia

This particular activity is applicable to countries which are rich in mineral resources.

The teacher forms a Science Club in the school. Groups of pupils can be asked to undertake a research project on one of the local mineral resources. Pupils work in their spare time for 2–3 months. Tasks can be

(1) identify any mineral resource in the local vicinity,
(2) find out about any indigenous industry, local craft using this mineral,
(3) find out where else in the nation and in the world this mineral is found,
(4) what are the various uses of the mineral,
(5) what is the possibility of developing beneficial small-scale industry from the mineral

On the whole it involves the local community, planning, design, data collection, research, and understanding techniques involved. By undertaking such a project, the students should be able to:

(a) suggest appropriate mining methods,
(b) decide the average life span of the mine and suggest ways of redeployment of workers when the mine closes,
(c) the importance of the mineral resources to the standard of living in the community, in the nation,
(d) suggest possible steps that might be taken to reduce the problem of diminishing mineral resources, i.e. recycling, reclaiming, more efficient usage, substitutions etc.,
(e) list problems, hazards, pollution and suggest their own solutions.

In Zambia, for example, the Basic Science syllabus in grade 7–9 includes the following on mineral resources.

1. To study copper and its extraction.
2. To study the results of man's usage of the country's mineral resources.

When this topic on mineral resources was taught, pupils were encouraged to undertake the project work as extra curricular activity in almost all schools in Zambia. The results were very positive. This led to an awareness of the resources (especially copper) Zambia has, and its implications in society among the secondary school pupils.

In 1978, a group of pupils identified an area where there was clay which could be used for making pottery (local people were making pottery out of it for their use). The complete study by pupils created interest, among the higher authorities and it is a site of a new pottery works.

Similarly at another area in Zambia pupils identified a quarry which produced fine talc $(Mg_3, Si_4, O_{10}(OH)_2)$, the possibility of commercial use of it being looked into.

Conservation of resources

ROBERT LEPISCHAK

We live in a world of finite resources; the mineral resources, the "building blocks" of development should be judiciously used by the present generation to ensure a resource base for future generations. Although the earth contains all the metals of the world the useful elements are usually so diluted in the rocks that they are available only when geological events have concentrated the material and the concentration is readily available for exploitation. The evolution of mineral deposits requires eons of geological time which over-shadow the mere centuries of human history and the ensuing use of Mother Earth's resources. Some earth materials, mineral fuels such as coal or oil, once used are not recoverable. Other earth materials such as iron, copper, lead, zinc, and aluminium, only to mention a few, remain tangible and are therefore reusable or recoverable. For example, coal once burned is a dissipated resource; the aluminium, in a container, does not dissipate, the container may be used for another purpose or may be melted down, so as to recover the aluminium, which can then be shaped into another object of use to people.

In a world of diminishing resources it becomes essential that materials made from finite resources be reclaimed and reused where and whenever possible. Recovery is, of course, seldom practised when it costs more, in terms of collection costs or energy use, than producing new material.

TABLE 14.5. *Recyclable waste (figures in thousands of tonnes per year) for the U.K.*

Material	Consumption	Identified total losses	Percentage potentially recoverable	Value of this (1979) price) £ million
Ferrous metal (steel)	26,000	2,800	36%	55
Copper	660	79	22%	15
Aluminium	694	131	25%	23
Zinc	353	92	38%	10.5
Lead	325	72	8%	3.3
Tin	17	11	36%	26
Thermoplastic	1,320	512	64%	66

(from S.I.S. Book G Mineral Resources)

Methods of resource conservation

Strategies for resource conservation include:

1. *Reclamation* – or what could be simply called reusing items or parts of items,
   e.g. (a) milk/soft drink bottles – after collection these items are cleaned and refilled for use, in some cases as many as ten (10) times.
   (b) automobile reclamation centres – parts of derelict autos are adapted as "used parts" on other autos.
2. *Recycling* – the reuse of waste in a production process
   e.g. (a) in house or industrial scrap recycling, scrap iron used in cast iron or steel production which are "shavings" from the production of blooms, billets or slabs and metallic shapes,
   (b) post consumption recycling – scrap iron from old machinery, automobiles, industrial equipment which is added to the charge and becomes cast iron or steel which is then shaped into a new consumer product.

What materials can be recycled?

(a) *Domestic refuse and mixed solid industrial waste.* Research is in progress in several countries on the separation of general rubbish into its components. This involves processes such as screening, magnetic separation and sink/float separations. The various components are dealt with below.

(b) *Metals.* In the same way that industrial scrap is efficiently used by industry, scrap merchants can also dispose of objects made of recognizable metals, such as copper, brass, or lead.

Every year we throw millions of tonnes of steel into our domestic dustbins, mostly as "tin cans". It is fairly easy to separate this from other refuse by magnetic means, but it is difficult to remove the labels on the food cans. These cans are made of tin-plate, sheet steel with a layer of tin on each side. A square metre of tin-plate, contains about 11 g of tin and no satisfactory de-tinning process for cans has yet been devised. Tin is easily melted, but heating tin-plate simply alloys the tin to the steel, producing a quality of steel useless for almost every purpose except the manufacture of low quality cast iron. Industrial tin-plate can have the tin removed by an electrolytic process, but this is not possible with dirty old cans.

(c) *Glass*. Broken glass is called cullet. Scrap cullet in industry is remelted and used in the glass factory. Cullet from domestic refuse could be remelted, but there are difficulties. Different types of glass have slightly different properties, the most obvious being colour. Green cullet would be most unwelcome in a factory producing colourless bottles, though a mixture of colours would not matter if green or amber bottles were being made. Glass-making machinery is designed to use molten glass of a particular stickiness (viscosity) and cullet of unknown origin might affect the quality of the glassware produced. The cullet must be clean and free from metals, particularly iron or aluminium, and cleaning and sorting it is expensive.

It is expensive also to collect and carry the cullet to the glass works, though a process developed in the U.K. separates glass by crushing, producing a material like sand which can be used as a filler in paints, plastics, bricks, floor tiles, etc.

The ingredients for making glass are cheap. Though environmental groups protest against the use of non-returnable bottles (which are light, but used only once) some firms find it cheaper to make new bottles than to collect and re-use old ones.

Many of the deposits on the returnable bottles are not claimed and perhaps the return of containers could be more strongly encouraged by raising the price of a deposit. The more efficient use of containers would then be possible.

If standardized containers were to be used for a range of popular commodities as is already done for milk, beer, and soft drink bottles, then this would encourage their return or recycling.

The amount and type of material recycled in a country will depend on a number of factors; some of these being:

(i) the degree of development of a country (contrast Western European countries to countries of central Africa, or to India),

  (ii) the demand for a particular recyclable material on the regional, national or world market,
 (iii) government policy on reuse of particular material,
 (iv) effectiveness of environmentally conscious community groups,
  (v) costs of actual collection and extraction of the desirable material.

However any amount of material reclaimed or recycled is material which extends the use of finite resources.

  3. *Substitution and more efficient usage* – industrial conservation and tradition have dictated that certain materials are used for particular purposes. New needs and technology have lead to many changes in the use of minerals.

Tin is relatively expensive and very vulnerable to technological progress and substitution by other materials especially for packaging. Fifty years ago, tin was used to plate steel cans. Today about half the cans produced in Britain and the U.S. in fact do not require any tin at all. Also by using thinner coats, a given amount of tin now covers a much larger area of steel than it did 30 years ago. The change from "hot dipped" to electrolytic tinplating has meant therefore that the amount of tin used per can has been decreasing. The world used about 7½% more tin-plate at the start of the 1980s than at the start of the 1970s – *but tin consumption was down 5%*.

There is also tin-free steel coated with chromium which has been in use (on a small scale) since the late 1960s.

About half of the copper used today is in electrical applications. However, aluminium (only 11% as dense as copper) is replacing much of the copper used for overhead cables. Use of aluminium has been increasing about twice as fast as copper in recent years. Plastics now compete with copper for uses such as piping and with steel in carbodies.

Products of the petrochemical industry have replaced traditional clay or brass water jars used in India.

Industrial processes have produced materials which do not decompose or wear out as readily:

  (1) aluminium alloy is used in auto construction in lieu of sheet metal, thereby limiting corrosion,
  (2) special steel alloys used in shafts and ball bearings have an exceptionally long life span,
  (3) Teflon coatings on contact surfaces outlast wood or metal surfaces used in similar situations.

Perhaps in a less direct way mineral resources are used more efficiently as a result of engineering or construction processes which make automobiles more energy efficient and aerodynamic. Improved insulation techniques in homes and commercial buildings can lead to more efficient use of mineral fuels. The drive for greater efficiency will mean that our resources will last longer.

Student activity (primary level)

AIM: To have pupils, through activity:
      1. Determine alternate uses for "once used" materials.
      2. Alter "throw aways" to adapt them to another use.

PROCEDURE: Bring a container with a pot pouri of articles, empty jars, boxes, tins, etc. and have pupils decide on alternate or unique uses for the materials.

    . . . this activity should act as an introduction to alternate uses of throw aways and should act as a catalyst for discussion on home and community recycling examples i.e. are items being thrown away or reused in the home? how does the village or community dispose of items or reuse them?

Student activity (middle school level secondary level)

AIM: To have students compare and contrast producers and consumers of a mineral resources relative to data provided and by an associated map activity relate the information in terms of a comparison between the role of developed and developing nations in the total scheme.

Who produces copper?   ## Who uses copper?

   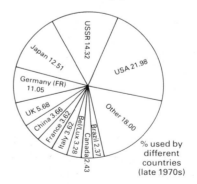

Teacher resource:

Over two-thirds of world production of copper concentrate comes from just 6 countries – the US, USSR, Chile, Canada, Zambia and Zaire. Production in Zambia and Zaire did not begin until earlier this century.

The US alone uses nearly ¼ of the world's copper. The US, USSR, Japan and Federal Germany together use nearly ⅔. The US and USSR mine much of the copper they use – but Europe and Japan import much copper from Central Africa and South America.

Fig. 14.5

PROCEDURE: 1. On an outline map of the world locate and identify the following countries – U.S.A., U.S.S.R., Chile, Canada, Zambia, Zaire, Peru, Poland, Philippines, Australia, S. Africa, U.K., Germany (F.R.), China, France, Italy, Belgium, Luxemburg, Brazil,
2. Relative to the divided circles Fig. 14.5, colour code the developing countries (gold) and the developed countries (green).
3. Using the same colours as above code the map used in section (1),
4. Discussion and implications of the observations, made by the students, should be discussed and related to the economic, social, political, and environmental implications such a distribution has.

Student activity (secondary level)

Relate to the teacher resource material provided in the information section. Students should consider the integration of factors which would affect recycling relative to energy consumption or energy savings in recycling materials. Consideration should be given to:
1. Does recycling conserve material?
2. Does recycling require more energy than producing the original material?
3. What is the actual cost?
4. How can people affect the above variables?

Coal in the Kruger National Park
PETER SPARGO
Introduction

By a strange irony South Africa is custodian of two immensely valuable assets: a quite remarkable proportion of the world's wild life (both animals and plants) on the one hand and of its mineral wealth on the other. Until recently the possession of these two great assets has rarely produced conflicting demands – and most people have assumed that there was no reason why they should.

However, towards the end of the third quarter of 1979 it was learned that the South African Geological Survey was carrying out prospecting in an area in the far north of the Kruger National Park known as Punda Milia-Pafuri – in spite of the fact that the National Parks Act expressly forbids prospecting in such parks. The object of the prospecting was to determine the extent and quality of a deposit of a special type of coal known as coking coal which was believed to lie beneath the Park. The definite possibility of full-scale mining in the Park was also mentioned.

Even though no information was released concerning the size or depth of the deposit the very possibility of mining in the Park provoked immediate, vehement and widespread protest and debate throughout the whole of South Africa. It soon became apparent, however, that the two parties involved viewed the proposed mining operation from very different points of view.

On the one hand the South African Iron and Steel Industrial Corporation ("ISCOR") – a huge semi-State organization charged with the responsibility of providing South Africa with adequate supplies of iron and steel to ensure industrial growth, saw the coal deposit as the source of an essential ingredient in the process of iron and steel manufacture – and the manufacture of these two commodities is of such supreme national importance that in ISCOR's view its claims had undisputed priority. If South Africa's fast-growing population needed jobs, then industrial expansion was the only way to provide these jobs. But industrial expansion meant more iron and steel and this meant more coking coal. South Africa is not well endowed with coking coal and therefore this deposit of high-quality coking coal had to be exploited or the country might become dependent upon imported supplies. The argument seemed logical and unanswerable.

The conservationists and environmentalists, on the other hand, saw the Kruger National Park as a priceless, irreplaceable national asset which had been jealously guarded against all comers since the beginning of the century and was now the home of large numbers of species of animals and flowers, some of which were in danger of becoming extinct elsewhere in Africa and some of which already existed only in the Park. In particular they viewed the Punda Milia-Pafuri region in the north of the Park as being the most ecologically precious sector of the whole Park, containing as it does more rare species than any other sector of the Park, as well as numerous springs and archaeological remains. Finally, the argument went, if a section of South Africa's greatest and most famous national park could be mined so easily (and in spite of being protected by the law), what hope would there be not only for the rest of the Kruger Park but for any other national or provincial park in the country? The proposed mining operation had to be stopped at all costs. Once again the argument seemed logical and unanswerable!

The situation very rapidly developed into a classic "development versus preservation" confrontation with, in many cases, more heat than light being generated! Arguments frequently moved from the rational to the emotional and the real issues often disappeared under the welter of words. Because of the importance of the principles involved this particular problem is valuable as a stimulus to class discussion on this type of issue, not just in South Africa but throughout the world.

The Kruger National Park

Before discussing the problem of coal mining in the Kruger National Park in any meaningful way it is important to describe the location and features of the area in which the proposed mining operation is to take place, for the essential problem with which this case study deals is not merely about the necessity for mining as such, but where that mining is to occur.

The Kruger National Park is unquestionably one of the truly great nature reserves of the world, for not only is it very large, but it also contains an astonishing quantity and variety of wild life of many types.

Situated in the north-eastern corner of the Transvaal Lowveld, the Kruger National Park was established in 1898 as the Sabie Game Reserve, only receiving its present name in 1929. It has an area of 19,010 km² (c. 2,000,000 hectares) and extends from the Crocodile River in the south to the Limpopo River in the north – a distance of over 340 km (Fig. 14.6). It stretches from the Mozambique border in the east to a surveyor's line in the west, averaging 60 km in width. The whole of the 1,000 km perimeter of the Park is now fenced, both to keep animals within the Park and to eliminate the spread of diseases such as the much-feared foot-and-mouth disease.

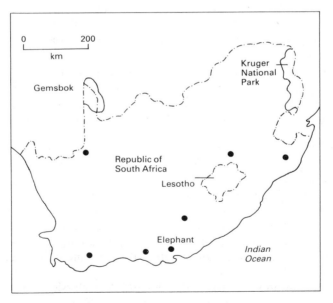

FIG. 14.6. The position of the Kruger National Park.

Both because of its sheer size and the fact that its great north–south length means that it cuts across several biological zones, the Park is host to a quite remarkably large and diverse number of species, both flora and fauna. For example, the total number of species of fauna which inhabit the Park is nearly 700, made up as follows:

Birds	432 species
Mammals	188 species
Reptiles	94 species
Fish	46 species

The population of large animals, for which the Park is world-renowned, is particularly impressive and a 1971 animal count revealed the following populations:

Hippopotamus	3,800
Zebra	20,300
Leopard	650
Giraffe	6,500
Buffalo	21,500
Blue Wildebeest	15,000
Impala	162,000
Kudu	6,500
Waterbuck	3,600
Eland	440

(apart, of course, from large numbers of elephant and lion!). Although less spectacular, the flora of the Park is also most impressive, for it contains flowers, trees and grasses impressive both in numbers and diversity. Many of these species occur nowhere else in the world.

The Northern Kruger Park

The present proposal is that mining should take place in the northern part of the Park, in the Punda Milia-Pafuri region, and it is therefore important to note that this region is in many ways the richest in the Park. For example, there are two fish, one frog, five reptiles, seven bird and five animal species occurring in this region which are found nowhere else in the country, and in some cases nowhere else in the world. In addition, numbers of other plant and animal species occur only in this northern area: 33 trees, 5 fish, 3 frogs, 16 reptiles, 50 birds, and 12 mammals. Finally, the area is the source of a number of perennial springs – a precious resource in a dry area such as this – and the location of numerous valuable archaeological sites.

The proposed mining operations will therefore take place in an area of exceptional richness, in terms of flora, fauna, water resources, and archaeology.

The problem of coking coal

At the heart of the problem of coal mining in the Kruger National Park are the peculiar properties and particular importance of a type of coal known as coking coal. This is a variety of coal which, when heated in the absence of air, forms hard, non-crumbling coke known as "metallurgical coke". This is a key ingredient in the production of iron in a blast furnace and is therefore regarded as a material of great national importance.

Comparatively few coals produce metallurgical coke and although South Africa has very large reserves of coal unfortunately only a comparatively small proportion of these are coking coals. Hence in South Africa coking coal assumes a greater importance than it might do in the many countries in which it forms a higher percentage of the total coal reserves.

Using this material with a class

The manner in which the case study is structured will depend upon the teacher's own personal style, as well as the maturity and ability of the class. However, the following has been found to be a successful approach, using two or three class periods:

(i) The teacher introduces the topic briefly, outlining the key problem involved: the conflicting demands of an expanding industrial society's needs for coking coal on the one hand, and the increasingly urgent need for large-scale preservation of animals and flora on the other. In this introduction, which should take no longer than 10 minutes, the teacher should make every effort to present each side of the case as fairly, accurately and impartially as possible (whatever his or her own personal feelings in the matter!). Key data should be presented to the class, either on a brief handout or using an over-head projector or chalkboard.

(ii) The class is now divided into two, or more, "teams" and each is requested to prepare a case either supporting or opposing the development of coal mining in the Park. If necessary a further short handout can be distributed providing additional information for use in preparing a case.

In discussion with each group it must be pointed out that although "hard" data is important in preparing their case, it is perfectly legitimate to bring in what might be called "other factors", e.g. moral, ethical, or religious principles.

The length of time allotted to this phase of the exercise will largely depend upon the time available but should not be less than 30 minutes. In preparing their case each group must decide who is the most appropriate person to present their findings to the class as a whole, i.e. to act as their spokesman.

(iii) The class comes together again and the leader of each group presents his/her group's argument. This is a fairly formal presentation of a reasoned argument and no interjections or questions should be allowed.

(iv) The matter is then thrown open to general debate, with group leaders being allowed a short period to open an attack upon their opponent's arguments (not their opponents!). The role of the teacher here is to act as impartial chairperson unless a pupil of sufficient experience is available, encouraging pupils to engage in rational debate, to guide the discussion into previously-unexplored paths or to stimulate flagging discussion by the use of appropriate questions.

Examples of such questions are:

To what extent are the present inhabitants of a country bound by some sort of "moral trust" handed down to them in the country they have inherited – for example, for its wildlife *and* its mineral wealth?

(b) In the same way, to what extent are they custodians of this inheritance for future generations?

(c) If a national park is protected by law from prospecting operations, what right does a government have to carry out such operations without changing the law?

(d) If the mining of coking coal in a national park results in the creation of jobs, and therefore a higher standard of living for many people, is this not more important than preserving some animals and plants, even if they are rare ones – after all, this is not the only game park in Africa.

(e) Do human beings have a special responsibility for *all* life on Earth, i.e. for plant and animal life as well as human life?

(f) Other steel-making processes are more expensive than the traditional blast furnace process but do not make use of coking coal. Should South Africans be prepared to accept more expensive iron and steel thereby eliminating the need for coking coal and hence save the Park? But what if this more expensive steel not only costs more, but also makes the country less competitive in world markets in terms of exports?

(g) Would it be acceptable for ISCOR to purchase an area of land exactly equal to that needed for mining – and then donate this to the National Parks Board to be added to the park, as was done by the Phalaborwa Copper Mining Company some years ago?

(h) How important are the views of people who will live in the area adjoining the Park and who will obviously be seriously affected by the mining operation, e.g. new jobs, greater wealth in the area, etc.?

(i) Is it realistic for ISCOR to promise to restore the mined-out land to its "former state" after they have completed mining?

(j) Let us assume that although the coal deposits lie under the Park, they are sufficiently deep for mining to be carried out entirely from outside the Park, i.e. by sinking vertical shafts there and then tunnelling horizontally below the Park. Would this be acceptable.

(k) Is it reasonable to argue that wildlife might happen to be in South Africa, but that we really hold it "in trust" for the whole world? How should this belief affect our view of the problem?'

(l) "A mine is for now – a game park is for ever" is a slogan. What do you think of it?

(m) In a country such as South Africa with a rapidly growing population (c. 400,000 per annum) surely the creation of jobs, and therefore prosperity, is more important than anything else?

(n) South Africa is a relatively wealthy country. Why doesn't it buy its coking coal from overseas, even if it is more expensive, and thereby save the Park?

(o) The mining operation proposed by ISCOR may well only involve a relatively small area of the Park – say 5%. Surely this will not really affect the Park very much?

(v) Although taking a final vote on the issue "proves" very little, pupils almost invariably enjoy this finale – especially as many of them are now in combative mood! From an educational point of view it is always instructive to ask the class how many of them changed their view on the issue as a result of the exercise.

Conclusion

Although minerals are a source of wealth and essential for manufacturing industry, their exploitation is not without environmental impact and social cost. In this chapter we have seen how the nature of these impacts may be taught to pupils and students by means of simulations. It will be clear that decisions about mineral exploitations involves choices based on values. Thus the value of a mineral to an economy needs to be weighed against the value of a landscape, or that of maintaining a viable ecosystem. Further we have seen that any attempt to conserve minerals through recycling should help to lessen the demand for new minerals. It will also directly and indirectly lessen the environmental impact since waste metal, glass etc. will be reclaimed and the pressure to extract new minerals will be lessened.

The use of land, water and mineral resources on our planet needs to be a wise use, inspired by a regard for the needs of all the earth's people and not just the favoured few.

Appendix 1

Papers Available to the Land, Water and Mineral Resources Group

Aalst van, H. F.	Education for developing water supplies.
Aalst van, H. F.	Water for Tanzania.
Barrett, E.	Education for mineral resource extraction and use.
Barrett, E.	China clay – A teaching unit for secondary schools.
Basa, E. Y.	Ground water.
Blum, A.	Water – drop by drop.
Bunker, C. A.	Panguna copper mine – its impact on the environment.
Coggins, P. C.	Mining in developing countries.
Ellis, J.	Using "Man and the Biosphere" posters.
Ellis, J.	Predicting the uncertain. Learning from traditional resource use.
Ellis, J.	The many faces of wood in dry lands. Grazing in a changing environment. The use of soil degradation.
Ellis, J.	Desertification: a teaching unit for secondary schools.
Graves, N. J.	The use of land, water and mineral resources.
Graves, N. J.	Bauxite extraction: a teaching unit.
Haubrich, H. *et al.*	Save the Rhine: a teaching unit.
Katz, M. B.	The training of village-rural geologists in developing countries.
Linskog, P. A. and Linskog, R. U. M.	The importance of hygiene education in obtaining a health impact through improved water supply and sanitation, with examples from Malawi.
Mattigod, S. V.	Teaching pedology.
Morrish, H.	Land use: a case study.
O'Connor, A.	Studying problems of land use in East Africa.

Okpala, J. I. N.   Some problems of land use in Nigeria – Strategies for developing students' awareness of effective use of land.

Rawling, E.   Urban planning strategies: a student workshop example.

Spargo, P. E.   Coal in the Kruger National Park. A decision making case study.

Spargo, P. E.   The Orange river project: a case study.

Stimpson, P. G.   Land use choice in a marginal semi-arid environment.

Vedanayagam, E. G.   Case study of the Periyar–Vaigai Project.

Weetman, G. F.   Education for forest conservation in developing countries.

Yakubu, J. M.   A case study of technology in relation to land use in Ghana.

Index